the
IOWA MASTER FARMER AWARD HISTORY BOOK

D1213992

INDEPENDENCE PUBLIC LIBRARY
210 - 2nd STREET N.E.
INDEPENDENCE, IOWA 50644
319-334-2470

Published by:
The Iowa Master Farmer Foundation
c/o *Wallaces Farmer*
Des Moines, Iowa

Printed by:
Sigler Printing
Ames, Iowa

Library of Congress Control Number: 2007937753
ISBN: 978-1-888223-82-8

Cover design by Aaron Butzen

Cover photo, courtesy of *Wallaces Farmer,* was taken at the 1928 Master Farmer banquet in Des Moines. Parts of the 1926, 1927 and 1928 classes are pictured.
Front row kneeling, from left: H.E. Barringer, Lewis Newton, Bert Schuelke, Hervey Hazen, Frank Everett, Otto Schultz, Seth Miller.
First row standing, from left: E.L. Hill, Roy Pullen, Burrell Foster, Paul Strickler, Earl Elijah, John Smith, Theodore Gronna, O.J. Kalsem.
Back row, from left: A.B. Myhr, Dan Schnitijer, Earl Watts, Lenus Hagglund, H.D. Backhaus, Adolph Schultz, E.E. Tracy, George Christophel, Ray Redfern, Charles Kirkpatrick, Fred Nelson, Geroge Steen, Oscar Johnson, John Hunt, Lewis Morris.

Special thanks to the Iowa Farm Bureau Federation for their generous support in printing this history book.

Special thanks to Pioneer Hi-Bred International, Inc. for their generous support in printing this history book.

PIONEER®

A DuPont Company

ACKNOWLEDGEMENTS

Many people helped make this book a reality. Our heartfelt appreciation goes to all those who responded to our call for help. Thanks also to those who offered encouragement and support throughout the project.

Several individuals who went out of their way to make this project successful deserve special recognition. First is **Jerry Goldsmith** of Clarence, Iowa. This whole project was his idea. He proposed a history book of Iowa Master Farmers in 2006 when he was historian for the **Iowa Master Farmer Association**. The rest of the IMFF board, officers and members of the **Iowa Master Farmer Association** are to be complimented for supporting the project as well.

Ron Swanson, Galt, Iowa, 2006 president of the Iowa Master Farmer Association, approached the Iowa State University Greenlee School of Journalism and Mass Communication about the possibility of an intern taking on this project.

Aaron Butzen, a recent graduate of the Greenlee School, did a yeoman's job of scanning and editing articles and photos, writing copy, and doing all of the design and layout of the book as an internship.

Dave Popelka, Sigler Printing, Ames, Iowa, was extremely helpful from the beginning by providing suggestions and advice regarding book design, layout, format, etc.

The Iowa Farm Bureau Federation has staunchly supported the Iowa Master Farmer Foundation since its inception in 1999. Farm Bureau contributed $2,500 toward printing. Thanks to Farm Bureau and **Barb Lykins**, Farm Bureau's Director of Community Resources for their help.

Pioneer Hi-Bred International, founded by Henry A. Wallace in 1926, has always had historical ties to *Wallaces Farmer* and the Iowa Master Farmer Award program. Pioneer contributed $2,500 toward printing. Thanks to **Lou Ireland** and Pioneer for their help.

Howard Holden, retired Iowa Agricultural Statistics Service deputy state statistician, volunteered many hours retrieving and compiling historical data used to help paint a picture of how Iowa agriculture has changed since 1926.

Jim Sage, Waterloo, Iowa, a Master Farmer and historian for the Iowa Master Farmer Association, wrote several of the historical introductions leading off the chapters.

Neil Harl, Iowa State University economist and agricultural law specialist, wrote the Foreword. He also did a masterful job editing and finalizing historical information and data in the chapter introductions.

And finally, the staff at *Wallaces Farmer,* Iowa's Farm Progress publication, coordinated the project. **John Otte,** economics editor, also wrote many of the chapter introductions and worked with Howard Holden sorting out the historical data. **Kellie Grolmus**, editorial assistant, provided invaluable assistance in proofreading copy and pages. **Frank Holdmeyer**, executive editor, worked closely with the intern, Aaron Butzen, offering guidance and assistance when needed.

To all of these people and to those organizations and people not mentioned by name, Thank You!

FROM THE EDITOR

A NOTE FROM THE EDITOR:

All of the articles on each class of Master Farmer Award winners have been reproduced as they were originally published in *Wallaces Farmer*, with only minor editing. We did this in order to maintain the historical perspective. In doing so, however, we sacrificed, to some extent, consistency in writing style and layout design throughout the book. We believe readers will appreciate seeing how the writing style in the magazine has evolved over the years.

It is also important to note that the date on each article in the book reflects the issue date of *Wallaces Farmer* in which the original article appeared, not the date the awards were given that year.

Some confusion may be caused by the apparent lack of a 1962 Master Farmer class. However, up until 1963, the Master Farmer Awards were presented in the year following the year of the award class. Therefore, the 1926 winners were honored in 1927, the 1927 winners in 1928, and so on. In 1963, *Wallaces Farmer* began naming the class according to the year in which they received their awards, so those Master Farmers that received their awards that year were part of the Class of 1963, not 1962.

The Iowa Master Farmers have had a profound effect on the shape of Iowa and national agriculture over the years. We hope you enjoy reading about the history of these valiant men and women as much as we have enjoyed assembling it. Happy reading!

FOREWORD
by Neil E. Harl

When *Wallaces Farmer* instituted the Master Farmer recognition in 1926, few would have foreseen the enormous change in agriculture in the coming 80 years. No period of comparable length in the entire history of the human family saw greater change in the agricultural sector. As many have observed, the change was unprecedented. A major part of the revolution in the agricultural sector in the last eight decades has been attributable to two major technological themes: the technology of seed and genetics, and the technology of power.

In February of 1937, just past the age of three, I was assigned by my father to sit in an old corncrib and "butt and tip" the selected ears from the drought-stunted 1936 crop. That process involved shelling off the irregular kernels at the ends of the ears that would not feed through the planter plates evenly. The ears would then be put through a hand corn sheller to become the seed for the 1937 crop. That was the way open pollinated seed was produced. Hybrids had been introduced a decade earlier but were slow to be accepted by depression-weary farmers.

Our yields in 1937 were much better than 1936 – roughly 40 bushels per acre. But my father's eye was caught by the even better yields on some plots in the neighborhood. In 1938, he turned completely to hybrid corn. Within less than a mile from where I sat in February of 1937 butting and tipping corn, we have produced 220 bushels per acre in recent years on the same land. That is a measure of the huge impact of the technology of seed and genetics, augmented by fertilizers and other inputs.

The effects of the technology of power were no less astounding in the decades to come. We were farming with horses until late 1946 when Dad acquired a new John Deere B. While that was viewed at the time as a fairly powerful tractor, it sits like a pygmy in one corner of our machinery storage shed that now houses the tenants' tractors that run upwards of 200 horsepower. The result has been a dramatic reduction in the backbreaking work of producing and harvesting crops and doing other farm work. And it's also meant a huge increase in the size of farms and a concomitant drop in the number of farms. Our two tenants – a father and son – farm what were 10 homesteads in the early Twentieth Century.

Both the technology of seed and the technology of power tended to be output increasing in nature. By the laws of economics, that meant the benefits from the new technologies were largely passed on to consumers in the form of less expensive and more plentiful food. It has been difficult for farmers, other than for innovators and early adopters, to hold onto the gains from technology. And it's meant a dramatic decrease in the size and economic vitality of many rural cities and towns.

At the conclusion of a recent semester-long seminar attended by mostly retired Iowa State University faculty and staff who had grown up on farms, I asked whether their parents, uncles and aunts, and grandparents would have voted in the mid-1930s to refuse the new technologies had they known then what the impacts would have been. Not one hand went up. The lure of less physical work, the belief that more acres farmed would bring more prosperity to their operation, and the conviction that the extra power would permit them to be better farmers were powerful motivating forces. The fact that technology would diminish the local community crossed few minds at the time.

The long and storied history of the Master Farmer recognition program has provided an enduring beacon of what it means to be a truly outstanding farmer in those decades of constant change. A track record of outstanding crop and livestock production has always been a part of the picture. But it's been much more than that. Being a Master Farmer has meant: selfless community service; exemplary soil and water stewardship; and careful attention to the family. It's meant honesty in dealings with neighbors; supporting the public interest whether it be schools, the church or the community; and a willingness to lend a hand to a neighbor in need.

This volume is a suitable milestone in the history of Master Farmer recognition in Iowa. The values so visible in the program since the days of Henry A. Wallace as editor of *Wallaces Farmer* (and the other Wallaces who preceded him) continue to rank highly and serve to re-validate the program every year.

Neil E. Harl
Ames, Iowa
Spring 2007

the IOWA MASTER FARMER AWARD
by Aaron Butzen

In 1925, Clifford V. Gregory, editor of *Prairie Farmer* magazine in Illinois, set in motion a movement that would change the face of farming in our country forever. In an effort to reward and recognize excellence in farm citizenship, Gregory and his colleagues initiated the first-ever Master Farmer award program, honoring 23 men at a banquet in Chicago on December 2, 1925. Several other Standard Farm Papers caught on to the idea the following year, and by 1927, 300 men in 21 states had been named Master Farmers.

The motivations behind the movement were multifarious. A book about the award published by *Pennsylvania Farmer* in the 1920s defined the aim of the award as follows:

"The purpose of the Master Farmer movement is to dignify agriculture by recognizing and dramatizing its successes; to encourage farmers to take pride in their calling; to inspire farm boys and girls by showing them that outstanding success is possible in agriculture as in other occupations—not only the success that is measured in money, but what is more important, the success that comes from an upright and useful life in family and community."

As noted above, it was clear from the outset that the award was about more than farming, also encompassing involvement in family and community affairs. So in 1926, when *Wallaces Farmer* instituted the Iowa Master Farmer Award, it made perfect sense to use the magazine's motto—"Good Farming, Clear Thinking, Right Living"—as a basis for the Master Farmer scorecard.

This precept for farmers' conduct held award nominees to a higher standard of ethics, requiring that Iowa Master Farmers not only skillfully manage their farms and market their products, but also invest their time and money in the pursuit of a successful home and community life.

The movers and shakers behind the Master Farmer movement felt it was necessary to bestow upon farmers the same type of recognition received by exceptional individuals in other vocations. According to Secretary of Agriculture William Jardine in 1928, "The basic character of agriculture in our national economy makes it especially appropriate to recognize among farmers the same ability, initiative, business sense, and enterprise that are so widely recognized in other fields of activity."

The editors of *Wallaces Farmer* agreed with Mr. Jardine about the merits of such a program, and announced they were accepting nominations for the first annual Iowa Master Farmer Award in the April 9, 1926 issue of the magazine. On January 13, 1927, the first Iowa Master Farmer banquet was held in Des Moines to recognize the 1926 award winners. Eighty candidates had been nominated for the honor. *Wallaces Farmer* editors made personal visits to over 40 of them. In the end, the judges gave unanimous approval to 14 men. These first 14 Master Farmers came from all parts of Iowa, from Shenandoah to Spirit Lake, operating farms that ranged from 90 to 360 acres.

As times, trends and technology changed over the past 80 years, diversity has remained constant among winners of the Iowa Master Farmer Award. From 1926 through 2007, *Wallaces Farmer* has awarded 410 Iowans, even though the number of annual awardees has been pared down to maintain the prestige of the award. The awards program has been held every year since 1926, except during times of national distress—from 1932-1937 during the Great Depression, and from 1942-1945 during World War II.

Nomination Blank---Iowa Master Farmers

THE editors can visit the candidates suggested. The judges can select the men to be honored. But you, the neighbors and friends, must do the important thing—nominate the men who are to be considered. We appreciate your cooperation in helping us bestow recognition where it is deserved.

Candidate's Name..Postoffice...

Location of farm (how to find it)...

Age........... Years of schooling......................

Years as farmer......... Years on present farm..........

Acres owned...... Acres rented...... Acres operated......

If owner, has he ever been a renter?....................

Amount owed on land owned...........................

Amount of land or money inherited......................

....

....

Describe farm operations briefly.........................

....

....

....

....

....

What responsibility has he taken in school affairs?.........

....

....

....

....

Offices held in township and county government............

....

....

....

....

Offices held in cooperative organizations—creamery, shipping association, REA co-op, elevator, SCS district, etc...........

....

....

....

....

....

....

....

Offices held in farm organizations, civic or service organizations, etc. ....

....

....

....

....

....

....

Other positions of responsibility in the community...........

....

....

....

....

....

(Over)

A portion of the old Master Farmer nomination form

Originally, the awards were given in the year following the year of the award class—that is, the 1926 winners received their awards in 1927, the 1927 winners in 1928, and so on. In 1963, the program began naming the winners in the current year, so although the program didn't actually skip a year, there is no Master Farmer class of 1962.

One unique characteristic of the *Wallaces Farmer* Master Farmer program began with the award class of 1959, when Larry Cain, steward of the Cerro Gordo County farm, received the first-ever Master Farmer Exceptional Service Award. This award has been presented several times over the years when an individual doesn't exactly fit the Master Farmer classification but has spent his lifetime helping and serving farmers and agriculture. Many Iowa Extension specialists and university professors are among those who have received the award for helping to improve the vocation of agriculture for all.

Soon after the Iowa Master Farmer program got its start, the award winners recognized the need to organize in order to promote a closer relationship among generations of Master Farmers. Immediately following the 1928 banquet, the two existing classes of Master Farmers met and formed the Iowa Master Farmer Club. The Master Farmer Club began meeting annually to conduct business, congregate, and socialize with all past and current Master Farmers.

In the mid-1950s the Iowa Master Farmer Club decided to use club funds to aid the education of agriculture and agriculture communications students, and began sponsoring scholarships at Iowa State University. These continue today as a partnership with *Wallaces Farmer*.

In 2002, the Iowa Master Farmer Foundation was formed to help ensure the future of the scholarships and the awards program. That same foundation made the decision to sponsor the creation of this history book. Also in 2002, the Iowa Master Farmer Club changed its name to the Iowa Master Farmer Association.

The Iowa Master Farmer Award has a long and rich history which is documented in the pages of this book. However, the book is only the current snapshot of a program that has persevered through eight decades and countless changes in technology and lifestyle. The Iowa Master Farmer Award is an honor that will doubtless endure as long as the world needs to be fed.

Intern Aaron Butzen hard at work

TABLE OF CONTENTS

CHAPTER 1
~
1926 - 1932: Pre-Depression

Following relatively good farm prices from 1900 to 1920, Iowa experienced a precipitous economic decline in the next decade. Land values crashed after World War I as the demand for commodities weakened. Some Iowa farmers were able to improve their well-being by adopting new practices to lessen the burden of common farm chores.

For example, a few farmers "upgraded" to pedal-powered milking machines. Others used wind power for pumping and storing water. Farmers still used live horsepower for fieldwork but some were acquiring tractors. With horses, walking behind a plow or disk was tiring. When the horses needed a rest, the farmer could rest as well. Horses provided transportation to a neighbor's farm, creamery, school, church or town.

Threshing rings build legends
Entire neighborhoods had threshing rings. Some men loaded oat bundles, which were hauled to the threshing machine with teams of horses. Some farmers pitched the bundles into the threshing machine. Still others hauled away grain and one or two managed building the straw stack.

Someone had to rise early to stoke the boiler on the steam engine to have power when the threshing crew arrived. In addition to regular chores, farm wives prepared meals for the threshing crew. Tales of those hearty threshing dinners remain legendary today.

The advent of the internal combustion engine brought tractors powered by kerosene or gasoline. The new technology meant farmers needed less time to plant and harvest crops. Tractors took a lot less time to fire up in the morning than a steam engine. Automobiles provided transportation to church, school and town.

Communication trims isolation
Other improvements in rural life came quickly as well, such as rural roads. Rural telephone cooperatives improved communication. Radio brought news into rural homes. The U.S. Postal Service developed Rural Free Delivery (RFD) and private enterprise brought electricity to a few farms along major highways.

Iowa State College, in its eighth decade, was a vital part of the Agricultural Extension Service, which evolved in this period providing helpful educational services for farm families. Several farm organizations were formed to lobby state and federal governments for the needs of farmers who were vulnerable to the effects of oversupply of farm commodities.

Henry C. Wallace (U.S. Secretary of Agriculture, 1921-1924) and members of Congress emphasized the need for farmers to work together for the common good and urged that cooperative associations be formed to aid in purchasing supplies and marketing products. The federal government had little interest at this time in playing a role in boosting farm prices.

1926 Iowa Farm Facts

FARMS & INCOME

Number of Iowa farms	214,000

LIVESTOCK

	Inventory	*Average price*
Cattle and calves	4.2 million head	$8.00/cwt (beef)
Hogs and pigs	10.1 million head	$11.68/cwt
	Production	*Inventory*
Chickens (Layers)	2.4 billion eggs	23.1 million birds
Milk	5.2 billion lbs.	

CROPS

	Harvested acres	*Yield*	*Production*	*Avg price*
All Hay	3.4 million	0.99 tons/acre	3.3 million tons	
Corn	9.5 million	39 bu./acre	371 million bu.	$0.69/bu.
Soybeans	10,000	15 bu./acre	150,000	$2.54/bu.
Oats	6.4 million	31.6 bu./acre	201 million bu.	
Wheat	387,000	21 bu./acre	8.2 million bu.	

The Master Farmer medallion

1926

IOWA MASTER FARMERS

~ January 14, 1927

What makes a man rank as a Master Farmer? What standards must he reach to make it fitting for us to point to him as an example for younger farmers to follow? What sort of farm management and operation is required? What leadership must he furnish his community? What aims, plans and ideals must he help build for his children, his church and his schools?

Last April, we told of our plan to honor a group of these leaders among Iowa farmers. We printed our scorecard and asked for nominations. Out of the 80 nominated, 14 were voted by judges as worthy of the title, "Master Farmer." The scorecard that was used grouped the requirements under the three heads: Good Farming, Clear Thinking, Right Living.

The first part of the scorecard covers the operation and management of the farm. Whether the candidate has carried out a program that increased the fertility and crop-producing power of the soil is the question of first importance.

That the 14 men selected stand high in this regard is borne out by the records. More than one-half doubled the yield of corn since they began the operation of the farms they now own. All have increased yields very materially.

By practice, these men have proved that a definite rotation including the most efficient legumes, is the foundation of profitable farming in Iowa. On 11 farms, this has involved the use of limestone; on seven, more than half the farm has been given an application. Tiling, weed eradication, the use of improved seed, and better methods of cultivation have been important in increasing yields.

Efficiency in handling livestock is one of the most important factors in making Iowa farms profitable. Efficiency calls for many things. All of these men try to feed well-balanced rations. Enough legume hay produced at home to meet livestock needs is the aim of all of these Master Farmers. All have raised alfalfa for this purpose. Two of them had none in 1926, due to winter killing. Silage is used on 11 of these farms.

In 1926, 11 of these men raised their hogs on clean ground. Seven had been doing this regularly for a long enough time to classify them as pioneers in using the McLean system. Profitable farming in Iowa generally involves hog raising. It is rather significant that every one of these men ranks high as a hog raiser. Some are good purebred hog men, some are outstanding market hog producers, some are primarily feeders of purchased hogs. All have made money with hogs. Cattle fattening, baby beef production, beef cattle breeding stock and dairying are found on different farms. Each man, in his specialty, is a good cattleman.

If men are producers of high-yielding crops and made money handling cattle and hogs, the effective use of labor, machinery and buildings was found to accompany these things.

The second part of our scorecard dealt with the items grouped under "Clear Thinking."

We gave first importance to their financial standing and methods, and plans of handling business. Nearly all kept very complete and detailed records of the farm business. Only two failed to take a yearly inventory; and only three did not work out the total income and expenses, and net income for the year. All but one kept a record of income and expenses as the items occurred. Two kept detailed cost of production and daily labor records.

The relation of income and expenses for the last five years was studied and most of these Master Farmers made a very favorable showing. A perfect record was not made, however. Each year of the five did not show a profit above a return on the investment after expenses and labor was paid.

What is wise distribution of surplus income for farmers, especially during the past five years? Eight of these Master Farmers have spent part of theirs giving children a college education. Two others are carrying endowment insurance that matures when their children reach the age for college attendance. All but two men carry life insurance that requires part of their surplus income. Several of them carry amounts far in excess of that carried by most farmers. Payments on farms, farm and home improvements, and support of church and church school are items that call for large parts of the net incomes of these Master Farmers.

If a farmer does clear thinking, he is bound to be interested in the schools of his community. Each of these men has served as an official in the schools his children attend. More than half have served in such positions for 15 years and several for more than 20 years.

Clear thinking involves an interest in farm organizations. Not only is membership held but leadership given from among these men. Every one of these has belonged to and served as an officer in some leading farm organization. All belong to shipping associations; several are interested in co-operative creameries, elevators and feed companies. All but two are officers of mutual insurance companies.

Farming is a continuing business. The operation of the farm, and community work and activity, will need to be done after we pass on. Each of these men is helping sons or others to prepare to take his place when the need arises.

A thoughtful interest in public affairs is part of clear thinking among farmers. They are the state's heaviest taxpayers and most directly affected by many items of legislation. More than mere voting is required. Service in township, county and legislative office, as well as on boards having supervision over public and semi-public affairs has been performed by these Master Farmers. These men have done this work as a duty and not for the honor of office.

The third division of our scorecard deals with "Right Living". This involves giving the farm family the best surroundings for a happy, useful existence. It means the best training possible for the children. It calls for an interest and activity in those agencies that build for higher aims and deals in the home and community. It calls for friendly relations with neighbors and businessmen.

Each of the homes represented has a comfortable house, large enough and well-adapted to the needs of the family. Shade, shelter and fruit are provided. Several have provided surroundings of unusual tastefulness and beauty. The homes that 11 of these men have provided for their families are modern and contain all the equipment and devices considered desirable to make life and living comfortable. The other three fall only a few points from reaching this standard.

High school training for all the children and for nearly all college training has been given or is planned.

No man was refused consideration because of lack of interest in church and church affairs. Yet it was found that no one who measured up to the standard set in other things failed to belong to some church and have a part in its affairs. More than half were Sunday school teachers. Nearly all serve in some official capacity in the church of their choice.

The Master Farmer offers leadership not only in religious work but in club work and other young people's activities. Such an interest was not required for consideration, but all were found to have a part in this phase of "Right Living." Nearly all were distinct leaders in club work.

In our scorecard, we left a place for additional points to be given for exceptional merit in a special field. Each of these men had a specialty for which additional credit was given; this specialty varied from a soil fertility program to church work, from efforts to bring town and country people closer, to outstanding leadership in club work.

George W. Christophel, of Bremer County, has farmed in Iowa for 20 years. He originally came from Illinois. He farms 100 acres, bought 13 years ago. The land had no buildings or trees and was badly depleted in fertility, needing tiling, lime and clearing of rock. A fine set of buildings has been provided, the land made productive and all put in rotation. Alfalfa and sweet clover are grown. A dairy herd and hogs are the chief sources of income. Mr. Christophel has served in an official capacity for schools, farm organization and church. He is, at present, serving his second term in the state assembly.

George Godfrey, of Kossuth County, is 42 years old. He farms 320 acres; the first half was bought 13 years ago, the last half eight years ago. He began using sweet clover regularly in the rotation 12 years ago. He has doubled corn yields on the land under cultivation when bought. He specializes in baby beef and pork production. He is exceptionally efficient in his use of labor. Mr. Godfrey has taught one full term at Ames and three winter short courses. He is active in church work. His leadership among farmers made him a delegate to the last national Farm Bureau meeting.

Lenus Hagglund, of Page County, is the oldest of the Master Farmers. He operates 360 acres with the aid of two sons. Crops are largely marketed by feeding steers and raising hogs. He bought part of this farm 32 years ago. He served as a school official for over 20 years. He was the first Farm Bureau president in his county. His oldest son was among the first in club work in Iowa. Four children have attended college, two graduated. He is a member of the state assembly.

Fred W. La Doux, of Dickinson County, has farmed in this county 32 years; seven on this farm of 137 acres. An exceptionally fine set of buildings has been erected and crop yields have more than doubled. A corn yield of 85 bushels in 1926 made the record among the Master Farmer group. He is a leading Chester White hog breeder. He shifted from cattle feeding to dairying three years ago. Mr. La Doux is on the Spirit Lake school board, is county president of his farm organization, and has devoted time to giving town people an understanding of farm problems.

Charles D. Kirkpatrick, of Keokuk County, was born on the 320-acre farm he now operates. He has done exceptional work with a permanent soil fertility program, corn breeding, and cost and business records for farming. He is a writer on farm and economic problems. Mr. Kirkpatrick has given much time to church and young people's activities.

William McArthur, of Cerro Gordo County, is 40 years old. He and his brother operate 360 acres. Definite rotations, including soybeans and sweet clover, cattle feeding, improved seed and tiling have doubled yields. He is a leader in the production of soybeans and adapted seed corn. He maintains a pure-bred herd of Polled Herefords. Mr. McArthur has been an extremely valuable leader in the local farm organization, shipping association, mutual insurance, co-operative buying, school, church and the county fair.

H.S. Martin farmed, in Jasper County, 24 years. For two years he has operated 640 acres near Taintor. He is an outstanding hog raiser and cattle feeder. Corn yields have been raised

50% in five years, to an average of 65 bushels. He has a soils test plot in cooperation with Iowa State College on his 80-acre farm near Newton. He keeps complete cost of production records. He has furnished leadership in farm organizations.

E.F. Morris, of Hardin County, operates 110 acres. He has run this farm for 29 years, the first few years as a tenant. He began the use of lime 10 years ago. His corn yielded 65 bushels in 1926, 75 bushels in 1925. Hogs are the largest source of income. A small herd of Polled Shorthorns is kept. Buff Rock chickens are a major source of income. He has devoted much time and study to schools and school problems. He is a leader in the church and cooperative affairs of the community.

Lewis Morris, Polk County, is 54 years old. He farms 230 acres that was bought 16 years ago. A dairy herd was maintained several years but sold three years back, partly because he felt it might interfere with college attendance for his children. All land under cultivation has been limed, or will be, before spring. One hundred and sixty acres received an application of acid phosphate in 1926. Hog feeding is the major livestock enterprise. Leadership in school, church, club work, and Farm Bureau is furnished by Mr. Morris. He has had an active part in the Farm Business short course at Ames.

Fred W. Nelson, Story County, is 40 years old. He was born on the 240-acre farm he operates. He markets his crops through fattening cattle and raising hogs. He seeded sweet clover in 1916 and during the last four years has used it regularly in rotation. His leadership and activities have been unusual for so young a man. He is county president of the Farm Bureau, and an officer since its organization. He has served in an official capacity in school, township, church and lodge.

Dan J. Schnittjer, of Delaware County, operates 198 acres. He has owned his farm for 17 years. An exceptionally well-adapted set of buildings has been built. He is a dairyman,

cattle feeder and hog raiser and feeder. Feeding purchased hogs is the largest enterprise, as many as 2,000 head being handled. Mr. Schnittjer is active in the Grange and Farm Bureau. He is a leader in church, school and cooperative organizations.

P.P. Stewart, of Fayette County, farms 320 acres. He has operated this farm 22 years, the first nine as tenant. He is one of the leading dairymen of the state. Dairying is the major enterprise and the business is built around the Holstein herd. Mr. Stewart has furnished outstanding leadership in farm organization, school and club work activities. He is a member of the state fair board.

Earl Watts, Page County, farms 240 acres. He came to Iowa from Arkansas 24 years ago. He bought 160 acres of soil-depleted, weed-infested land 22 years ago. It is now part of his very fertile, finely-improved farm. An exceptionally fine set of buildings has been erected. Hog raising and cattle feeding are the livestock enterprises. Mr. Watts has had a real part in making school, church and farm organization programs effective in his community.

William Wendt, of Bremer County, has operated the farm he now owns since his marriage 31 years ago. It consists of 90 acres. His entire farm has been tiled. A regular rotation is followed, with corn yields of 60 bushels. He is an outstanding hog raiser and has a good grade dairy herd. Mr. Wendt has been active in club work and he has served as a leader in all farm and cooperative organizations in his community.

G. W. CHRISTOPHEL

Bremer

Hog Raising and Dairy Farming

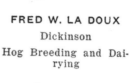

GEORGE GODFREY

Kossuth

Baby Beeves and Hog Raising

LENUS HAGGLUND

Page

Hog Raising and Steer Feeding

FRED W. LA DOUX

Dickinson

Hog Breeding and Dairying

C. D. KIRKPATRICK

Keokuk

Grain Production and Hog Raising

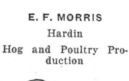

WILLIAM McARTHUR

Cerro Gordo

Cattle Feeding and Legume Production

H. S. MARTIN

Jasper

Hog Raising and Cattle Feeding

E. F. MORRIS

Hardin

Hog and Poultry Production

LEWIS MORRIS

Polk

Hog Feeding and Corn Production

FRED W. NELSON

Story

Hog Raising and Cattle Feeding

D. J. SCHNITTJER

Delaware

Dairying and Hog Feeding

P. P. STEWART

Fayette

Dairying and Cattle Breeding

EARL WATTS

Page

Hog Raising and Cattle Feeding

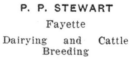

WILLIAM WENDT

Bremer

Hog Raising and Dairying

The 1926 Iowa Master Farmers

IOWA MASTER FARMERS

1927 ~ January 13, 1928

In what way do the men who make up the group that have been designated as Master Farmers differ from the general run of folks operating farms in Iowa? They are not perfect in their methods of farming, even though they have done a better job of handling their own farm business than most of us. They are subject to 1,001 handicaps and unexpected changes due to variable weather, markets, soil conditions and so forth, to which others are subject, and they do not have a perfect score in overcoming these. But as a whole, this group has succeeded unusually well in meeting and conquering the problems that have confronted them. They have done more than merely handle the problems involved in running the farm. They have furnished constructive leadership in the life and activities of the community in which they reside. And by this is meant more than merely the holding of official position in schools, township, government, co-operative organizations, general farm organizations and churches. As real leaders they have worked at the job not only of directing the activities of the organizations, but of encouraging and developing the abilities of those among whom they live and work.

Must Have High Standard of Home Life

But a Master Farmer must not only achieve a reasonable degree of success in the operation of his own business and the organized activities that are a part of good community life and living. The standard of the home life must also be high. This calls for giving the family the best surroundings possible for a happy, useful existence. It means interest and effort devoted to education, in the widest sense. It means also that the Master Farmer and his wife must be interested in a constant effort to raise the aims and ideals of their family and their community.

A reasonably high achievement in the all-around requirements that go with being a Master Farmer appear to require permanency. Farmers that moved several times during their period of farm operation seem to fail to measure up to the requirements. This group of 16 has operated the farms upon which they live for an average of 23 out of 25 years of farming. Only one has been an owner-operator of a farm other than the present one, and he moved to the old home place when he made the change.

In the selection of the group of 14 Master Farmers in 1926, and 16 in 1927, the scorecard that was used grouped the requirements under the three heads: Good Farming, Clear Thinking, and Right Living.

The first part of the scorecard covers the farm operations and the degree of success of these. In the selection of the group of 16 men honored, there was no partiality shown as to the sizes of the farms. Operators of farms ranging in size from 120 to 720 acres are in the group. The average size was 308 acres. Six were 240 acres or less in size. Fifteen out of the sixteen are owners of all or part of farms they now operate. In the selection of this group, there was no bias against tenant farmers. However, when a man has been farming 15 years or more and has made good as a farm operator, and proved a definite factor in community life, he and his family have generally bought a farm and taken over its operation. The one tenant on our list has operated the same farm for 16 years on the stock-share plan.

A program that increases fertility and crop yielding power of the land operated in a fundamental standard for the selection of men for the Master Farmer group. In this regard, each has a creditable record. Six have doubled the corn and legume yields on their farms since they began farming in their present location. All have increased the yields of grain and legumes. This has meant the feeding of all or nearly all the grain produced to livestock, the careful utilization of manure, and use of rotations containing legumes. This increase has also been brought about by the use of improved varieties of corn and small grain, a shift to more efficient legumes, the use of limestone and phosphorus in some form, tiling, and the putting into cultivation of land formerly not tillable.

All of these men are growing alfalfa, and 12 out of 16 are users of sweet clover. All have applied limestone in considerable amounts, except three. These three men are located on farms where alfalfa and sweet clover grow readily without the application of lime. Eight are carrying out a program of systematically applying limestone to all the land under cultivation, and have covered more than half their tilled land. Eight have used super-phosphate (acid phosphate) in considerable amounts, and, of these, four are using it regularly once in the rotation. Rock phosphate has been used by four men; one is covering his whole farm systematically.

Six of this group have given every new variety of oats produced at the Iowa station a careful trial, and every one of the 16 is using one of these improved varieties. Five of the group have entered the corn grown on their farms in the state yield test with creditable showing. All but two are growing strains of corn that through the state and county yield tests have been proven good for their location.

Marketing crops produced by means of livestock is typical of Iowa Master Farmers. Efficiency in handling livestock is required if farm profits are to be made. More than feeding balanced rations is necessary. Livestock must be adapted to the farm and to the interest and inclination of the farm operator. This is as true of Master Farmers as of the rest of us.

Hogs an Important Source of Income

We find that on every one of the farms this group operates, hogs are an important source of income. Eleven out of 16 follow the McLean system of hog raising in all its details. Nine have been pioneers of this in their home communities. All are producers of market hogs. On all the farms, over a period of years, hogs have been profitable. This is because these men have followed the work of experiment stations, use minerals, well-balanced rations, make liberal use of pasture crops, and vaccinate against cholera.

On 15 of these farms, cattle are a major enterprise, and in his specialty each is a good cattleman. In this group there are three men who maintain herds of specialized dairy breeds, and two who have herds of dual-purpose cattle. All are cow-test association herds, four of which have led their local associations one or more years. On eight of these farms, the fattening of purchased steers is a major enterprise. Two specialize in baby beef production. One farm has a general-purpose herd of cows, part of which are milked and the remainder nurse calves. Four of this group have made sheep a major enterprise.

Effective use of labor, machinery and buildings has been found to accompany skillful and profitable crop raising and livestock handling.

The second part of our scorecard deals

with the items grouped under "Clear Thinking." To be considered a Master Farmer, we require that a man must have achieved a creditable financial standing and must have kept a record of his business transactions. Nearly all have kept complete and detailed records of their farm business. All but two took an annual inventory, and 12 worked out their total expense and net income each year. Two keep daily labor records, and four others keep diaries of the farm operations.

Most of the group made a highly favorable financial showing for the last five years. All were in better shape financially than five years ago, and more than half showed a profit above interest on the investment for the whole period.

But more than a mere making of money is required of Master Farmers. The use they make of surplus is equally important. All but two carry life insurance—some a surprisingly large amount for farmers and men whose incomes have never been large. Payments on farms, of course, absorb a good deal of the surplus of families in this group because eight are operating farms not completely paid for. But these men have not allowed indebtedness on the farm to absorb all of their surplus when a wise plan called for use of part of it for other purposes. New homes have been erected by three men in this group within the last six years. Additional machinery, and installation of modern conveniences in the house have taken a considerable share of surplus income of this group.

Seven of the Master Farmers have spent part of their surplus income in recent years giving a college training to children. Four others are paying for endowment insurance policies maturing at the time their children reach college attendance age. Our Master Farmers' families in their distribution of their income have supported liberally their churches and various activities connected with the church.

If a farmer thinks clearly, he is interested in the schools in his community. Fourteen out of this group have served as officials in the schools their children attend. Nine have served as a school official for 10 years or more.

Interest in farm organizations is a necessary part of a well-rounded life in a farm community. In this group not only membership, but an active part in leadership is key for each man. Every one has belonged to and served as an officer in one of the general farm organizations. Master Farmers living in communities that have cooperative creameries, elevators, or shipping associations are not only members but are holding places of responsibility in these organizations.

Farming is or should be a continuing business. Children should be raised and trained to take our places when we pass on. Three men have already taken into partnership a son to carry on the operation of the farm. Four others will take this step within the next four or five years, according to present plans.

Under "Right Living" are grouped those outward features by which we attempt to measure the things that should build happy, contented homes.

On each of these 16 farms is a comfortable house, at least fairly well-adapted to the needs of the family. Twelve of these families live in houses having the modern conveniences that make life and living more comfortable. The remaining homes are largely modern but lacking in one or two respects.

High school training or its equivalent has been provided for all the children that are old enough from the families of these Master Farmers. College training has been given in nearly every case where the children reached that age.

No one nominated was refused consideration because of a lack of interest in church affairs. Yet it was found that 13 not only belonged, but held a place of responsibility in the church organization to which they belong. All the Master Farmer families attend, give financial support and have some part in the local church of their choice. The Master Farmers not only furnished religious leadership but nearly every one is a leader in club work and other young people's activities.

There were nearly 100 nominees for Master Farmer to whom personal visits were made and their farm business, home life and community activities studied in the selection of this group of 16 Master Farmers. Each in this group of 16 is well aware of many failures in coming up to the ideal they set for themselves. Each also falls short in some of the things we wish to find in our ideal Master Farmers. Nevertheless, we feel their records of achievement well merit the designation of Master Farmer, and they are worthy of being pointed to as examples for younger farmers to follow.

The 1927 Master Farmers are:

Carl T. Anderson has operated a 400-acre Washington County farm as a stock-share tenant for 16 years. He markets each year over 500 head of hogs. For five years, he has handled his hogs strictly according to the McLean system. He feeds two to six cars of steers each year. He has spread nearly 500 tons of limestone. Anderson is a leader in local farmers' institute, general farm organizations and church.

H.D. Backhaus, of Worth County, has operated the 220-acre farm he owns for 23 years. He has specialized in raising market hogs and sheep. He has planned and built an unusually convenient and well-adapted set of farm buildings. He helped organize and has served as an officer in the following: cooperative elevator, creamery, shipping association and Farm Bureau.

Frank Beath has farmed in Adams County for 36 years. He operates 340 acres, 260 of which he owns. Raising and feeding baby beef is his specialty. Hogs are also a major source of income. He is carrying on a definite liming program. Mr. Beath is an outstanding leader in Farm Bureau and club work in his county.

A.J. Blakely, Poweshiek County, was born on the farm he has operated for 17 years. He farms 260 acres, of which he owns 130. He specializes in Delaine Merino sheep. A strain of this breed has been bred continuously on this farm since 1868. Mr. Blakely has served as an officer in the following: shipping association, State Wool Growers' Association, county club work, church board and Sunday school.

R.R. Clampitt owns and operates 570 acres in Hardin County. He has been farming 26 years. Purebred Milking Shorthorn cattle is his leading source of income, although hogs are a major enterprise, and sheep and draft horses are raised and sold. Mr. Clampitt is a constructive leader in the consolidated school and its activities, and active in cow test and breed association work.

E.L. Hill, of Dallas County, has farmed in his present location for over 40 years. At present a son operates the home farm of 720 acres in partnership. Fattening cattle—10-15 cars annually—is the leading source of income. Raising and feeding hogs is also a major enterprise. Mr. Hill has been a leader in community enterprises and farm organizations.

John M. Hunt is an owner and operator of 347 acres in Hardin County. He has farmed for 20 years, 14 as an owner. Cattle feeding and hog raising are chief sources of income. He was one of the first in his community to use lime, which is being supplied to all land under cultivation. He has been the leader and president for 18 years of the Four-County Winder Fair, at Ackley. He is active in church and general farm organizations.

Oscar W. Johnson, of Marshall County, has been farming in his present location 18 years. He operates 250 acres. Four to six cars of cattle are fattened each year. He is an extensive user of limestone and a large grower of alfalfa. Mr. Johnson has served as an officer in the Farm Bureau, shipping association, consolidated school and church.

George W. Leffler, Van Buren County, graduated from Ames in 1904, and has been on the farm he now owns since graduation. He operates 320 acres. He was a pioneer in tiling in his community. Cattle feeding and hog raising are the major livestock enterprises. Mr.

Leffler has given much time to the development of local community social life, club work and farm organizations.

A.B. Myhr, of Winnebago County, farms 120 acres, which he owns. He has operated this farm for 22 years. Dairying and hog raising are the major livestock enterprises. He is carrying on a soil fertility experimental plot. Mr. Myhr is active in the work of county fair, boys' and girls' clubs, cooperative elevator, creamery, shipping association, school and church.

Roy T. Pullen, of Clay County, farmed as a tenant in Sac County five years before buying the farm of 160 acres he operates. All the farm buildings, including an excellent house, and unusually good windbreaks, orchard, shrubbery and shade, have been put on the place in 16 years. He is a pioneer on growing popcorn in Clay County. Mr. Pullen has served as president of the farmers' elevator, shipping association and county Farm Bureau, and on the board of his church and county fair.

Ray Redfern, Des Moines County, has farmed 23 years. He has owned 160 acres for 17 years and rents an additional 80 acres. He specializes in producing seed corn and certified seed oats. He raises and feeds baby beef and hogs. Mr. Redfern is active in schoolwork and in his local church. He has held every office in his county Farm Bureau, helped organize the state federation, and is a member of the executive board. He is active in the Iowa Corn Growers Association and the Iowa Experiment Association.

Adolph Schultz, of Pottawattamie County, began farming for himself 23 years ago, on the farm he now owns. He operates 277 acres, 197 of which he owns. Hogs and baby beef are the important livestock enterprises. Alfalfa and sweet clover are regularly grown on all land under cultivation. Mr. Schultz has had an active part in a community band and orchestra for nearly 30 years—four years as a teacher. He is an outstanding leader in farmers' organizations. He has taken a leading part in church,

school and community social activities.

John N. Smith, of Jones County, has operated the farm which he owns for 40 years. At present, he is running it in partnership with a son. The farm contains 275 acres. Hog raising, fattening steers and dairying are the livestock enterprises. Mr. Smith is carrying on a definite liming program. He has been a leader in church, school, Farm Bureau, shipping association and cooperative creamery affairs, and served as an officer in each. He is gradually retiring from these activities, with those he has helped train taking his place.

George R. Steen, of Muscatine County, has operated a farm for 18 years. He bought the 139 acres he now owns from his father, nine years ago. He is carrying on a systematic liming and soil building program. Dairying and hog raising are the leading livestock enterprises. He has specialized in seed corn production in the state corn yield contest and helped to organize the Iowa Corn Growers Association. He is active in the local Grange and church work.

E.E. Tracy, of Chickasaw County, has owned and operated the farm where he lives for 38 years. The farm is being operated at present in partnership with his son. The farm contains 320 acres. Purebred Red Polled cattle are the leading livestock enterprise. Mr. Tracy has been active in the cooperative creamery and general cooperative company and in school affairs. He is gradually retiring, having five sons and sons-in-law farming in the neighborhood to take his place.

MASTER FARMERS OF 1927

C. T. Anderson
Washington

H. D. Backhaus
Worth

F. H. Beath
Adams

A. J. Blakely
Poweshiek

E. L. Hill
Dallas

J. N. Hunt
Hardin

O. W. Johnson
Marshall

G. V. Leffler
Van Buren

A. B. Myhr
Winnebago

R. T. Pullen
Clay

Ray Redfern
Des Moines

Adolph Schultz
Pottawattamie

J. N. Smith
Jones

George Steen
Muscatine

E. E. Tracy
Chickasaw

R. R. CLAMPITT, Hardin County

The 1927 Iowa Master Farmers

IOWA MASTER FARMERS
~
January 25, 1929

Here they are! To the 14 Master Farmers selected in 1926, and the 16 Master Farmers named in 1927, are added these 15 1928 Master Farmers. Iowa greets them with pride.

"Good Farming, Clear Thinking, Right Living" is the standard by which these men are judged. Out of 135 nominees, these 15 seemed to the board of judges to meet most nearly the demands of this motto of *Wallaces' Farmer*.

These Master Farmers have proved that farming is more than a method of earning their daily bread and accumulating enough money to keep them out of the county home. Farming, as they know it, involves living on the land they till, close by the livestock they raise and feed. It means making a home. Their accomplishments are measured, therefore, not only by the corn they raise and the hogs they market, but by the homes they provide for their families, and the friendly aid they give their communities.

Elijah

Reasonable Share of Modern Conveniences

Barringer

According to the standards set by *Wallaces' Farmer*, Master Farmers must provide for their families houses that are well-enough built and equipped to aid in the living of happy, useful lives. This calls for a home with a

reasonable share of the so-called modern conveniences. This standard has been met by all of this group of Master Farmers. Five of the 15 have built new, all-modern homes since 1922. On the other hand, five have houses built 30 or more years ago. These older houses, two of which were built upward of 50 years ago, have been rearranged, and in all running water, electric light, furnaces, screened porches and built-in features have been provided. Four out of the five old houses have bathrooms with complete fixtures, and the fifth was planning on this additional convenience when visited by the representative of *Wallaces' Farmer*.

The intermediate group of homes—houses neither new nor old—were all provided with water system, furnace, electric lights, bathroom and power washer. The homes of all the 15 were large enough to provide ample room, not only for the convenience of the immediate family, but to take care of visitors and hired help without crowding.

But more than the right kind of a house is required. Surroundings of the home must be in keeping. Fields over-run with morning-glory, cockleburs or Canada thistle, that crowd out the corn, oats and clover or reduce their yield, must not be found on the farms of Master

Everett

Foster

Farmers. In the same way, the chickens and pigs must not crowd the grass, flowers and shrubbery, and children out of the house-yard. These requirements, the 1928 Master Farmers have met.

But right living calls for more than good physical surroundings. It means the best possible training for the children. This involves schooling, of course, but it also includes more than that. It means reading material of the sort that builds and not merely fills. It means interest on the part of the Master Farmer and his family in those things that build higher ideals in the homes of the community.

More than a county school education should be the standard set by Master Farmers for their children. In this year's group there are 45 children among 14 families. Among those who have reached or passed the age for high school, all have attended high school or its equivalent. Only one has left high school without completing his course. Eleven out of a possible 16 attended college. Nine completed a college course.

Church membership and attendance have never been set up as a requirement for achieving the title of Master Farmer. But this year, as in the two previous years, the men who reached the standard set in the management of their farms and their livestock, and in the providing of a good home and educational facilities, who were interested in their community enough to support and help build up farm and cooperative organizations were all interested in a church in their home community. More than mere membership and financial support is the standard that has been set by these Master Farmers in regard to the church

Hazen

and its activities. Eleven of these men are serving their churches as officers. Among this group of Master Farmers are two choir leaders and five or six Sunday school teachers and superintendents.

Gronna

All Active in Farm Organizations

All the Master Farmers selected have been active in general farm organizations. In this group, four have served as local officers of two farm organizations. Seven have served or are serving as president of the county Farm Bureau.

With one exception, each has served as an officer of one or more farmer-owned cooperative organizations. Four have been directors or presidents of cooperative creameries. Nine have served on the boards of cooperatives handling grain and feeds. Seven have been mutual telephone officials, and an equal number have served mutual insurance companies in an official capacity. Three have been officials of cow testing associations. Nine have served as president or on the board of directors of county fairs, and two on the board of supervisors of their counties. Ten have helped direct local shipping associations. In the group this year are the president and former vice-president of the state shippers' association.

Each, with one exception, has served as an officer of the local or consolidated school. More than half of the 1928 group has so served for 10 or more years. Eleven or 12 have served as township trustees or clerk. In addition to the official and organization duties, these men have found time to serve their communities in numerous unlisted activities such as being active in bringing a cooperative

Kalsem

creamery into being, educating their neighbors in a constructive plan of road improvement or arousing a desire for and pride in a high standard of maintenance of a local cemetery. The question arises as to whether these men have done all these numerous activities well, and if so, if this outside work has not been at the expense of efficiency in the operation of their own farm business.

Miller

Building Up the Soil

These men have set a high standard of farm operation. They have put into operation plans for building up soil. These plans vary in details but all are sound and constructive. Programs in this field have raised and are raising crop yields and are making profits.

All have used limestone, three in small amounts, however. The other 12, finding it highly desirable and profitable, are applying it as part of the regular program to all or most of the tilled land. They have used on an average about 250 tons. All grow alfalfa. Ten seeded sweet clover in both 1927 and 1928. All but two have tried superphosphate and nine are using it regularly once or more in the rotation. One is using rock phosphate. The use of limestone and phosphate when it is required to make the best use of land and crops, and the carrying out of a definite rotation, including the most efficient legumes, is the foundation of profitable farming for the 1928 Master Farmers.

Turning the grain and forage produced into meat and livestock products at a profit is the second step. Not one of these men market any large amount of grain direct, except for seed. Seven are regular feeders of purchased steers, and fatten from 50 to 250 head each year. Two others fatten cattle some years. On five of the farms dairying is an important source of income; on two it is the most important. One Master

Newton

Farmer produces purebred cattle for breeding. Balanced rations, legume hay, study of markets, and cow testing associations go with cattle feeding and dairying as these men practice it.

As on most Iowa farms, hogs are the leading enterprise in regard to net income on a majority of the farms operated by this group. Several are outstanding producers of market hogs. Four raise 300 head or more yearly.

No Cholera on These Farms

Thirteen out of the 14 that raise hogs in considerable numbers vaccinate regularly year after year whether cholera is present in the community or not. As a regular practice they have been doing it an average of 13 years.

Whether in improved methods in crop or livestock raising, in club work or rural church affairs, in the organization of a cooperative creamery or in the running of an efficient school system, this group of Master Farmers offers constructive leadership. Here are a few notes about each of the 15:

Edward Reimer, of Crawford County, began farming in 1898 on the 260 acres he now owns. This man is an outstanding raiser and feeder of cattle. The farm operations are built around this enterprise. His judgment of feeder cattle is so highly valued by other men fattening cattle in his community, that he buys for a number of them at the Denver cattle show. This year he had orders for nearly 40 cars. Mr. Reimer has been active in Farmers' Union and Farm Bureau. He has given much time to club work and has served as officer for the local bank, school and elevator.

C. Everett Smith, of Jasper County, has operated the same farm of 160 acres for 19 years. He is carrying out a definite liming program and has the first corn yield test plot in Jasper County. He is an outstanding hog raiser. Mr. Smith has served as presi-

33

dent of the county Farm Bureau and as master of the local Grange; he is president of the county fair. He is extremely active in church work.

Otto F. Schultz, of Poweshiek County, in partnership with his brother Henry, owns and operates 440 acres. They have been partners in farming for 33 years. Beef cattle and hogs are their major livestock enterprises. Mr. Schultz has been a school and bank official, member of the board of supervisors, and has served as president of the Farm Bureau and chairman of club work. An adequate system of graded and graveled roads reaching every town, township and community in Poweshiek County has been one of Mr. Schultz's pet projects.

Paul Strickler, of Appanoose County, is 40 years old. He was raised in Centerville, where his father was engaged in business. After attending college he spent four years in Idaho, raising cattle. Fifteen years ago he began farming on a seriously depleted 80 acres on the edge of Centerville. Mr. Strickler recently bought two other farms. These are operated on a stock-share plan and are being built up by the use of lime, of which he was the first extensive user in the county and by legumes and Jersey cattle. He is not only trying to have the partners on these farms make money, but wants them to become interested in community and farm organization activities. He himself devotes a good deal of time to Farm Bureau work.

Seth N. Miller, of Warren County, is 60 years old and the oldest of the 1928 Master Farmers. He began farming 38 years ago. He owns 280 acres, 80 of which he operates himself, the remainder being operated by a nephew on a stock-share lease. Mr. Miller was one of the first extensive users of agricultural limestone in Warren County. His farms are among the leading ones in the county in crop yields. Mr. and Mrs. Miller retired from active farming a

Reimer

Schuelke

few years ago, but found living in town more tiring than farming and returned to active farm operation five years ago. They have two children, both college graduates.

Earl Elijah, of Cedar County, operates the largest farm of the 1928 Master Farmers, 800 acres. Of this, 480 acres is rented and 320 owned. He began farming in 1913, and is an outstanding cattle feeder. He is a graduate of Cornell College and Ames. Mr. Elijah is carrying on a definite soil building program, including lime and phosphate applications. He has served as president of the school board, Farm Bureau, lumber company and shipping association.

Harold E. Barringer, of Palo Alto County, began farming 21 years ago. He is the owner of 304 acres and rents additional land. He has limed nearly all the land he owns that is tilled and uses superphosphate regularly. He is one of the largest growers of alfalfa in the county. He is an outstanding hog producer and raises 300 to 400 yearly. Mr. Barringer is county Farm Bureau president and is active in school, cooperative organizations, county fair, church and Masonic lodge.

Burrell C. Foster, of Washington County, was born on the farm he operates, 42 years ago. Dairying, cattle feeding and hog raising are the livestock enterprises on his farm. Not many Iowa farmers make both dairying and the fattening of purchased steers major enterprises on their farms. But this man does, and both enterprises are well managed and have been profitable. He is using limestone, super and rock phosphate, alfalfa and sweet clover to increase soil fertility and crop yields. Mr. Foster is president of the local Farmers' Institute and has served on the school board and board of supervisors. He was one of the leaders in organizing the Wellman Cooperative Creamery.

Theodore Gronna, of Allamakee County, has operated the farm of 203

Schultz

acres he now owns for 25 years and rents additional land. He is carrying on a definite liming program and uses superphosphate regularly. Dairying with Milking Shorthorns is the major livestock enterprise. Mr. Gronna has been especially interested in the development of higher-yielding, better-adapted corn and small grain, and their distribution in his community. When his own strain of corn was beaten in the state yield test, he began growing and distributing the higher yielding corn. Mr. Gronna has been active in school affairs, cow testing work and general farm organizations. He is a member of the cooperative creamery, store, shipping association and town community club.

Lewis T. Newton, of Marion County, is 54 years old and has farmed for 17 years. For 20 years previous to that, he was a coal miner. At this work he saved enough money to make an initial payment on his home place, which he bought 18 years ago. He now owns 240 acres, of which 120 acres are in the home farm. For five years he has rented 557 acres, which is operated under a stock-share lease. Each year 400 to 600 hogs are raised. Mr. Newton has served as officer of the school and Farm Bureau, and is active in the local cooperative company.

Livestock That Pays Profits

Henry C. Vaske, of Dubuque County, began renting part of the 230 acres he now owns in 1897. Dairying is the major livestock enterprise. He was one of the first Holstein breeders in his community and bought his first grade Holsteins the first year he farmed. He has used a purebred bull ever since he started with Holsteins. He helped organize a

Strickler

cow test association. His herd leads the association. Hogs and poultry are also important enterprises. The buildings on the farm, all of which were planned and built by Mr. Vaske, are unusually well adapted to the farm. Mr. Vaske has served as an officer in the local church and school. He has been a leader in dairy club work and in the Farm Bureau, shipping association and local Holstein association.

Smith

Bert Schuelke, of Buena Vista County, owns and operates 320 acres. He was among the first to use sweet clover, limestone and alfalfa in his community, and has nearly doubled yields in the 17 years he has operated this farm. He feeds over 200 cattle yearly and raises 300 hogs. He fattens the largest amount of livestock of any of the 1928 Master Farmers. He is an officer in the Farm Bureau and shipping association, and director in county fair, elevator and hospital.

O. J. Kalsem, of Story County, began farming in his present location 34 years ago. The farm contains 380 acres. He is carrying out a definite liming program and has practically doubled crop yields. He is one of the largest users of sweet clover in Story County. Mr. Kalsem is an outstanding cattle feeder. He is president of the Iowa Livestock Shippers' Association and has served as officer in the cooperative elevator, creamery, church and school. The consolidated school, which he helped build and organize is one of the outstanding ones in the state in the training it gives.

Growing Melons and Apples

Frank F. Everett, of Mahaska County, operates a farm of 256 acres. He is carrying out a lim-

Vaske

ing program and uses superphosphate regularly. Hog raising is his major enterprise. In addition to ordinary crops, this man grows a few acres of melons and sweet potatoes. In cooperation with Iowa State College, he has carried on extensive experiments with different methods and materials for the control of the insects and diseases that attack watermelon and cantaloupes. He has also carried out crossing experiments with melons to test out possibilities of thus controlling wilt.

Hervey E. Hazen, of Lee County, has operated his father's farm for 16 years on a stock-share basis. He is the only tenant in the 1928 group of Master Farmers. He graduated from Ames in 1909. He is an extensive user of limestone. Mr. Hazen produces purebred cattle, hogs and sheep. Apple growing is a major enterprise. He has been operating a large, mature orchard nearby, and by proper care and spraying has made it profitable. Also, a young orchard of 15 acres has been planted on the home farm. Mr. Hazen is a leader in school and church activities, Farm Bureau, club work and shipping association.

IOWA MASTER FARMERS
~
January 18, 1930

Anderson

Bode

Again we announce the selection of a group of Iowa Master Farmers. In age, these 16 men vary from 39 to 80; in land owned or operated, from 70 to 1,300 acres; in location, they range from some of the rough lands of southern Iowa to the most fertile soil found in Muscatine, Linn, Tama and Crawford counties.

All 16 have been good farmers and businessmen, making good use of their advantages and opportunities for themselves and their families. More than this, every one of these 16 has made the land he operates more fertile and productive than when he started operating it as tenant or owner.

These men have more than made money and fertile, well-improved farms. They have tried to provide for their families' homes, surroundings and training that will prepare them to make a success of living. The interests and efforts of these Master Farmers and their wives have extended beyond doing well for themselves, their farms and their own families. They have had visions of better communities, better and more prosperous neighbors, well-trained, hopeful boys and girls with high aims and ideals, growing up on the neighboring farms and in nearby towns. They have

contributed time and thought and money to make these dreams come true through strong and helpful cooperative and mutual service organizations, and through better schools, roads, and churches that meet and help solve the problems of life.

They have had faith enough in the future of agriculture to work enthusiastically for and through scouting and club work, farm organizations and community clubs.

We honor these men not for what they have in land and livestock primarily, but for what they have shared with others in planning for and giving time and money to make better, happier communities.

Merely making money farming is only one-third or one-half the problem of success. So long as farming remains a way of life as well as a means of making a living, the man who is interested only in more and bigger crops and better and more profitable livestock, is only one-third or one-half a success as a farmer. Without vision of something more than "more land, more corn, more hogs," farm families and farm communities perish.

Hence the standard for Master Farmers is based on something more than "Good Farming." Of course, good farming comes first, with all

Davis

Dunham

Fox

it carries in the way of good crops, proper rotations and soil building; the breeding and feeding of efficient and profitable livestock; effective and desirable fencing; and farm buildings that meet the farm needs for housing the crops and livestock.

Without good farming, farm families can not provide the conveniences and comforts and surroundings for farm homes that make for the raising of happy, helpful, satisfied sons and daughters. And without the income that good farming is required to give, it is not possible to devote the time and money to church and community and farm and cooperative organizations that must be furnished if communities are to grow in strength and usefulness.

These 16 men, from as many counties in all parts of Iowa, have accomplished this all-around job of doing well for themselves, the land, their families and their communities.

None of these men has done a perfect job in meeting the ideals that would make a "perfect Master Farmer." Each of them knows that he has fallen short of his own ideal of "Good Farming, Clear Thinking, Right Living," and has told us so. Some have been stronger in one line of activity, some in others. All, however, have reached a high standard and are worthy to be honored for their work. Not only for what they have accomplished, but that they and the many others who are doing equally good work may be encouraged to go forward in the path of unselfish, constructive leadership in farm communities in all parts of Iowa, we tell of the achievements of this group of Master Farmers.

Hueck

A Granger for 20 years, an active member of the Farm Bureau since its organization, and director and former president of the local fair, William C. Anderson, of Muscatine County,

George

is a real leader in farm organizations and community activities. The 240-acre farm, which he has operated as tenant and owner for 25 years is one of the most productive in his county. He is a leading breeder of Poland China hogs in the state and has an excellent herd of Shorthorn cattle. Mrs. Anderson is a leader in girls' and women's clubs and Farm Bureau work.

Farming 480 acres of land, with a definite soil and crop improvement program, and turning the crops produced into pork, beef and milk in a very efficient manner, is the chief business of Harry J. Bode, of Kossuth County. He finds time to serve as president or director of five mutual and cooperative organizations. As a township trustee, he helped drain and grade all the roads of his township. He has been extremely active in parochial school affairs. He has the largest family of any of the 1929 Master Farmers—seven children.

Bees, 300 stands of them, are a part of the farm business of James C. Davis, of Wayne County. A fine Jersey herd and hogs are the other major livestock enterprises on this 165-acre farm. Mr. Davis was one of the first users of limestone and growers of alfalfa in this part of Iowa. He was winner of the Wayne County 1929 alfalfa growing contest and has one of the oldest cooperative soil test plots in southern Iowa.

The Oldest of Iowa Master Farmers

Among the cattle on the farms of Z.T. Dunham are direct descendants of the cattle his father brought from Jackson County to Crawford County 80 years ago. Z.T. Dunham has bred Polled Durham and Polled Shorthorn cattle since 1883 and helped found the breed organization. Three sons and a son-in-law operate

Holland

Kennedy

the 1,300 acres of Crawford County land owned by this man. He is 80, the oldest of Iowa's Master Farmers, and still active in the direction of the home place of 640 acres, which has been operated by his son Arthur on a partnership basis for 30 years. He has been and still is a leader in church and school affairs, in the local fair and boys' club work.

A convert from cattle feeding to dairying, about 13 years ago, Harry B. Fox, of Sac County, has one of the most carefully bred and highest producing Holstein herds in Sac County. He is also an outstanding producer of Poland China hogs for breeding and market. On the 200 acres he owns and the 120 acres he rents, Mr. Fox is carrying out the best soil and crop improvement practices. He was a pioneer in his community in the use of limestone and alfalfa. He and his family are active in the Farm Bureau, church and community affairs.

In addition to being leaders in their church, in club work, the Farm Bureau, cooperative and community organizations, W. M. George, of Bremer County, and his wife, find time to do a good job of running a 360-acre farm. They own 240 acres and rent 120 acres. Dairying, with over thirty Holstein cows milked, market hogs, and poultry are the major livestock enterprises. Mr. George took the two-year agricultural course at Ames. He is the youngest of the 1929 group of Master Farmers.

Believing in the value of dual purpose cattle for southeastern Iowa and the old family farm that he operates, Frank Holland has spent

McElhinney

much of the last 25 years building up one of the best Milking Shorthorn herds in Iowa. He has been active in the breed organization and served at many state and national livestock shows as a judge of this breed. He

was one of the first users of limestone and superphosphate in his county, and has systematically built up the soil and crop yields of the 300-acre farm. He has devoted much time to the Farm Bureau, his church and school.

Knight

Born, and raised until fourteen years of age, in Keil, Germany, John Heuck, of Clay County, is one of the best informed and most enthusiastic students of soils and soil fertility problems among Iowa farmers. He has cooperated with Iowa State College and extension workers in soil and fertilizer experiments, crop rotations, testing corn yields and seed treatments for disease. He worked as a hired hand on Iowa farms several years, beginning when sixteen years old. He then farmed for nine years as a stock-share tenant in Tama County. From 1906 to 1912, he operated a lumber and implement business in Everly, and since that time he has been operating a farm in his present location.

After studying at the University of Iowa on a law course, for two years, R.C. McElhinney, of Tama County, decided that corn growing, hog raising and cattle feeding were more to his liking. He owns and operates 401 acres. He fattens 100 to 150 head of cattle each year. He is an exception to the general tradition that a good cattle feeder is never interested in milking cows, and has an excellent herd of Milking Shorthorns. Good schools for farm folks are his greatest outside interest. He has served as a school officer since 1904, and had much to do with the building and success of the Geneseo township consolidated school. He is the president of the county Farm Bureau and state director. He is a leader in Sunday school and church.

Club work and church activities take a lot of time

Michel

Poundstone

of Charles B.F. Michel and family, of Linn County. Serving as president of the county Farm Bureau and of the shipping association takes a lot more of his time. In partnership with his son, he manages to carry out a systematic soil building program and do an extra good job of raising hogs and fattening cattle on his 246-acre farm.

Making the most out of 160 acres, both in the way of high yields and profits, has been most systematically done by Harry E. Poundstone, of Wright County. A definite rotation, using sweet clover and alfalfa as the legumes, and best improved strains of seeds, has given the yields. A well-bred Holstein herd and the best of market hogs and poultry are marketing the crops profitably. He has been active in school affairs, Farm Bureau, cow test association, and mutual electric high-line building.

Raising neither corn nor hogs, Sam Kennedy, of Cerro Gordo County, is one of Iowa's largest farmers in size of business. He is Iowa's outstanding vegetable crop producer, marketing 22 or more carloads of onions, onion sets, cabbage and potatoes each year. He owns 400 acres, and in 1929 rented 30 acres more. He has been Iowa's champion sugar beet grower four of the last five years. He is a thorough student of peat land problems and the most successful user of this soil in Iowa. He has served as county Farm Bureau president, is active in the local fair, and is president of the Clear Lake Commercial and Rotary clubs. He has given much time and effort to Boy Scout work.

A school officer for twenty-seven years, master of the local Grange and overseer in the state Grange, active in club work, a director in the cooperative creamery and a leader in his church,

Royer

John S. Knight, of Clayton County, works for and with his community. His farm of 70 acres has practically all been limed, and by a definite crop rotation since 1907 has been improved in fertility. A small but select Holstein herd and market hogs raised on rotated pasture for over twenty years are the chief sources of income.

Mrs. Royer, First Master Homemaker

Profitable market hogs, fat steers, eggs and poultry are helping W.H. Royer and his wife pay for their 240-acre Dallas County farm. A definite crop rotation and use of alfalfa and other legumes have largely increased yields. Both have been active in the Farm Bureau, school affairs and church. He is president of the local cooperative oil company, a bank director and township trustee. She was chosen in the first group of Iowa Master Homemakers.

Farming as a stock-share tenant on a 160-acre farm, George E. Sauerbry, of Fayette County, is carrying out a definite cropping and soil building program, including liming, fertilizing, tiling, etc. He is a constructive breeder of Durocs and Holsteins. He is county Farm Bureau president and active in the local Holstein association. He and his family are extremely active in club and church work.

Besides raising the most hogs of any of the 1929 Master Farmers, Everett Stewart, Washington County, also fattens cattle. He has operated his father's farm of 200 acres on a stock-share lease since 1912, and recently bought an adjoining 80. He is carrying out a liming and soil building program. He and his family are leaders in church, club work and school affairs. He is an active member of the Farmers' Union and has been an officer of the county Farm Bureau since its organization.

Stewart

Sauerbry

1930

IOWA MASTER FARMERS

~

January 17, 1931

"I would enjoy visiting with you but as far as filling out your records, there is no use. I am no Master Farmer. Why waste your time?" This was the answer of John McKeegan, of Lyon County, when I asked him if he could spare the time to fill out our Master Farmer record.

This was the kind of reply I heard many times in visiting the 108 men from which the 15, 1930 Master Farmers were selected. Like Mr. McKeegan, the others realized their shortcomings in trying to accomplish the most for self, family, farm and community. The outstanding attribute of the 1930 nominees seemed to be modesty, not only among the 15 men selected, but among nearly all of the number that lacked so little of making the standards. Parents, wives, children, neighbors and friends were given most of the credit for the things accomplished.

We feel that in this group we have 15 worthy exponents of "Good Farming, Clear Thinking, Right Living." Of course, they have not done a perfect job of increasing crop yields, getting rid of noxious weeds, and raising and feeding profitable livestock. Neighbors and friends can doubtless see a better arrangement of farm buildings that could be made, a better or more economical way to have provided good shelter for crops and stock, and a home better fitted to the family requirements. Others might have raised and educated their children in a different manner, or divided the time available for community activities differently among churches, schools, cooperatives, mutuals and general farm organizations.

Have Faith in Their Communities

All of these farmers believe that being successful means more than doing a good job of raising corn and hogs, or its equivalent. They have faith in their communities and neighbors and give time, money and thought to helping make life and living better for others as well as themselves and their own.

The oldest of the 1930 group of Master Farmers is William A. Hollowell, of Marion County, who is 69 years of age. The youngest is Joseph Lengeling, of Carroll County, who is 43; the average age is 56 years.

This group of Master Farmers represents larger families than those of the previous four years. There are 70 children among the 15 families, an average of four and two-thirds per family. Two men set a new record for Master Farmer circles with 10 children each. These men are Rudolph C. Hopp, of Mills County, and Edward Houston, of Crawford County. Each is the father of five sons and five daughters.

Baker

Boatman

The ancestry and background of these Master Farmers and their wives make up a fair cross-section of the general run of Iowa farm people. Four of the men were born on the farms they now operate. Three more were born in the counties in which they now live. Two more were

Grunewald

born in Iowa, but in different counties. One was born in each of the states of Indiana, Pennsylvania and Virginia. Two were born in Germany and one in Ireland. Of the wives, seven were born in their home counties and four others in Iowa. Four represent the states of Missouri, Maryland, Wisconsin and Illinois.

The birthplaces of the 60 parents of the Master Farmers and their wives tell an interesting story. The greatest number, 21, were born in Germany. Seven came from Ireland, and six claim Iowa as their native state. Four parents came from Indiana and Illinois. Three were born in Vermont. Sweden furnished two of the parents, as did each of the states of Virginia, Maryland and New York. Missouri, Michigan, Ohio, Connecticut, Pennsylvania, Canada and England each furnished one parent.

The 1930 Master Farmers haven't moved around much since they began farming. Jesse J. Boatman, of Poweshiek County, has been in his present location the shortest length of time, but he lived within sight of his present location, on a smaller farm, eight years before. Ten of these men have lived on the farms they now own for 25 years or more.

"Have Done Nothing Striking Here"

When I stopped Henry J. Grunewald, of Benton County, at his fence-building job to visit with him, he remarked: "We have done nothing striking here. My father before me laid out this farm and operated it, and had it in fine shape when I be-

Hopp

gan to operate it as a tenant. We were partners for 14 years, and it was then and with his help that I started many successful practices that I have continued since I bought the place in 1914."

While the remainder of the group had not worked as directly with their fathers for as long a time as Mr. Grunewald, every one of this group gave much credit to parents and home experience for their success.

Hollowell

First of all, these men have been and still are good farmers. Every one has made a significant increase in crop yields on his farm and several have doubled corn yields. And they have done this while the farms were being paid for, improvements being built, and families being raised and educated. And these men are not resting on past achievements in soil building and crop improvements, but are still trying out new strains of corn and small grains and working out rotations better adapted to their soils and livestock needs.

When I visited Joseph Lengeling, of Carroll County, I was particularly interested in looking over his purebred hogs because I knew that a litter of his pigs had been entered in the Swine Record of Performance work at Ames. Was his the type of hogs that used the least feed to produce 100 pounds of gain? Would these pigs produce the most valuable carcasses? Would they gain most rapidly? Neither he nor I could answer the questions, but we enjoyed guessing. Several others of this group of Master Farmers produce purebreds that they sell as seed stock; two sell hogs as breeding stock; three sell purebred beef cattle; and one, R.G. Kinsley, of Clayton County, has for years sold purebred Jerseys. W.A. Hollowell keeps purebred horses and sells stallions. But in spite of purebred livestock enter-

Houston

prises on several of these farms, this group of Master Farmers all follow the type of farming that we class in Iowa as general farming. All grow corn and oats and legumes as major crops, the bulk of which are marketed through livestock. Thirteen raise hogs as a major source of income. E.H. Stevens, of Fremont County, has fed purchased hogs for several years. The 15th man, R.C. Hopp, of Mills County, was for a generation one of the most extensive hog raisers in Iowa, but at present is only raising a few because of a shift in farm operations and a very serious disease infection of the whole farm a few years ago. Ten out of the 15 are cattle feeders, and eight have dairy herds as a major source of income. Five make chicken raising a major enterprise, and three have flocks of sheep.

Greatest Changes in 50 Years

When talking about the changes that had taken place since he started farming, I asked Mr. Hollowell what were the two or three greatest changes in farming since he began, a half-century ago. His answer was: "First, taxes. They have jumped from 30 or 35 cents per acre to $3.50 or $4. The second is the amount of machinery required to profitably operate a farm. In the early days, a walking plow, a walking cultivator, a harrow and a wagon were the main farm tools. Not nearly all the farmers had corn planters and few had binders. The third greatest change is the number and method of raising hogs. Fifty years ago, a tight yard with corn, water and a little shorts for feed, was the approved hog-raising method. Cholera was the ever-present menace, but nothing could be done about it."

Four of the Master Farmers are

Jager

using phosphorus fertilizer regularly in one form or another, and five more are testing it out on their farms at the present time. Every one of these men is growing the more efficient legumes, alfalfa and sweet clover, although a majority are still using red clover.

Kinsley

"If you had only waited a few years before you made your visit, our farm would have been more worthy of consideration, I believe," said Jesse J. Boatman, of Poweshiek County. "Our soil building program is only well started, and during our 11 years on the place, we have hardly got started on our farmstead and building improvements."

Mr. Boatman has been on his farm the shortest time of any of this group of Master Farmers, 11 years. And, as with any farmer who is trying to pay for a farm, educate a family, and at the same time build up the farm and farm buildings, 11 years is too short to complete the job.

Mr. Boatman operates the largest number of acres of any of the 1930 group, 680 acres. Of these, he owns 240 acres. Joseph Lengeling, Carroll County, operates the smallest farm, 120 acres. The average size of farm is 322 acres. All have title to all or part of the land they operate. William A. Hollowell, of Marion County, has been farming the longest, 49 years—35 years in his present location.

The first visit I made to the farm of Rudolph C. Hopp, of Mills County, he was not at home.

"Where is he?" I asked. "Visiting farmers in the community, helping to organize a mutual or cooperative rural fire protection association," I was told.

Later when I found Mr. Hopp at home, he told me that this new type of a cooperative had been organized, the money raised to buy the truck,

Lengeling

arrangements made with the fire department of the nearby town to man the truck, and the truck purchased.

These Master Farmers have all done pioneering in rural organization, and continue to give time and effort to organizations that they believe will help other farmers and their families in their communities and counties. Five of these men have been presidents of their county Farm Bureaus, and six others have held other offices in this organization. The wives of three have been county chairmen of women's work in the Farm Bureau. Another Master Farmer has been master of the local Grange. All are active members in general farm organizations.

Thirteen have served and are serving as officers of from one to a half-dozen cooperatives and farmers' mutual organizations, elevators, creameries, feed companies, electric power lines, telephone companies, mutual insurance companies and shipping associations.

Ten have served as officers of their consolidated or township school boards for periods of 10 to 23 years and the remainder for shorter periods; and four have sons who are now school officers.

A majority of the Master Farmers and their wives have served the churches and Sunday schools of their choice as officers and teachers. All of this group of 15 families are members of or help to maintain church organizations. A wide variation of church choice is found in the group – Lutheran, Congregational, Baptist, Presbyterian, Methodist, Catholic and Universalist.

Doubling crop yields on his 200-acre Ringgold County farm has been accomplished by H.K. Baker since he bought it, 28 years ago. He was one of the first to apply limestone in his county, having started 17 years ago. A total of 400 tons have been used. He pioneered in the use of improved seed corn and small grain. Sheep and hogs are his major livestock enterprises, and he has started a herd of milking Shorthorns. As president of the consolidated school board and local bank and as an active supporter of the church and the Farm Bureau, Mr. Baker has helped build up his community.

Lubkeman

Being president of the Poweshiek County Farm Bureau and an active participant in school, cooperative and community affairs takes a great deal of J. J. Boatman's time. Nevertheless, he does this, as well as operate 680 acres of land, of which he owns 240 acres. A constructive soil-building program based on legumes, lime and phosphate is being used. Eighty-five bushels of corn per acre were grown on his highest-yielding field in 1930.

H. J. Grunewald, of Benton County, was born on the farm he now owns. He operated this farm as a tenant for 14 years before he bought it in 1914. He operates 540 acres, of which he owns 240. Cattle feeding and hog raising are the largest livestock enterprises, but a good Holstein herd is kept on one farm. The poultry enterprise is the largest of any of the 1930 group. Mr. Grunewald is a pioneer in the use of alfalfa and limestone. His judgment and support are much appreciated in farm organizations and cooperatives. He is particularly active in livestock marketing organizations.

Has Farmed 49 Years

W.A. Hollowell, of Marion County, has farmed for 49 years, 35 years on the 315 acres he now owns. He has limed nearly the entire farm and was a pioneer in the use of alfalfa and sweet clover. Purebred Percheron

McKeegan

horses and Shorthorn cattle are raised, but hogs and fat steers are his leading sources of income. Included in his service to his community are his work as a church official for 50 years, a school officer for 20 years, and president of the county Farm Bureau eight years.

Producing milk for the Omaha market is the chief livestock enterprise on the 300 acres of Mills County land operated by R.C. Hopp and his two youngest sons. Until recently, he was one of the largest scale cattle feeders and hog raisers in western Iowa. Continuous growing of alfalfa for 36 years makes him one of the pioneers with this crop for the whole state. Mr. Hopp, who was born in Germany, has farmed in Mills County for 40 years. He is an outstanding leader in Farm Bureau and club work and is active in farmers' mutual and cooperative organizations. There are 10 children, all mature—five sons and five daughters.

Raising the largest number of hogs of any of the 1930 Master Farmers and feeding steers that commonly top the market are two achievements of E.W. Houston, of Crawford County. But his family of five sons and five daughters is his source of greatest pride. Mr. Houston operates a 240-acre farm which, through the systematic use of good rotations, including alfalfa and sweet clover, has been made one of the most productive in his community. He is a leader in farm organizations, a speaker at farm and public gatherings, and a leader in the Knights of Columbus.

W.F. Jager, of Mahaska County, shares the operation of the home farm of 328 acres with his youngest son. The oldest son operates a second farm owned by Mr. Jager. Mr. Jager has doubled the crop yields on his farm, limed nearly the entire area, and pioneered in the use of alfalfa and sweet clover. Hogs, beef cattle and sheep are the chief sources of income from the farm. Mr. Jager is a

Miller

former master of the Grange. Both he and Mrs. Jager take an active part in farm organizations and club work.

The farm business of R.G. Kinsley, of Clayton County, is built around a purebred Jersey herd kept for production of cream and breeding stock. The 360 acres owned have been operated the last five years in partnership with two stock-share tenants. Mr. Kinsley's herd has been in a cow test association for 12 years. The high cow in the herd produced 815 pounds of butterfat in the last record year. Mr. Kinsley is active in the Farm Bureau, a leader in cooperative creamery organizations and president of the Iowa Dairy Council. Previous to 1913, he lived in town and ran a hardware and implement store, but from 1901 to 1913 he operated a farm with hired help.

On the smallest farm among the group, 120 acres, Joseph Lengeling, of Carroll County, has developed a fine herd of purebred hogs, which he markets largely as breeding stock. Potatoes, cream, baby beef and poultry all contribute to the income and diversity. He has doubled corn yields through good rotations, including alfalfa and sweet clover. He pioneered in using lime and phosphate. Mr. and Mrs. Lengeling are both active in farm organization and in their church.

Measured in high crop yield and return per acre, the 160-acre farm of H.L. Lubkeman, of Franklin County, stands at the head of the group. This farm, which is operated in partnership with the youngest son, is outstanding in the production of pork. Dairying and baby beef production are also combined successfully on this farm. Mr. Lubkeman, who came to the United States from Germany when 17 years, is an outstanding leader in cooperatives, Farm Bureau and club work and in his church.

Helping make cooperative and community enterprises succeed and

Reed

keeping up strong farm organizations, better schools and churches have taken a large part of the time and interest of John McKeegan, of Lyon County. These interests have not interfered with making his farm one of the most productive in his community, and he is doing an excellent job of producing market hogs and feeding baby beeves on a large scales. A purebred Shorthorn herd is also kept on his 240-acre farm.

Rinker

Four major livestock enterprises—a dairy herd, market hogs, chickens and sheep—give a diversity of work and income on the 160-acre farm of Frank L. Miller, of Grundy County. A fine set of farm buildings, built by the owner, and an outstanding flower and shrubbery display make this farm unusually attractive. Both Mr. and Mrs. Miller are active in farm organizations, school, church and club work.

Cattle feeding, a Shorthorn breeding herd and market hogs combine to use, to the best advantage, the grain and hay produced on the level land and the pasture on the rough land on the 480-acre farm of Alex Reed, of Jackson County. This farm, which Mr. Reed operates in partnership with his two sons, has been made one of the most productive in his county through the use of good rotations, lime and phosphate. He is bank, creamery and Farm Bureau president, and a school and church official.

H.H. Rinker, of Boone County, operates his two farms in partnership with his two sons. At the home place, 280 acres are rented in addition to 150 acres owned. Crop yields have been doubled on owned land and are being rapidly increased on the rented land through good rotations, including alfalfa and sweet clover. Sheep and steer feeding are the leading livestock enterprises. Mr. Rinker is a leader in his church, consolidated school, shipping association and the Farm Bureau.

Fattening both purchased steers and feeder hogs in large numbers is the livestock program of E.H. Stevens, of Fremont County. He was one of the first users of lime in his county and was one of the first in the county to lime all cropland systematically. He has doubled his corn yields. Mr. and Mrs. Stevens are active in Farm Bureau, school, church and club work.

Stevens

IOWA MASTER FARMERS
~
January 23, 1932

Representative of the much larger group of farmers that are furnishing inspiring and constructive leadership in their communities throughout Iowa is the group of 1931 Master Farmers. These 10 farm operators have done, and are doing, the jobs of making their farms more easily and fully tilled, increasing fertility, and doubling crop production because of this and because of the use of improved seed and improved methods. They are raising better and healthier livestock and at lower costs. And, while doing "Good Farming," they have not forgotten "Clear Thinking" and "Right Living."

The interests and the needs of their families and their communities have shared in the time, money and planning of these Master Farmers. They have provided good homes and home surroundings and educational advantages for their children. They have worked for and helped to bring to their communities better and stronger schools, churches, cooperatives and community and farm organizations.

This group of 10 average 51 years of age— the oldest 70, the youngest 39 years. The 10 have a total of 35 living children. They have been farming an average of 27 years. Only one has moved since he started farming. Their farms average 276 acres in size. All own part or all they farm except one, who operates an orchard farm on a partnership basis.

Walter L. Beck, of Des Moines County, owns 225 acres that he bought in 1918; he rents 60 acres. Previous to buying, he farmed in partnership with his father and three brothers. Fertility and crop yields have been sharply increased through the use of lime, phosphate, complete fertilizers and a systematic rotation. Choice beef cattle and market hogs have provided a profitable method of selling crops. An outstanding leader in his church and very active in school affairs, Mr. Beck is also a leader in club work, an officer in an oil company and an elevator company and vice-president of the local bank.

Roscoe B. Blinks is one of the outstanding cattle feeders and hog raisers in Linn County. He is a pioneer in liming, having begun 18 years ago. He has started over his farm for the second time with limestone. He is a regular user of phosphate and mixed fertilizer. He has nearly doubled crop yields both on the 120 acres he rents from his father and the 91 acres bought in 1922. Mr. Blinks is president of the county Farm Bureau, active in church work, an officer of the cooperative oil company and president of the Cedar Valley Farm Business Association.

Robert M. Clark, who operates a 100-acre Polk County farm, is exclusively a fruit grower, with apples his specialty. He is 39 years old, the youngest of the 1931 Master Farmers. Beginning 16 years ago with 26 acres of trees that had been uncertain as to yield and profit, he has built up to 50 acres of bearing trees and 20 acres of recently planted trees. Measured by production, profit, quality of fruit and work in new sorts and improved practices, he is one of the best apple growers in Iowa and the middle-west. He is on the executive board of the State Horticultural Society, and was for seven years president of the Iowa Fruit Growers' Association.

John Collison, of Carroll County, owns 777 acres, which he and his three sons operate. Fattening choice baby beeves, 300 to 500 yearly, is the chief livestock enterprise. Five hundred or more hogs are raised yearly. In handling both these livestock enterprises, unusual skill and ability are shown. An unusually good job of fitting the farm and tractor machinery into economical farm operation has been done. Though holding few official positions in organizations, Mr. Collison is a leader in his community and county whose much sought advice and counsel have proved sound and constructive. He and his family are consistent supporters of their church and church schools.

Herman Franzenburg began farming as a tenant 25 years ago on the 200-acre Benton County farm he now owns. Though the land was fertile and well tilled when he began farming, he has raised crop yields nearly 50%. He has a most carefully planned farm layout, with three groups of uniform-sized fields fitted to rotation and livestock programs. Mr. Franzenburg is an outstanding hog raiser and feeder of baby beeves. He and is family are active in school and church work and in cooperative and community organizations. He is one of the outstanding leaders in boys' club work in eastern Iowa.

Louis Hadenfeldt, of Buena Vista County, has farmed in the same community for 28 years, the last 19 as owner of the 160 acres he now operates. With tiling, good rotations and livestock feeding, he has increased acre yields about 50% and trebled the crop and meat production of the farm. He is one of the outstanding hog raisers and cattle feeders in northwestern Iowa. He has been a valuable officer of the local shipping association, elevator and consolidated school, and he and his family are active in their church.

Mrs. J.E. Hoopes, the first woman to be given the title of Iowa Master Farmer, specializes in the growing of garden seeds, such as tomatoes, asparagus, melons and the other vine crops on her 125-acre farm in Muscatine County. Beginning as truck farmers in 1884, she and her husband went into the seed business and became leaders in their specialties in Iowa and the middle-west. A business partner with her husband until his death, 16 years ago, she has continued as an outstanding leader in her field. The oldest of this group, Mrs. Hoopes continues to be active in her farming, her church and community affairs. She is a leader of the Iowa Vegetable Growers' Association.

D.F. Kruse, of Sioux County, farms 375 acres, of which he owns 200 acres. Tiling, regular growing of legumes, liming and cattle feeding have contributed to the 50% increase in yields he has achieved. Hogs are the major livestock enterprise, closely followed by beef cattle. He has served his community as president of the farmers' elevator for 10 years and as an officer in the school, telephone company, shipping association and oil company, and is a church trustee.

Fred R. Mitchell, of Hardin County, owns in partnership with his two sisters, the 240-acre farm he operates. Though his father, who operated this farm for 50 years, was an outstanding farmer, this man, through a liming program, phosphate, more efficient legumes and improved seed, has been able to push yields sharply upward. He is a feeder of market-topping baby beeves and is a most efficient pork producer on a large scale. A college-trained musician, Mr. Mitchell has developed an excellent choir in the community church. He is an officer of the Farm Bureau, elevator, shipping association and telephone company, as well as president of the county fair and federal farm loan association.

John W. Swalin came from Sweden to Pocahontas County in 1887, when 19 years old. He began farming on 85 acres of unpromising, swampy land, 40 years ago. The 285 acres of fertile, well-tiled land now owned and operated in cooperation with his sons include the original 85 acres. Liming, early and regular use of alfalfa and sweet clover, drainage and livestock feeding, have made possible the more than doubling of crop production. He is an outstanding raiser of hogs. Mr. Swalin is one of the leaders in his church, and has served his community as an officer of the telephone company, elevator and Farm Bureau. There are eight children—the largest family of any of the 1931 Master Farmers.

MASTER FARMERS OF '31

This year we add ten new names to the Iowa Master Farmer roster. They are as follows: Top, left to right—Fred R. Mitchell, of Hardin county; John W. Swalin, of Pocahontas county; Mrs. J. E. Hoopes, of Muscatine county; John Collison, of Carroll county, and Walter L. Beck, of Des Moines county. Bottom, left to right—Herman Franzenburg, of Benton county; D. F. Kruse, of Sioux county; Roscoe B. Blinks, of Linn county; Louis Hadenfeldt, of Buena Vista county, and Robert M. Clark, of Polk county.

The 1931 Iowa Master Farmers

CHAPTER 2
~
1938 - 1942: Pre-World War

Following the stock market crash of 1929, the United States and world economies declined steadily. Widespread unemployment and little consumer purchasing power for food adversely affected Iowa's already weak farming economy. Livestock and grain prices plummeted to all-time lows.

One family, in 1932, sold a Guernsey milk cow for $7, which paid for the total cost of the birth of a child, hospitalization for mother and baby (10 days) and the doctor's bill.

Times were tough all over. For decades, rural Americans migrated to cities seeking jobs. High unemployment during the depression reversed the migration for awhile. People moved back to the farm where they could at least grow food.

Wallace leaves legacy
In 1933, Henry A. Wallace became U.S. Secretary of Agriculture. The attitude of the federal government changed. Washington launched a concerted effort to restore the economic well-being of American citizens.

Wallace contended that with 25% of the U.S. population living on farms, improving the economic conditions on the farm could go a long way toward improving the entire U.S. economy. Production controls for livestock and crops were enacted with federal benefit payments going to those farmers who participated in the programs. The permanent legislation, giving the Secretary authority to balance demand and supply, became known as the Agricultural Adjustment Act (AAA) of 1938.

Farm mortgage relief for agriculture came about with loans provided to farmers on crops they raised. In 1935, the Rural Electric Administration was established to provide low-cost loans to bring electricity to every farm. Private utility systems were not able to achieve this. One of the major benefits was electricity for lights, and for operating milking machines and other electrically-powered farm equipment.

Dust Bowl spawns conservation
In the mid-1930s, little rainfall and extremely high temperatures brought on a severe drought. From 1934 to 1936, crops, livestock and people suffered through what became known as the "Dust Bowl" days.

Jim Sage, Waterloo, Iowa, remembers extremely cold temperatures and heavy snowfall in January and February 1936. However, by summer they had to take their mattresses outside on the lawn in order to sleep at night.

The dust storms of the Dust Bowl helped launch the Soil Conservation Service (SCS) in 1935 to stimulate soil and water conservation on individual farms.

Farmers adopt technology
As a young man, Henry A. Wallace began experimenting with various strains of seed corn in an effort to improve the quality and yield of one of Iowa's basic crops. The hybrid

corn Wallace developed resisted insects and diseases, and boosted yields 15% to 20% per acre. In 1933, farmers planted around 40,000 acres using the new hybrid seed corn instead of open-pollinated varieties. By 1940, 75% of the corn planted was of a hybrid variety.

In the 1930s, Wallace struggled with an anomaly. As a scientist, he worked to boost yields with hybrid seed corn. He knew that higher yields trimmed costs per bushel. In Washington, he tried to reduce total crop production through federal farm programs. He hoped tightening supplies would pull prices higher.

Rubber tires and standardized power take-off systems developed during this time helped make planting and harvesting crops much less tedious. Pull-type, and eventually tractor-mounted, corn pickers became essential machinery on the farm.

Ag scientists studied ways to boost livestock production. Crossbreeding and selective breeding along with better feeding practices improved the quality and quantity of meat, milk and eggs for consumers' tables.

1938 Iowa Farm Facts

FARMS & INCOME

Number of Iowa farms	215,000

LIVESTOCK

	Inventory	Average price
Cattle and calves	4.5 million head	$7.81/cwt (beef)
Hogs and pigs	8.2 million head	$7.73/cwt
	Production	Inventory
Chickens (Layers)	2.4 billion eggs	19.5 million birds
Milk	6.4 billion lbs.	

CROPS

	Harvested acres	Yield	Production	Avg price
All Hay	3.1 million	1.62 tons/acre	5.1 million tons	
Corn	9.8 million	46 bu./acre	453 million bu.	$0.46/bu.
Soybeans	308,000	21 bu./acre	6.5 million bu.	$0.67/bu.
Oats	6.0 million	35 bu./acre	209 million bu.	
Wheat	583,000	16 bu./acre	9.3 million bu.	

1938

IOWA MASTER FARMERS

~ January 28, 1939

To remind Iowa again of the importance of rural leadership, *Wallaces' Farmer and Iowa Homestead* resumed this year its selection of Iowa Master Farmers. Four new men have been picked to join the distinguished list of Iowa Master Farmers. They are: Allan B. Kline, of Benton County; Benjamin C. Neal, of Linn County; Orie F. Irwin, of Sac County; and Herbert W. Buck, of Adair County.

These men were nominated by their neighbors. Their farms and records were inspected by the editors of *Wallaces' Farmer and Iowa Homestead,* and they were finally selected by a board of judges composed of the following: Mark Thornburg, Iowa's Secretary of Agriculture; George Godfrey, Master Farmer and director of agricultural relations at Iowa State College; W. H. Royer, president of the Master Farmers; and Clifford V. Gregory, associate publisher of *Wallaces' Farmer and Iowa Homestead* and founder of the Master Farmer movement.

The new Master Farmers were presented to the state at a dinner at Des Moines, the evening of January 18.

As readers of this paper know, Master Farmers are selected because they are capable farm managers, because they are leaders in community work, and because they maintain the right kind of homes. They exemplify our motto, "Good Farming, Clear Thinking,

Right Living."

The new Master Farmers live up to this standard.

Allan Kline, of Benton County, is known to many farmers for his work in farm organizations. He is at present vice-president of the Iowa Farm Bureau Federation, served as president of his county Farm Bureau for years, and has been active in various cooperative enterprises in his community.

He's a good farmer, too, though not an orthodox one. He owns and farms 440 acres of rolling, well-drained land in Benton County, and produces hogs by the carload.

Low Overhead

He keeps his sows and gilts out in the fields, uses straw sheds and "A" houses, raises two litters a year, and turns out all the way from 300 to 1,000 head of fat hogs a year. And

he does it at a very low overhead cost. Kline uses crossbred hogs and gets big litters and vigorous pigs. For early spring litters, he keeps the sows and their pigs in the "A" houses for the first two weeks and then moves them to straw sheds, so the houses can be used by another crop. The older pigs are moved from field to field, as pasture and feed require. They are kept in straw sheds in winter. When time comes for spring work, the sheds are torn down, the straw

Kline

and manure spread around the field, and everything is set for a big crop. Meanwhile, the pigs move on to alfalfa or bluegrass pasture.

All of the farm has been limed, with an application averaging 3 tons to the acre. As to fencing: "I'm always building fences," Kline says. "We keep shifting the fields around to fit the needs of the rotation and of the hogs."

Electrically Equipped

The power line has helped the Kline farm home to be equipped with lights and electric stove, water system, hot water heater and other electric devices.

The Kline children, Robert, 17, Charles, 16, and Winifred, 14, probably think the best things about the place are the swimming pool and the tennis court. Both improvements were built with farm labor in spare time, and at low cost.

At 43, Allan Kline is younger than the average Master Farmer. Most Master Farmers are over 50, a majority close to 60.

Orie F. Irwin, of Sac County, gets back to the average age. He is 52. He owns and operates 560 acres of land in Sac County, where they still remember there was once a drought. Irwin points to a double row of stumps out in his front yard to prove it. The old windbreak was killed by dry weather.

Irwin was born on the farm where he now lives. It's a bigger farm now, though, than it was when his father was alive. And it has one of the best sets of buildings for a cattle-feeding enterprise that you'll find.

Sac county folks say that Irwin has been the backbone of a lot of community work for years. He was on the county corn-hog committee, served for years as township Farm Bureau chairman, has been a director in the farmers' evening school at Sac City, and has been useful to the community in many other ways.

Cattle Are Long-Fed

As a cattle feeder, he has played things as safe as a feeder can. He buys light stuff, puts them on a long feed, and has his money in the feed rather than the cattle. He raises some calves, but buys most of them. The yearly output of fat cattle is around 300 head.

He makes extensive use of pasture, 100 acres being in a mixture of bluegrass, timothy, alsike and bromegrass. Recent seasons have been hard on pasture, but 1938 was good, and he hopes for better grass seasons in the future.

Irwin is in the hog business, too, in a big way. He raises over 300 head a year, using spring litters only. And he raises them on clean ground. The pigs have to be up to 100 pounds and vigorous before they are turned in to follow the cattle.

"You still have to watch them like a hawk," he says. "You can't keep cattle feeding yards free of disease when you buy feeders. But we keep things as clean as we can; we don't turn out hogs until they are well grown, and when any pig looks a bit off feed, we jerk him out of there in a hurry."

The two Irwin children are through college and away from home, the daughter married and the son a club agent in another county. Mrs. Irwin has a well-equipped house to work in, with electricity and other improve-

Irwin

ments added to a home built a good many years ago.

Forty Years on Farm

Down in Adair County's rolling land is another new Master Farmer, Herbert W. Buck. Mr. Buck, 52 years old, owns 182 acres and rents 90 acres additional land. He has lived on this farm since 1898. His father died when he was 16, and he didn't get as much schooling as his boys have had, but he has improved the farm and enlarged it.

In Adair County, as in many southern Iowa counties, erosion is the great enemy. Gullies slash across farms and rob the land.

Buck inherited part of the farm, but he also inherited a gully. His battle against the gully is part of his distinguished record. The gully looks pretty tame now. Walk down it from the road toward the pasture at the foot of the slope and you find a ribbon of grass that stretches along over what used to be a gash in the earth. You find locust trees planted at strategic points, and you find, down below, a pond, a dam and a few acres devoted to timber.

Buck

Buck tried terraces and dams across the gully long before the Soil Conservation Service started its project in Adair County. But when the project began, he joined up at once.

"We got our first set of good terraces ready in 1935," he explained. "And they paid out that year. You see, we only got one good rain that season, but that made the corn crop on those strips below the terraces. The rain soaked in and was used when the crop needed it. On land like this, but without terraces, the crop just dried up."

Stopping Erosion

The farm is two-thirds limed. Sweet clover, red clover and alfalfa are being grown. The fields are being re-fenced to fit the new pasture and strip-cropping plans that are designed to defeat the threat of erosion.

Buck keeps 24 Angus cows, raises the calves, and feeds them out to 1,000 pounds. Last year he raised 63 spring pigs and 100 pullets. Both the pigs and pullets are raised on clean ground, well away from the buildings.

In the farm home, Mrs. Buck has an oil-burning refrigerator and an individual electric plant to supply light and power for the washing machine. Water is piped in from the windmill tank. The bathroom and the septic tank were put in years ago.

"It cost me only around $100 to fix up the bathroom and outlets, at the time I did it," said Mr. Buck. "It was money well spent. Too many of us wait until we retire and move to town before we get things like this. I think we need them worse on the farm now."

The Bucks have three children—one boy in high school, a girl in junior college, and the older boy is renting a farm nearby—and he is a good fighter against erosion, too.

Buck was active in community club work before the Farm Bureau was organized, was an early director in that, is an elder in the Presbyterian church, has been in the AAA programs, helped with 4-H Club work, and is a leader in the soil conservation district.

Over in Linn County, when you ask about Ben Neal, the neighbors begin to warm up at once. Neal, 58 years old and owner and operator of 350 acres, has made a place for himself as a community leader, as a sensible farmer and as a good friend.

Fine Old Home

He was born in this community, and moved onto his present farm 30 years ago. The Neals still live in the fine old brick house built by Colonel Robert Smythe on this place around 75 years ago. The house has modern improvements now, of course.

Neal has served as president of the Linn County Farm Bureau, was the first AAA chairman in the county, is a director in the Linn County Cooperative Oil Company, and is active in the local church and in other community affairs.

His two boys, Howard and Denny, are married and working with their father on the farm. Two daughters are married, and the youngest daughter is starting to college.

Neal is a general farmer, raises his own hogs, and buys cattle to feed. He raises two litters of pigs a year, and plans to keep from 20 to 30 sows in the breeding herd.

A detailed study of his farm records shows him far above the average as a farm manager. One man, commenting on his nomination as a Master Farmer, said, "He is a man of exceptionally-high character, is greatly respected, and is a genuine community leader." Another spoke of his high regard for Neal's "judgment and integrity. He has an analytical type of mind and does his own thinking."

Ben Neal and his two boys, Howard and Denny

1939

IOWA MASTER FARMERS

~
January 13, 1940

Every year, *Wallaces' Farmer and Iowa Homestead* helps select a few more Iowa Master Farmers. For 1939, the new Master Farmers are: J.D. Misbach, Iowa County; Will Yates, Osceola; Dayton W. Mather, Floyd; P.C. Thedens, Buchanan; and Herbert Schneckloth, Scott County.

What are they like? The following article by Donald R. Murphy tells of visits to their farms.

At Marengo, in Iowa County, they told me to drive south till I came to a low hill with a row of white pines on each side of the road. That would be Misbach's. I inquired about the white pines first thing. "I planted those myself 37 years ago," J.D. Misbach told me. "I remember a neighbor stopping by to tell me I'd never get any good out of them. I have, though. And the boys will get more."

Mr. Misbach is 65. He has done a good job of tree planting on the place. His father, settling on the same farm in the 60s, put out short-lived, quick-growing trees. J.D. has replaced all of them, except for one soft maple grove.

The Misbachs settled on this place to stay. Wiese, the oldest boy, unmarried, is on the farm now. So is Myron, who married last summer. When the 100th anniversary of the first Misbach's coming to Iowa County is celebrated, there will be folks of his blood still on the same place.

J.D. has eased up this fall and moved to town. This is partly to give the boys a free hand on the farm, and partly because he feels he is getting to the place where long days of hard work don't go so easily.

"I found out this summer that I was listening for the dinner-bell at 11 o'clock," he said. "That's how I knew I was getting old."

He'll keep working after he retires. He owns another farm which he looks after. He is director or committeeman in the Farm Bureau, the mutual insurance company, the cooperative oil company, the cow testing association and the AAA. As chairman of the county committee on tenant purchase loans, he has a lot of work to do in helping renters get started on farms of their own.

The Misbach farm contains 320 acres. J.D. Misbach and the boys

Misbach

feed cattle and hogs, milk a few cows, use lime, grow legumes, and raise big crops of corn.

In cattle feeding, Misbach usually buys calves in October and feeds for a year. This past year he handled 125 head. He has about 20 sows farrow in the spring, eight or 10 in the fall. Eight cows are usually milked, and the herd ranks high in the local cow testing association. The cattle are wintered on whole soybeans (1½ pounds a day) and all the silage they will eat. The racks are always full of alfalfa or soybean hay. Minerals are fed, too, and some oats.

In the spring when the silage runs low, the calves go on sweet clover pasture and run to a self-feeder filled with corn and cob meal, with some protein added.

Uses Plenty of Lime

Orchard grass has been tried out for August feed. Sweet clover and other legumes grow well. Misbach started liming 20 years ago, using 2 tons to the acre. Some fields have been covered twice.

The Misbachs have a big family—seven children. "I've driven thousands of miles taking kids to school at Williamsburg," he told me. All of the children are out of high school now. Four are college graduates.

Misbach himself went to the country school and no farther. "We didn't go to high school then," he explained, "or for a long time afterward. When my oldest boy was through country school, nobody went to high school around here. But times had changed when the others came on."

It was 106 degrees that day, but the corn looked green and vigorous. The Misbachs— father, son, and grandsons—had been putting manure on that corn land for 60 years. That makes a difference!

"I'm looking for a man who can make a good living on less than 160 acres," I told Will Yates, of Osceola County, when I drove into the yard. "I've got 123 acres," he said, "and we get along." Yates is 50. He knows what it is to

Yates

go broke, to buy in at high prices, to have drought and disaster strike.

He was born on the farm in Osceola County, went out to Montana and farmed for a while, came back in 1919 and bought equipment and stock in the high time.

Fortunately, he didn't buy the farm then, but waited until 1934. He has done well since.

Yates makes his money off his Holstein herd, and his pigs. The herd is a dandy; big cows with bones in the right places and udders that look ready to fill a pail apiece. The herd average is 450 pounds of butterfat per year.

Ronald Yates, now back on the farm after two years in college, helped start his father on a purebred herd. It must have been 13 years ago that Ronald got a purebred heifer in club work. Now all the herd is purebred. Seventeen cows are being milked.

The herd has developed largely from two cows; one, 11 years old, is still milking. Both were high producers. A new bull has a dam with a 699-pound record as a two year old. He should put a few more pounds on the herd average.

Yates raises around 70 pigs a year and has both spring and fall litters. There has been some disease trouble lately, in spite of the fact that he changes hog lots. He uses a Hampshire-Spotted Poland cross, sells at six months, weighing 200 pounds or more.

Poultry is important on the farm, too. Three hundred laying hens and pullets are being kept this winter.

When you look at Yates' community record, you wonder that he gets any farming done. He is vice-president of the Osceola county cooperative creamery, director of the mutual insurance association, director of the farmers' elevator, president of the cooperative oil company, and an officer in the Farm Bureau.

There are three children. The daughter is a college graduate; the older boy took two years at Ames and decided to come home and take a fourth interest in the dairy herd. The younger boy is at home going to school.

P.C. Thedens, of Buchanan County, is a newcomer; he moved here from Illinois in 1903. But in 36 years, you get acquainted.

You also find the time to drain a lot of land, help put up the consolidated school, raise a family, and feed out a lot of cattle and hogs.

Anyway, Thedens did. He is 74 now, and has one married son at home and another on a farm across the road. But he still says how the 325-acre place is to be run.

He raises around 30 calves a year, buys as many more, feeds for a year and sells at around 1,000 pounds. Two hundred pigs are raised a year. He has been using a Hampshire boar on Duroc Jersey sows.

And, like a lot of other cattle and hog men, he finds it worthwhile to milk a few dairy cows.

Mr. and Mrs. Thedens have the biggest family of any of this year's Master Farmers.

P.C. Thedens, left, and son George

There are nine children. Two boys are farming, and two girls married farmers in the same community. Four of the other children live in Buchanan County. All of them went through high school. One girl finished college.

Theden's big job in the community has been the consolidated school. He has been its president for 20 years. He has served as Farm Bureau director, as township trustee, as county supervisor and as president of the local bank.

The Mather house stands at the bend of the Shell Rock River. From the front yard, you can look at it for miles up a stream kept bank-full by the dam below at Greene.

Along the river, in pastures hemmed in by electric fences, spring pigs were fattening when I stopped at the farm. Sows with fall pigs were in other waterside pastures.

The dairy barn held 46 cows. Their average last year was 379 pounds of butterfat. And behind the buildings, stretched out the rest of the 345 acres in the big Mather farm.

Dayton W. Mather is 51, started farming across the county line in Butler, sold out in 1920, got cash, waited until he thought the boom was over, and bought back—this time in Floyd County—about 1922.

"It was too soon, of course," he told me. "I paid too much for the farm, just about enough to balance the profit I made on the other place."

His hog farming takes the eye. Mather raises 200 to 300 pigs in the spring; 100 in the fall. He uses sweet clover and alfalfa for clean ground pasture, divides the herd into units of

The Mather home, located at a bend of the Shell Rock River

his land in legumes and raised an average of 85 bushels on his 112-acre allotment of corn land.

Every acre on the place has been limed. He raises Belgian horses, is active in school affairs, has been secretary of the Farm Bureau, president of the township school board and township committeeman in the AAA.

Schneckloth's neighbors say he knows when to buy and sell cattle as well as how to feed. His market judgment has brought him money.

Mr. and Mrs. Schneckloth have three children. The oldest boy is married and starting to farm. The second boy, Donald, made a notable record in club work this year.

50 or 60, puts a big waterer in the center of a field split four ways by electric fence.

Clean-ground methods pay, he says, and the pigs look healthy. Mather uses a crisscross system, started with Poland China sows, used Hampshire boars for two years, then Poland boars for two years. Then back to Hampshire again.

He has limed every acre on the place. "The test showed I needed 3 tons to the acre," he said. "I put on four."

In the community field, Mather has served on the board of the Greene cooperative creamery, as a director in the oil company, as a township AAA committeeman, and as president of the Floyd County Farm Bureau.

Mr. and Mrs. Mather have a daughter and two boys, one in college and one back from college on the farm.

Herbert Schneckloth, of Scott County, is the youngest of this year's Master Farmer crop. He is only 45. He farms 360 acres, raised 60 litters this last year, averaging seven pigs per litter, fed out 96 head of cattle and kept six dairy cows.

In 1939, he kept 40% of

Schneckloth

1940

IOWA MASTER FARMERS

~

January 25, 1941

Iowa has four new Master Farmers. They are Fred K. Bruene, of Tama County; J. R. McKeown, of Shelby County; E.N. Neal, of Butler County, and Charles R. Mountain, of Polk County.

These men were nominated for the honor by their neighbors. Their selection was approved by a board of judges consisting of Clifford V. Gregory, associate publisher of *Wallaces' Farmer and Iowa Homestead* and founder of the Master Farmer movement; George Godfrey, of Kossuth County and Iowa State College (he is a Master Farmer himself); Mark Thornburg, Iowa's Secretary of Agriculture; and Robert M. Clark, of Polk County, president of the Iowa Master Farmers Club.

Most counties have a Master Farmer now. Most Iowans know what Master Farmers are like. But for those who don't, the description is: A farmer who does an extra good job of running a farm, and of helping to run a family and a community. Unless he is pretty good at all three, he doesn't qualify.

Fred K. Breune, of Tama County, is a good sample of the kind of man we like to select as Master Farmer. He is 52, has farmed on his present place or near it for 25 years, is chair-

Bruene

man of the county planning board, has served as an officer in a number of cooperatives, teaches in the Sunday school, has put three children through college and is sending two more.

He is now living on the same farm his father bought years ago, when the senior Breune came to Tama County. There was only a two-room house on the place then. The two-room house is still there, but you wouldn't know it. The Breune home is a large, modern, comfortable place—but the original two rooms are still in it.

Fred Breune's father must have felt at home there right up to the end. He used to sit on the porch and look over the fields in his last days. "Prettiest sight in the world!" he said. He died only a year ago, and Fred Breune, who had farmed the place for 10 years as a renter, became owner on the record books.

As a farm operator, Breune is a star member of the farm business association, is strong for lime and phosphate, and follows out approved practices. But he learned this out of bulletins and from other farmers, not at college. He is a graduate of Morningside College, and he took a Master's degree in psychology at the University of Iowa. Maybe the psychology degree helped him when he was Farm Bureau president and when he was elected to the legislature.

Breune farms 240 acres and makes his money from beef cattle, dairy cattle and hogs. All the farm except 20 acres can be cultivated. He milks 10 pure-bred Holstein cows, and does well with them.

Bruene feeds calves out to 800 to 1,000 pounds

Ordinarily, Breune keeps 15 to 20 sows for spring pigs. The pigs come late and are kept on pasture. Water is piped to the fields. The pigs are brought along slowly on red clover pasture, hand-fed oats, corn and skim milk through the summer and fall, and then put on the self-feeder for a finishing period of six weeks in late winter. Usually he heads these late-spring pigs for the February or March market.

When Breune came to the farm, the lots were full of necro. He had to move the pigs out on pasture. But now he thinks it pays to keep pigs out on pasture both for health and for economy gains.

He feeds out two loads of cattle a year, but handles these in rather an unusual way. He picks up calves at 150 to 200 pounds around his part of the state and feeds out to 850 to 1000 pounds. The

McKeown

finished product rates only common to good, but the costs are low. Of the added weight, about 400 pounds goes on through use of pasture and roughage. The final 300 pounds is put on with heavier feeding in the yard.

"I got my education in the livestock business in the stockyards over in Omaha," said J.R. McKeown, of Shelby County, our second Master Farmer. He was raised on a Pottawattamie County farm, but went to Omaha to work for a commission firm as a young man. "You learn what to buy and when, and when and where to sell," he declared.

Mr. McKeown has been buying and feeding and selling cattle ever since. It's a business that has more than its share of bankrupts, but McKeown has survived the collapse of 1920 and the depression of 1932.

The Omaha stockyards must have been a good school. Or else McKeown was an extra good student.

He is 64 years old now, and has been farming, except for those three years in the stockyards, ever since he was a boy. He came to Shelby County only 20 years ago, moved in during 1920 and bought a well-improved place of 215 acres right on the edge of town. That wasn't a good year to buy, but McKeown sold his old farm that year, too, and got clear on both deals.

Shelby County has been in the dry belt for some years now. McKeown has been in the AAA program, has tried to keep pastures up and get new pastures started, but most of the feeding has had to be dry lot or dry pasture feeding.

Things may be different now. McKeown's been getting a stand of alfalfa with late-summer seeding lately, although he's had to thicken it up in the spring. But he has 40 acres of alfalfa now and will have more.

He buys twice as much grain as he feeds and raises, but produces his own hay and silage. Sometimes this need to buy grain makes big cattle feeders leave the AAA. But McKeown stays in. This year he has only 62 acres of corn.

Cattle feeding is the big farm enterprise. He usually gets medium weight stuff in the fall for a six months' feed, then buys again in the spring, to sell in the fall. The cattle he has on hand now weighed 650 pounds when he bought them, will weigh 1,100 when he lets them go. "When cattle are high, buy medium grades," says McKeown. "When they're cheap, you can't buy too good stuff. There's not enough difference in price." As a rule, he feeds out five to seven carloads a year.

McKeown's in the hog business, too. He raises about 125 spring pigs and 40 to 50 fall pigs. He used to buy feeder pigs, but ran into too much trouble with disease. Lately, he has been having some difficulty with erysipelas

in the herd, but he raises the pigs on clean ground, changes it from year to year, uses alfalfa and bluegrass pasture liberally and manages to keep hog diseases in check.

He helped organize one of the first Farm Bureaus in the state, has been county president and director, and served for seven years as manager of the local cooperative shipping association.

Of his family of three girls and a boy, 50% have stuck to farming. One daughter married a farmer in Pottawattamie County and young McKeown is farming in Shelby County.

E.N. Neal with son Galen

"I don't move around much," said E.N. Neal, of Butler County. "I was born on a farm within a mile of this place, and we bought here—on a shoestring—in 1908. We had a good many years of scraping along. The place had no fences, the buildings were poor, and we didn't have enough machinery or much stock. Of course, we took some hard bumps in 1920 and 1932, like everybody else, but our hardest time was really back before the World War."

The farm looks different now. It includes 200 acres, of which 58 were in corn last year and 35 in alfalfa. There have been 920 tons on lime spread on the farm, and phosphate is beginning to be used. Neal went over the place first with 4 tons per acre and is now starting a second round with 2 tons per acre. For most of the place, a three-year rotation holds—oats seeded to sweet clover, sweet clover pastured, and corn.

Twelve sows are kept. The spring pigs come late, are carried along on alfalfa pasture, and sold in late winter. Neal is milking 14 cows.

A new enterprise, designed to use up more of the pasture and hay brought by the AAA program, is beef cattle. Neal has seven cows and bull of Burt Neal's linebred Shorthorn stock, with 20 head of grade Shorthorn females and is going to raise himself some feeders.

"We won't get into production until about 1943," he commented, "and that may hit the top of the beef cattle cycle when everybody is stocked up. Yet if my feeders don't cost me anything except hay and pasture, and I raise the hay and pasture, I don't see how I can go very wrong."

Neal's older boy, Galen, is back on the farm with him this year after three years in college.

In community affairs, Neal has been unusually active. He has been an officer of the Farm Bureau, a Sunday school teacher for 30 years, an officer in the local cooperative creamery company, was manager of the Iowa Farm Service Company, and led in starting the Butler County REA. He was project superintendent of the REA for several years.

Charles R. Mountain, of Polk County, is a breeder of high-production dairy cows. He has been raising purebred Guernseys for 32 years, starting in Cedar County and moving to Polk County in 1916.

In the herd now are 100 head of cattle, with 50 milking. The herd is making around a 600-pound average on butterfat, according to Advanced Registry tests. That's production!

Mountain sells milk in Des Moines. The city has grown since he moved to Polk County, so that his farm is now almost in the suburbs. Some day he may have to split it up into lots and move. Even now, he is handicapped by lack of space. He has 75 acres and rents 34 more, but that produces little more than hay, pasture and silage for his big herd. His 26 acres of corn hardly makes a dent in the grain supply needed.

With all that manure being put out, the farm is highly productive. Mountain has limed all the farm, uses lime with the manure, and has spread superphosphate on some of the fields.

Mountain

When a herd reaches a 600-pound average, picking a bull becomes an extra hazardous job. Many a good bull that will raise the average of a 400-pound herd would ruin a 600-pound bunch of cows. So the better the herd gets, the more difficult the problem of breeding is.

Mountain's answer to this is to raise his own bulls and to practice line breeding. One of his cows, former junior champion at the Iowa fair, is still producing well at 14 years, and made 832 pounds at 12. Her son is the present herd bull. Three of her daughters, three-year-olds, have records of 555, 631 and 649 pounds. That blood strain is going to be kept in the field.

In the community field, Mountain has been president of the Polk County Farm Bureau and president of the Iowa Guernsey Breeders Association. Mrs. Mountain helped start the first 4-H girls club in the county and has been president of the county Federation of Women's Clubs.

1941 IOWA MASTER FARMERS
~ January 24, 1942

Here are Iowa's four new Master Farmers, as I found them on visits to their homes last year. Nominated by their neighbors, approved by a four-man board, they are: Ray Coglon, Audubon County; Henry Dall, Ida County; Henry Olerich, Pocahontas County, and Alvin Prestemon, Allamakee County.

Henry Olerich
Pocahontas County

"When was it we planted alfalfa in that field across from the schoolhouse?" Henry Olerich asked his wife. "It must have been the year Rolfe had his first auto. Ours was the first alfalfa patch around here."

They agreed on 1904, not long after Olerich came to this farm in Pocahontas County. He is 68 now; has been on this farm 40 years. And every year has seen improvements to the place. Lime has been used. The alfalfa patch of 1904 had been expanded to 45 acres by 1941. And green manure. "I plowed under 30 acres of soybeans for green manure in 1940," said Olerich. "Had plenty of hay, it was late anyway, and I figured it would do more good turned under."

He has the green manure habit. Ordinarily, he seeds Hubam with his oats, pastures it in the fall, plows it under by spring.

While Olerich has treated his land well, has drained, limed and manured, his big interest has been in hogs. A purebred breeder for years, he has steered away from breeding extremes, always remembered that the ultimate end of a hog was the butcher shop.

On his steadily growing farm—it now covers 320 acres—there have always been plenty of good hogs. He has room for 100 spring and 100 fall pigs. He rotates the pasture, farrows spring pigs in the field with movable houses. There is one big hog house for bad weather farrowing. Another hog house handles hogs

Olerich parades 900-pound "Dynamite" around the barnyard

in the final stages of feeding.

In raising fall pigs, Olerich has the sows bred fairly late. He fears cold weather less than August heat and flies. No fall pigs are wanted until September. Some bred sows are always sold, the rest kept to raise boars and gilts for breeding demand.

Lately, with AAA hay supplies on hand, Olerich has gone in for more cattle. He has fed out steers, but now leans to cows and young stuff, fit to consume more hay, less concentrated feed.

There are six children in the Olerich family, four boys and two girls. One boy is farming nearby. Another is helping at home. All six went through college. The farm is well equipped; the home comfortable, modern.

In the community field, Olerich served as president of the county Farm Bureau for seven years, has served as church trustee, school director, and has cooperated with the AAA since the start of the program.

Ray Coglon
Audubon County

Ray Coglon, of Audubon County, was born on a farm a mile away from where he now lives. He hasn't moved far in his 49 years. The 80 across the road was bought before the boom. But the 80 on which his buildings stand was bought in 1919.

That wasn't so lucky, but Coglon has survived it. He finds 160 acres a good-sized farm, even if it is on rolling Audubon County hills.

He has put up a lot of fences on the place, to shift pasture, keep stock on clean ground. And there is plenty of pasture.

Ray Coglon

One reason for the pasture is the AAA. Another reason—and the more important one—is that Coglon is strong for erosion control. He helped organize this watershed into a conservation district of 2,200 acres. Contour planting, which he first tried years ago for himself, is now standard practice on many good farms.

I visited the place after an 8-inch rain last summer. There was some damage along the highway. The contour planting hadn't saved everything. But the Coglon farm showed few signs of trouble.

On July 8, he had a bluegrass pasture of 17 acres that hadn't been touched by stock that season. It had been limed, disked in the spring of 1940, seeded with red clover, alsike, sweet clover and alfalfa. For a test, there was a strip of TVA phosphate.

The grass and clover were high, waiting for the breeding herd of cattle to be turned in. He had 27 head of cows and yearling heifers that were to calve some time before this spring.

Coglon is a stockman. He sells cattle of his own raising and nearly all for breeding purposes. He keeps 25 head of breeding ewes, has four mares, and sold five head of horses off the place in 1940. He raises around 65 head of spring pigs, 30 fall pigs. And there are 150 laying hens.

To keep this stock going, he raises only 37 acres of corn, but since he has been getting a yield close to 70 bushels, that still piles up a lot of feed. He only buys around 500 to 600 bushels of corn a year to add to what he raises.

Besides his pasture land, he grows alfalfa.

There were 21 acres producing alfalfa hay in 1941, 18 more acres seeded to alfalfa.

Mr. and Mrs. Coglon have worked hard on the farmstead. The windbreak is a beauty—50 White Pine and 50 Norway Spruce. They were planted in 1926. In 1934, Coglon hauled 12 thresher tanks full of water to irrigate to save the trees. He had a good orchard, too, but the freeze of 1940 fixed that. There is one transparent left of the 30 trees, but he is planting again.

Some recent profits in farming have gone into the house. This year, the rooms were rearranged, a bathroom put in on the main floor, extra windows supplied, a furnace with a blower put in, an electric heater added (Coglon helped get the REA started). There is a new sink in the kitchen, with windows over it, so Mrs. Coglon can look out at dish-washing time.

In the community field, he's been active in the AAA township committee, has for a good many years served as township clerk, and has taken a part in church, Farm Bureau and cooperative. The Coglons have three children: Gertrude, 14; Raymond, 9; and James, 5.

Henry Dall

Henry Dall
Ida County

Farmers have fed cattle for a long time out in Ida County. In the Battle Creek neighborhood, too many filled-up feedlots in the hard years held stubbornly to their patch-hided steers while the market slipped and slid. Plenty of feeders went broke.

Henry Dall was not one of them. He has always fed cattle, still feeds, but he doesn't plunge. When I visited him last fall, he had 50 head on hand, weighing 800 to 900 pounds. He feeds from 75 to 100 head a year, plans to sell good, not prime, cattle, varies feeding plans to suit the season.

Dall is 64 years old, has lived on this farm 60 years. When his father retired, Dall took over the farm. That was back in 1900.

He raises around 100 spring pigs. They are farrowed in the hog house in April, put on pasture when three or four weeks old. Dall keeps the hog house clean, gets the pigs to pasture quickly, and has so far avoided much trouble with disease.

This is alfalfa country; the soil is sweet. Dall had 18 acres to cut for hay last year; had 25 acres of alfalfa and brome. He is fascinated by brome as a pasture crop, finds it fine for late summer; but is still experimenting with methods of seeding it.

One cash crop is hybrid seed corn. He raised 25 acres last year, and has been at this for the last seven years.

Dall has led a busy life in the community. He helped organize a cooperative store in Battle Creek 20 years ago, has been its secretary ever since. He is president of the county fire insurance association, has served on the Production Credit Board since its organization, was on the county FSA committee. He is a charter member of the county Farm Bureau, and an AAA cooperator.

Mr. and Mrs. Dall live in a big, two-story, white house, down a narrow side road that branches off from the gravel road out of Battle Creek. The fall day I visited there, flowers were still bright in the angle between the wings of the house. Too big a house, Dall said, for folks with no children. But there are plenty of boys in the community to follow Dall, to take profit from his example, even if they are not of his blood.

Alvin Prestemon
Allamakee County

We got lost on a twisting hill road in Allamakee County; the car slid down between walls of red maples, burnished oaks, into a little valley; the road seemed to be headed for no place. But there was a man at work on the side of the road.

"'Looking for Alvin?" he asked. "You took the wrong turn. But that gate into the pasture will take you to his place."

So we drove up to Alvin Prestemon's back door. His farm of 227 acres lies in a little valley back in the hills. There is bottomland pasture, some rolling land for crops, and a lot of timber pasture around both.

There isn't much farm land, or what a northwestern Iowa farmer would call farm land. The corn allotment is only 23.5 acres, an allotment made smaller by the fact that Prestemon prudently quit raising corn in the years when corn was cheap, and was penalized on allotments made on the historical basis.

But he raises plenty of feed anyway. Last year, for instance, he had 33 acres in oats and barley, 4 acres in soybeans, 28 acres in red clover, 17 acres in alfalfa. The balance was in pasture or timber. He is gradually and slowly opening up the timber land to make fair pasture.

The good pasture land, like one terraced 17-acre field on the slope, is likely to have sweet clover, alfalfa, and red clover in it as well as bluegrass. The legumes grow because he limed the farm lightly—1 ton to the acre—four and 15 years ago. He is now starting around again with an application of 2 tons per acre.

Prestemon has always lived in this neighborhood. His father bought the place—185 acres then—when Alvin was a boy. The elder Prestemon died when Alvin was 14. Alvin's mother died five years later. That left the boy head of family of eight children.

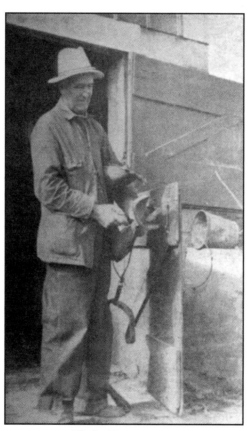

Alvin Prestemon

He bought this farm in 1909, gradually paid off the other heirs, fixed up the place, built a house. All the buildings on the farm were put up by him. Lumber from the farm was used in great part.

The house was built in 1913, before his marriage in 1920. Mrs. Prestemon says he did pretty well, but that if she had been around, there might have been stairs less steep, a few more closets. It's an attractive house, though, set back on a small knoll in the middle of the farm, and with a long lane out to the highway, a lane that takes lots of gravel in bad weather and lots of shoveling in winter.

Prestemon has done an unusually good job in getting the most out of the land and labor at hand. For years, when his brother was with him, he milked cows. When he had to depend on his own work alone, plus some help from a man living nearby, he shifted to beef cattle.

Now he raises calves from 22 Shorthorn cows, keeps a Hereford bull. The calves are put on 15 to 16 cows; he milks the other cows. Pasture, hay, and little corn bring the young stuff up to two years at a fair weight with a moderate amount of work and corn.

Prestemon raises around 100 pigs each year. That's where the corn goes. Usually about 70 pigs are raised in the spring, 30 in the fall. He keeps 20 ewes, sells as many lambs each year. There is a good poultry flock.

His corn yields are high. Because the allotment is small, he picks the best acres, uses manure freely, takes advantage of legume sod. The yield has gone as high as 80 bushels per acre.

Prestemon is 53 years old now. For many of those years, he has been active in the country church nearby; he has served on the county farm tenancy committee, on the production credit board. He helped organize and served as president of a town-country club where Farm Bureau people from four townships around Waukon get together with Waukon people once a month for entertainment and discussion.

The Prestemons have two daughters, both in college at the present time.

These are the 1941 Master Farmers for Iowa. There are bigger farms than these, farmers with larger bank balances, some farmers with more striking records of community development service.

But these men show what can be done in using the means ordinary people find at hand, in raising better crops and livestock, in making good homes, in helping the community.

In paying tribute to these men, *Wallaces' Farmer and Iowa Homestead* pays tribute to every other Iowa farmer who tries to build for the future, to protect his land, to maintain his community, to give his children a good start, to make his neighbors miss him sorely when he puts the plow in the shed for the last time.

CHAPTER 3
~
1946 - 1959: Post-War

World War II dramatically affected Iowa farm life. The government issued ration stamps to restrict food, gasoline and tire consumption. Iowa farmers geared up production to support the war effort. Scrap metal and paper drives, along with price controls, became a part of the American lifestyle. Wartime experiences quickly turned many young boys into men. Many did not return home.

Those who did return were eager to marry, start families and find places in the farming community. The GI Bill provided tuition for service men and women who wanted to further their education.

Mechanization of agriculture marched forward. Equipment became available as factories converted to peace time production, making "live" horsepower obsolete. Less need for oats to feed horses changed crop rotations. The diversification of crop and livestock production became more evident. Soybeans, as an alternative crop, provided protein for livestock and poultry rations. Self-propelled combines, grain storage, artificial corn drying and handling equipment came to the forefront.

ISU Extension provides information
Scientific developments at Iowa State College (Iowa State University after 1959) disseminated through the Extension service sparked a "chemical revolution." Insecticides such as DDT provided insect control and herbicides such as 2,4-D killed harmful weeds.

Changes in cropping systems and larger fields brought the need for better soil and water conservation. After World War II, every county promoted Soil Conservation Districts to help plan crop rotations, grassed waterways, contour planting and terrace construction on individual farms.

Artificial insemination of beef and dairy cattle intensified milk and meat production through the use of high-quality parent stock.

Home freezers became popular in preserving meat, fruits and vegetables. Farmers no longer needed to cut and store wood for cooking and home heating. Electricity, heating oil and/or propane provided rural farm homes with amenities comparable to urban living.

Print media, radio, television, and exhibits and fairs became an important part of farm life. In 1959, the first Iowa Farm Progress Show, sponsored by *Wallaces Farmer* magazine, highlighted the growing specialization and emphasis on modern management practices. Farmers could see firsthand how to hike efficiency, improve production techniques and perk up their bottom lines.

Prosperity gives way to crop surpluses
The period from 1940 to 1952 was the longest time of sustained prosperity in American agricultural history. With declining farm prices near the close of the Korean War, Iowa farmers again found themselves in a "cost-price squeeze," a reminder of the 1930s.

Farmers also faced a drought in the mid-1950s. Many left the farm, which brought about further consolidation of farms. Various federal programs were tried, such as the "soil bank," which took land out of production. But political pressure by urban interests reduced its effectiveness.

1950 Iowa Farm Facts

FARMS & INCOME

Number of Iowa farms	206,000
Crop production value	$491 million
Livestock production value	$1.9 billion
Iowa net farm income	$1.1 billion

LIVESTOCK

	Inventory	*Average price*
Cattle and calves	4.9 million head	$25.30/cwt (beef)
Hogs and pigs	12.6 million head	$17.98/cwt
	Production	*Inventory*
Chickens (Layers)	4.4 billion eggs	25.1 million birds
Milk	6.2 billion lbs.	

CROPS

	Harvested acres	*Yield*	*Production*	*Avg price*
All Hay	3.7 million	1.75 tons/acre	6.5 million tons	$16.6/ton
Corn	9.4 million	48.5 bu./acre	456 million bu.	$1.52/bu.
Soybeans	1.9 million	22 bu./acre	42.5 million bu.	$2.64/bu.
Oats	6.5 million	41.5 bu./acre	271 million bu.	$0.79/bu.
Wheat	250,000	22 bu./acre	5.5 million bu.	$2.03/bu.

IOWA MASTER FARMERS
~
April 5, 1947

Community building, farm leadership and farming skill count as *Wallaces' Farmer and Iowa Homestead* adds Howard Hill and Donald Bellman to the list of Iowa Master Farmers.

Hill, vice-president of the Iowa Farm Bureau Federation, feeds beef cattle and raises hogs on his farm in Dallas County.

Bellman has served on school board, on DHI Association, and is milk route chairman of Des Moines Cooperative.

G.D. Bellman, of Warren County, served on the county AAA committee and is director of Production Credit Association. A herd of 24 Holsteins and 30 litters of pigs a year are the basis of his income.

Howard Hill raises from 700 to 1,100 head of hogs a year and milks 14 dairy cows. He has served on the school board, farm forum, Farm Bureau and in the Western Policy Association. His father, Ed Hill, was one of Iowa's first Master Farmers.

IOWA MASTER FARMERS

~ *March 20, 1948*

Just how is a Master Farmer selected? Frankly, a lot of people from all parts of Iowa help *Wallaces' Farmer and Iowa Homestead*. Last year, for example, more than 75 farmers were nominated by their neighbors and friends.

Persons making a nomination fill out an official entry blank and scorecard. Then other neighbors and businessmen are asked for additional information.

If all scorecards give a high rating, one of the editorial staff of *Wallaces' Farmer and Iowa Homestead* makes further inquiries and visits the nominee.

Finally, the mass of reports gets to the four judges. The president of the Iowa Master Farmer group is always a judge. The current president is D.J. Schnittjer, Delaware County.

Iowa's Secretary of Agriculture and the head of the agricultural economics department at Iowa State College always serve as judges. So Harry D. Linn and Dr. William G. Murray acted as judges. Fourth judge is always the editor of this publication, Donald R. Murphy.

Master Farmers for 1947 are:

Connor

Carney Connor
Carroll County

Connor's home is in the Storm Creek bottom, north of Glidden. He owns 280 acres, rents an additional 120 acres from his father. His 120-acre farm is in the more rolling part of the county; he uses it as a grass farm in his cattle feeding.

Besides feeding cattle, Connor raises 150-200 hogs a year, milks 14-16 cows.

The Connors have seven children, four sons and three daughters. The oldest children are in college now.

Connor, 46, has found time to be active in community affairs. He has been township clerk, is a director in the local cooperative creamery and the farmers' elevator. He is president of the Carroll National Farm Loan Association, past president of the Carroll County Farm Bureau, a member of the Farm Bureau legislative committee, and county boys 4-H chairman.

Both Mr. and Mrs. Connor are active in their church.

Leigh R. Curran
Cerro Gordo County

One of the youngest farmers ever to receive the award, Curran, 40, is already known to many of you through his work as director of the Iowa Beef Producers Association and president of the North Iowa Fair.

He is also secretary of the local cooperative serum company, president of the Mason City Production Credit Association, director in a farmers elevator, secretary of the county Farm Bureau, officer in the Iowa Polled Hereford Association, member of the Mason City Rotary Club, and a strong supporter of 4-H work. He is active in the men's club of his church.

The Currans have three young children. His neighbors and the county Extension director mention his excellent crop rotation and his soil improvement work. One man said Curran has increased yields 40 percent.

Curran owns 320 acres, rents another quarter. In addition to his Polled Herefords, he raises several hundred head of hogs each year, and generally feeds some lambs. He is a member of a farm business association.

William H. Davidson
Cedar County

"Bill" Davidson, 46, is one of the group of Iowa farmers who paid their own expenses to Europe last summer. What is important about that trip is that Davidson, like several others, has given unstintingly of his time since then to bring the picture as he sees it to thousands of other farmers.

He represents the third generation of his family to operate the home place, 280 acres, which he rents from his mother. He owns 200 acres. He, too, is a livestock farmer. In the past, the emphasis has been on feeding cattle, but at the moment he has shifted into heavier hog production. He keeps a small herd of Holstein cows.

Davidson has used good soil-building rotations and has improved crop yields. He has started a complete soil conservation plan for his farm. Davidson and his wife have a son and a daughter, Davidson is an elder in his church, teaches a Sunday school class of high school boys and girls.

He has been, or now is, township trustee, president of the Stanwood school board, member of the county board of education, president of the Davenport PCA, vice-president of the county Farm Bureau, member of the state Farm Bureau's

Curran

74

livestock committee, and is a member of a farm business association.

Henry Kernen
Montgomery County

Kernen has operated his farm for 30 years. It is 160 acres. He started by buying a half interest in 240 acres, including the present homestead.

Kernen, like many other Iowa farmers, knows what it is to lie awake at night worrying about the interest and taxes.

Today, at 60, he owns his home. He is assisting his two grown children, a son and a daughter, both married, in the purchase of nearby 160-acre farms. He hopes his third child, a young son, will want to operate the home place.

Kernen did not pay for his farm by following time-tried methods of operation. He was among the first in his community to sow sweet clover; among the first to adopt hybrid corn, to rework his rolling land under an SCS plan.

Hog raising is his main enterprise, though he has fed cattle and has done considerable dairying.

He has been active in the local rural telephone company, a Farm Bureau director, Villisca evening school adviser, and a member of the Lions Club and the new Villisca landlord-tenant association. Much of his time has been given to bond drives and other community activities.

He is building a new home, has completed the grading and landscape work.

Davidson

Earl Lyon
Tama County

"Pete" Lyon, as his friends call him, has done several outstanding jobs. One is the improvement of the soil on the 160 acres he owns. He bought a rather unproductive farm in 1929. But it is paid for today, and corn yields have gone from 40 to as much as 100 bushels per acre.

He has a rotation that gives him plenty of pasture and hay, for one of his other projects—a high-producing herd of Jersey cows. That herd helped to attain the third objective—that of raising four sons who are interested in the home farm.

The oldest son is an Iowa State graduate, two of the sons are in school at Ames now, and the youngest is still at home. Duward, the second son, is a former state boy's 4-H Club president.

Lyon, 51, has found time to be a director of the local rural school, township clerk for 12 years, township AAA chairman for 10 years, a director in a farmers canning company, and a member of the county Farm Bureau board of directors.

He was one of the first to adopt many recommended soil conservation measures, and was conservation district commissioner for several years.

All the judges felt that the intimate cooperation of all members of the Lyon family deserved special recognition.

Marion R. Ringoen
Winneshiek County

Ringoen, 48, has an unusual background, in that he started his working life as a chemistry and physics teacher. He now farms a short 240 acres, specializing in Brown Swiss cattle and Duroc hogs.

On his farm, he grows only 40 acres of corn each year, but is producing as much corn as used to be grown on 70 or 80 acres of the same land. He has used both lime and phosphate on all his cropland, and is starting over the second time.

Ringoen has been active in school affairs as a director and president of the board. He has been county Farm Bureau president four years, a director in the local creamery. One of his major outside activities has been serving as president of the Hawkeye Tri-County REA. He is a trustee of his church.

The Ringoens have a son and a daughter. Their son graduated from high school last year. Robert holds the Iowa Farmer FFA degree. Their daughter is a graduate of Iowa State.

The Ringoens, like the Kernens, spend a lot of their spare time planning the home they intend to build when building materials become more plentiful.

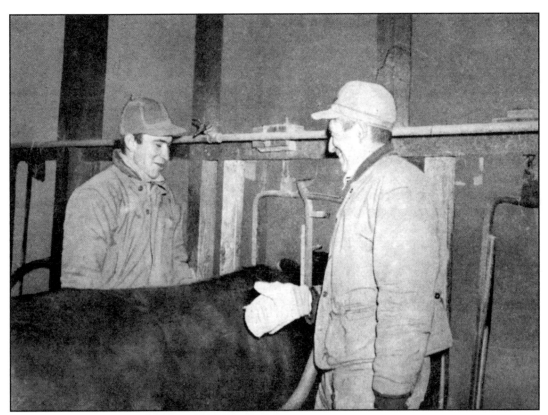

Earl "Pete" Lyon, at right, with son Howard

Marion R. Ringoen, at left, with son Robert

Kernan

IOWA MASTER FARMERS

March 5, 1949

In 1926, this publication started the program of honoring Iowa farmers for outstanding achievements in agriculture and good citizenship. That first year, 14 men were named Iowa Master Farmers.

The seven men pictured here just joined 110 men and one woman who have received the Master Farmer award since 1926.

Just how were they selected? A lot of people helped pick them. First came nominations. From all over Iowa, persons who are farmers or closely connected with agriculture nominated their friends and neighbors.

Accompanying the nomination was a scorecard. It covered three phases of farm activity — Good Farming, Clear Thinking and Right Living. Sometimes, several persons nominated one farmer.

Wallaces' Farmer and Iowa Homestead editors checked these nominees, filled out the additional field reports and scorecards.

Finally, a committee composed of the Iowa Secretary of Agriculture, Harry Linn; the head of the department of agricultural economics at Iowa State College, William Murray; the current president of the Master Farmer Club, Fred K. Breune, Gladbrook, and editor Donald R. Murphy ranked the contenders.

These seven men were named 1948 Iowa Master Farmers:

A.R. Clause
Greene County

Clause, 56, is one of Greene county's good livestock producers. His specialty is beef cattle and hogs. He farms 510 acres in partnership with two of his sons; owns 400 acres of that.

As an outgrowth of the boys' 4-H work, they also have a herd of purebred Aberdeen Angus cattle. A good rotation has been of help in building up the fertility of his land.

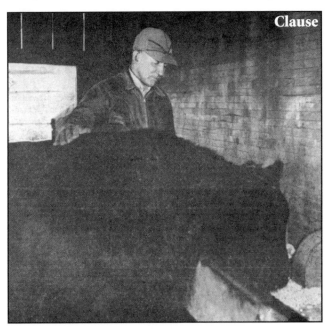

Clause

Clause is interested in efficiency; has a granary that doubles as a 12,000-bushel self-feeder for cattle. It will handle 100 head of steers.

He is active in community and church projects, was a charter member

Dubbert

of the Greene county Farm Bureau, is an SCS commissioner, and served on the school board for many years.

Clause is proud of the fact that, as president of the Grand Junction school board, he presented high school diplomas to all of his six children. Four of the children are college graduates; five are married.

Fred Dubbert
Pocahontas County

Not a grain farmer like many others in the Wisconsin drift soil area of Iowa, Dubbert, 52, specializes in pork and beef production. He raises around 30 litters of pigs a year; usually feeds 25 to 50 Whiteface heifers.

His buildings reflect planning to make choring easier and more profitable. His fertile farm reflects his knowledge of crops and soils, a subject he once taught at Iowa State College.

Dubbert has been active in Farmers Union, Farm Bureau, AAA, school and church work. He was on the Laurens school board 14 years.

His oldest son graduates from Iowa State College next June; after that, Dubbert plans to farm in partnership with him. Another son is in the navy; a daughter is in high school at Laurens.

Maynard Menefee
Dallas County

You don't have to be a big operator to deserve the Iowa Master Farmer award. Menefee, 40, operates a 90-acre farm. A former tenant, like so many other Master Farmers, Menefee purchased his farm through the Farmers Home Administration farm ownership program.

Menefee paid off the FHA loan in six years.

Menefee milks Holstein cows, has a herd average of 355 pounds of fat. One cow with a 520-pound record points the way to the kind of herd he wants. He also specializes in market hogs, and has a good poultry flock.

Menefee has been president of his county Farm Bureau, is active on his church board, on

Menefee

the Farmers Home Administration Board, and in other community activities. He has one young son.

Harry Reese
Adams County

Reese, 47, is a dairyman and pork producer. He has a fine herd of purebred Guernsey cattle and has made outstanding records in commercial hog production.

The only "Flying Farmer" in this group, he and his son own an airplane, plan to farm in partnership next year. Reese is chairman of the Adams County Soil Conservation District, has a complete soil conservation plan in operation on the 214 acres he owns.

His also is a program of increasing soil fertility with legumes, rotation pasture, manure, fertilizer and soil conservation.

Even with his big dairy herd and lots of hogs, he has given much time to community work. He has been a member of the Iowa Dairy Industry Commission, an officer of the Iowa Guernsey Cattle Club, active in the county Farm Bureau, in school and church affairs.

His daughter is married, lives on 160 acres near the home farm.

Reese

John P. Schnack
Clinton County

The first Master Farmer to be selected from a county famous for its good farmers and good livestock, Schnack, 47, owns 253 acres of land. He feeds cattle and also does an outstanding job of raising hogs.

Schnack has two sons and two daughters. The family has a very nice farm home. Schnack is active in a number of agricultural and church activities; gives freely of his time and energy to community affairs.

He came to this country in 1922, worked three years as a farmhand to pay for his transportation; started farming on a poor farm with his brother. Later, the partnership was dissolved.

Of that period, Schnack says: "If my brother and the landlord would have asked for the money due them, I couldn't have paid the bill."

In 1936, with a Federal Land Bank loan, he bought 153 acres and has since bought another 100 acres.

He has had to do a lot of building improvement on his farm and has brought it to a high state of productivity by

John P. Schnack, at left, with son Guenther

80

the use of lots of manure, long rotations and fertilizer.

Peter Sidles
Appanoose County

Sidles' farming operations stand out because of the way in which he planned his program to fit the problems of his area.

Poor soil has been tackled through long-rotation, livestock enterprise; erosion is being licked by contouring, strip-cropping and terracing, as well as with the livestock enterprise.

He carries a 40-cow beef herd, runs about 50 ewes. Enough hogs are raised to make use of all the grain produced on the farm.

Sidles, 53, is extremely active in school, church and agricultural affairs. He is especially interested in the twin southern Iowa problem of schools and roads. He is a long-time Farm Bureau member, an organizer of the county conservation district, and has been both an AAA and FHA committeeman.

He has five children. Two boys and a girl are college graduates; two younger sons are attending high school at Seymour.

Richard Stephens
Washington County

You probably have heard of Stephens, 46, as vice-president of the Iowa Farm Bureau Federation. He is also one of the state's outstanding large-volume commercial hog producers and a good cattle feeder.

He normally raises and feeds out about 1,000 hogs a year, may feed 100 to 150 cattle. Sows farrow in three groups—in September, February or March, and June.

Stephens started farming in 1926 on a place owned by his father. In 1933, he rented another place for cash rent. He bought his first 160 acres in 1936, now owns 760 acres.

Right now, the Iowa Farm Bureau takes most of the time Stephens is able to devote to outside activities. Yet it has not replaced his other interests. He still finds time to be active in local community, school, church and agricultural organization affairs. With all this, he still knows what it is like to work out in the hog lot.

Stephens has two sons. He says if he has a hobby, it is farm management.

Mr. and Mrs. Richard Stephens

IOWA MASTER FARMERS
March 4, 1950

Pictured on these pages are the six 1949 Iowa Master Farmers honored February 21 by *Wallaces' Farmer and Iowa Homestead*, at the annual Master Farmer luncheon in Des Moines.

These men may be typical Iowa Master Farmers; yet they are not typical examples of any set Iowa-farming pattern. No two of them farm alike, nor exactly like any other farmer.

Most important, they are doing an outstanding job of living and farming on the land they have to work with.

They may not be the best farmers in Iowa — many others at least are doing as well. They are, then, typical representatives of that top group of Iowa farmers who do so much for agriculture.

The Iowa Master Farmers Club got its start in 1926 when this magazine selected the first class of 14 men. With the 1949 winners, a total of 123 men and one woman have since received the award.

Through the years, the winners have been picked with the *Wallaces' Farmer and Iowa Homestead* motto in mind: "Good Farm-

ing, Clear Thinking, Right Living."

Each year, Master Farmer candidates are nominated by friends, neighbors and co-workers. Editors of this magazine then make field visits and submit written reports on the nominees.

Working from these reports, and calling on their own very wide acquaintance with people in agriculture, the judges select the winners.

The 1949 judges were: Donald R. Murphy, editor of *Wallaces' Farmer and Iowa Homestead*; Charles R. Mountain, Polk County farmer and president of the Iowa Master Farmer Club; Harry D. Linn, Iowa Secretary of Agriculture, and William G. Murray, head of the department of agricultural economics at Iowa State College.

The six 1949 winners are:

Dale Blackwell
Davis County

Blackwell, 41, is a first-rate farm operator with a remarkable record of activities outside the farm. His livestock operations are well balanced. If he has a specialty, it is his herd of Guernseys.

Blackwell

But he raises about 80 hogs, keeps a flock of sheep.

Blackwell started on the road to ownership with an FHA loan. Now he owns 260 acres, rents an additional 40. His soil conservation work has been outstanding, with emphasis on terracing of both cultivated land and pastures. He is a booster for lime, phosphate and pasture improvement. And he is always one of the first to adopt new varieties and new crops.

He has served his community in many ways. As a school director, as township trustee, as township assessor, as a director of the Dairy Herd Improvement Association, and of the telephone company. He has been Farm Bureau secretary and chairman and treasurer of the local conservation district. At one time he served on the county AAA committee.

The Blackwells have three children: Betty, 15; Rex, 13; and Jimmy Dale, 2.

Wilbur E. Goodhue
Polk County

Goodhue, 42, is widely known in central Iowa. He owns 500 acres and rents 200 more. During the last few years, his specialty has been efficient production of about 500 market hogs each year, plus cattle feeding.

At this time, he is in the process of changing his operations to allow for the use of more acres of grass and legumes. This switch

Goodhue

Lapke

will involve more pasture, more hay, fewer hogs raised, and a herd of 90 or 100 stock cows.

His efforts to attain greater efficiency in meat production have resulted in some unusual but very handy farm buildings.

Goodhue's farm is under a complete SCS plan; he is one of the commissioners of his local district. He also has been a township AAA committeeman and a member of the Polk County FHA Advisory Committee.

He served two years as county Farm Bureau president, has also been a township director. In 1949, Goodhue was on the boys 4-H committee. He takes an active part in all school projects.

The Goodhues have three children: Jimmy, 17; Betty Ann, 12; and Wanda, 7.

Zeno Lapke
Shelby County

This 42-year-old man probably has the kind of half-section farm you wouldn't want. He has spent 40 years of his life on this place; has made a fertile, productive farm from poor land.

He has done a wonderful job of soil conservation and soil improvement on a steeply rolling farm in the Missouri River loess soil area. His results have really helped sell soil and water conservation in an area where it was especially needed.

He has 80 acres of permanent pasture, 60 acres of brome-alfalfa, and 60 acres of clover in a normal year.

To use all the grass, he carries a herd of 20 to 25 Holstein milk cows and about 50 Angus stock cows. He raises about 150 spring pigs, farrowing them on pasture.

Lapke is active in conservation work, was alternate on the AAA, is county Farm Bureau president, has been vice-president. He is a director in the Western Iowa Bro-falfa Club.

There are 10 children in the Lapke family. They are: Bernard, 18; Clarice, 17; Lorraine, 14; Gerald, 13; Leone, 10; Kenneth and Carroll, 9; Eddie, 8; Marilyn, 6; and Kathryn, 3.

Arthur Linder
O'Brien County

Linder, 50, has a 420-acre farm that is just the opposite of Lapke's. Black and level, erosion is not serious problem.

Yet Linder uses plenty of grass in his rotation. He likes to feed cattle on pasture, though he has no permanent pasture.

He was one of the first in his community to plant hybrid corn, to use lime, to put phosphate on legumes, and to try new kinds of flax, beans or oats. Though he was one of the first to use a complete fertilizer, he does not need to buy much nitrogen.

Linder heifers are well-known on the Sioux City market. Cattle feed-

ing is his specialty, though he feeds a few hogs and milks a small herd of Holstein cows.

The family farmstead has a new windbreak, and this past summer the Linders built a new home.

Linder is busy off the farm, too. He is or has been a township school director, on the county livestock board, county fair board, township clerk, and county Farm Bureau president.

He has been boys 4-H leader and is a church trustee and on the church board.

There are three children in the family. Paul, 26, is in partnership with his father. Claris, 20, is a student at Morningside. Lois is 10.

Charles O. Nelson
Union County

Nelson, 49, owns 383 acres and rents 200 more. He is one of the pioneers in pasture improvement work and soil conservation work in his county.

He regularly raises from 100 to 175 acres of alfalfa-brome plus 30 to 50 acres of red clover. He has limed all his land.

Nelson has to handle a lot of livestock to

Arthur Linder and family at their new home on the O'Brien County farm

84

consume the roughage. Sheep are his long suit. He usually buys about 300 feeder lambs; in addition raises one bunch of February lambs and another of April or May lambs.

He feeds 50 steers a year, keeps 30 to 40 stock cows and about 15 brood sows.

Off the farm, Nelson has been treasurer of the school board, member of the Creston PTA, a township trustee, chairman of the local soil conservation district, and an FHA committeeman.

Nelson has served several times on the county Farm Bureau board and as treasurer. He is a member of the board of deacons and is a trustee in his church.

The Nelsons have four sons and a daughter. Dean, 21, is a student at the University of Arizona; Dale, 19, is at home; Charles, 14, is in high school; Everett is 8, and Phyllis is 4.

Lyle Sutton
Delaware County

Sutton is famous as a pork producer. From his 130 acre farm, during the wartime pressure for food, he fed out and marketed more than 4,000 hogs a year.

Today, he operates at nothing like that volume, has switched part of his efforts to cattle feeding. He plans to feed out from 1,500 to 1,700 hogs a year now.

Sutton has renovated and reseeded his 18 acres of permanent pastures. Alfalfa-brome is his meadow mixture—he keeps about one-half of his farm seeded to that. During much of the year, the alfalfa-brome pasture serves him as a "feed-yard" for his hogs.

Sutton

On the 112 crop acres, he grows roughly 30 acres of corn each year.

He served three terms as a director of Delhi consolidated school, was county war bond chairman, is a member of both the Grange and Farm Bureau.

He has been county Farm Bureau president. In his church, he teaches a men's class, is steward and trustee, and for three years was president of the Delaware County Sunday School Association.

The Suttons have three daughters, all married. They are: Mrs. Clayton Hansel, wife of a Clayton County dairyman; Mrs. Arthur Holthouse, wife of a Delaware County farmer, and Mrs. Paul Reeves, whose husband is a high school principal.

Charles O. Nelson, left, with son Dale

Here are the six 1950 Iowa Master Farmers. These men were honored February 21 by *Wallaces' Farmer and Iowa Homestead* at the annual Master Farmer luncheon in Des Moines.

Judges for the 1950 contest were: Peter Sidles, Appanoose County farmer, who is president of the Iowa Master Farmer Club; Donald R. Murphy, editor, *Wallaces' Farmer and Iowa Homestead*; Clyde Spry, Iowa Secretary of Agriculture; W.G. Murray, head, Iowa State College department of agricultural economics.

Clyde M. Core
Marion County

Core, 43, owns and operates 240 acres. A lifelong farmer, Clyde has lived on his present farm for eight years.

Holstein dairy cattle are the livestock specialty. However, Clyde has also maintained a herd of Angus breeding cattle and served as president of the Marion County Angus Breeders organization. He has also served as a member of the Iowa Dairy Industry Commission and as president of his county artificial breeding cooperative.

Core's farm was one of the first farms in Marion County on which a complete soil conservation farm plan was adopted. He has been a local group leader and a soil dis-

Core

trict commissioner.

In addition to doing a good job of farming, Core also has found time to serve his neighbors as township PMA committeeman, county Farm Bureau president, a member of the Pleasantville school board and on the board of his church.

The Cores have three fine children: Richard, Ronal and Nancy. All the children are at home.

J. E. Entz
Black Hawk County

Ed Entz, 54, has operated the same 414-acre farm for 33 years. Every acre of it is a credit to his stewardship. He started in Iowa as a hired man.

The Entz family includes three married daughters and two sons. The sons, John and Joe, are farming with their father. John also is married.

The livestock program includes production of Grade A milk from 25 purebred Holstein cows; feeding 100 steers a year either on pasture or in the dry lot; a breeding herd of Shorthorns; and a couple hundred market hogs a year.

He is president of the county Farm Bureau and has always been active in that organization; he is a long-time commissioner of his soil conservation district, and is on the board of directors of the La Porte

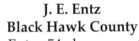
Entz

City bank.

For 12 years, six as president, Ed served on the Orange Township Consolidated School Board and is now a member of the county board of education. He has been a township AAA committeeman and a county supervisor.

And that's not all. Ed Entz is secretary-treasurer of Chicago Producers and has been president of his local shipping association.

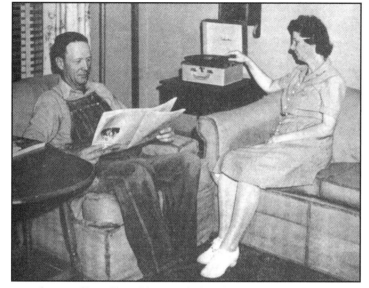
John Holland and his wife both enjoy good music

State College. Somehow, Holland has found time to serve on both county and state FHA advisory committees; to be a director and president of the Van Buren County Farm Bureau; to teach a Sunday school class; to serve on the board of directors of the new county hospital; and to help organize and be president of the Milton Community Fire Department.

John R. Holland
Van Buren County

This Iowa State College graduate and former school teacher has been farming land his great-grandfather broke out of virgin sod in 1841. John's father, Frank, was an Iowa Master Farmer in 1929.

The 165-acre Holland farm is well on the way to a complete grass farming system. Extensive use is made of roughage and grass silage.

The Holland Milking Shorthorn herd is nationally known. It is one of the oldest herds in the country; production records go back more than 40 years.

John, 51, has served two terms as president of the National Milking Shorthorn Society. He has judged at national shows.

The Hollands have two married daughters, another attending the University of Iowa, and a son at Iowa

Holland

Peter J. Johnson
Lyon County

Pete Johnson, 56, is extremely well qualified to join the Master Farmer Club. Dairying and hog raising are his livestock long suits.

His son, Leo, is married and farms with him. He has two married daughters.

With a herd of 25 Jerseys in milks, the Johnsons have consistently topped DHIA herds of similar size in the area; last year, on a 24-cow basis, the herd averaged 460 pounds of fat.

Close to 50 litters of pigs are raised each year on clean ground on the 320-acre farm. Johnson for years has followed approved SCS practices.

Years ago before the days of county agents, Pete helped organize the Inwood Institute to spread the gospel of better farming. He has been active in the Northwest Iowa Farm Business Association, is a county PMA committeeman

Johnson

Larsen

and on the county FHA committee.

He served four years as Lyon County Farm Bureau president; has been president of the Inwood Farmers Elevator; and is a director of the Inwood State Bank. He has been both president and a director in his DHIA, as well as chairman of the board of trustees of his church.

H. A. Larsen
Clay County

The Larsen home is one of the impressive farmsteads in Clay County. Larsen, 44, owns 180 acres, farms 247. He keeps in milk about 30 head of purebred Guernseys; last year the DHIA herd average was 399 pounds of fat.

About 200 hogs a year are a part of the program, as is an outstanding flock of chickens.

One of Larsen's hobbies or relaxations is working in his well-arranged shop. He gives special attention to labor-saving ideas. Out of this has come a feed-handling system that has saved miles of travel, tons of lifting.

The Larsen family includes four children, two boys and two girls.

A member of the county PMA committee, Larsen has also maintained an active interest in schools and school work. He has held offices in the Clay-Dickinson co-op oil company and in his DHIA. He has been county Farm Bureau secretary, has taught a class in Sunday school and has served on the church board.

Clark Stroburg
Taylor County

Taylor County's first Master Farmer, Stroburg, 55, has done an exceptional job of farming some of the rolling land in southern Iowa. He owns 520 acres.

Thirty years ago, he and his father used the first limestone ever to be shipped to Blockton.

Stroburg

Now the farm, including pastures, has nearly all been limed twice. Clark has almost 18 miles of terraces.

Recently, he has carried out a building improvement program, including a brick home. The home is equipped with electric radiant heat panels.

The family includes two daughters and two sons. One daughter and one son are married.

Stroburg raises Angus cattle and feeds out about 40 calves a year. He also milks 10 Holsteins, which are bred artificially. He raises about 300 hogs each year, using a Yorkshire cross. Only about 72 acres of corn are raised on the 520 acres.

Stroburg has been Taylor County Farm Bureau president, superintendent of his Sunday school, on the county FHA committee, a director in his artificial breeding cooperative, a member of the local creamery board, adjutant of his American Legion post, and an officer in the VFW. Since 1941 he has been a soil district commissioner, and for the past five years has been chairman of that group.

Stroburg is handy with his welder

88

1951 IOWA MASTER FARMERS
~
April 5, 1952

The six men shown on these pages are the 1951 Iowa Master Farmers. They were honored April 2 by *Wallaces' Farmer and Iowa Homestead* at the annual Master Farmer luncheon in Des Moines.

Since 1926, 135 men and one woman have received the honor. They were picked with this publication's motto in mind: "Good Farming, Clear Thinking, Right Living."

No one would claim that these men are the best farmers in Iowa. But they represent that top layer of farmers in Iowa who are serving agriculture as well as their home communities.

Candidates are nominated by friends, neighbors and others in agriculture. *Wallaces' Farmer and Iowa Homestead* editors visit their farms and make written reports to the judges.

Judges for the 1951 contest were William H. Davidson, Cedar County farmer and president of the Iowa Master Farmer Club; Donald R. Murphy, editor, *Wallaces' Farmer and Iowa Homestead*; Clyde Spry, Iowa Secretary of Agriculture, and W.G. Murray, head, Iowa State College department of agricultural economics.

Herbert Campbell
Washington County

Campbell is 41, farms 290 acres in Washington County. He has been farming since 1931, bought his present farm in 1940.

Campbell's principal achievement is in making over a rough farm with lots of gullies. He filled the gullies, reorganized the fields, started contouring, cut his corn acreage down to about 50 acres a year, went in heavy for alfalfa and brome.

He raises about 500-600 hogs per year, feeds cattle and sheep. But he passed up the lambs this year. Now he has about 80 head of a plain kind of cattle on feed.

In addition to doing an outstanding job of farming, Campbell has found time to serve his community. He is active in soil conservation work, has been county Farm Bureau treasurer, farm business association director, served six years on the local school board. He has been a trustee in his church and Sunday school superintendent for four years.

The Campbells have four children, three boys and a girl. The oldest boy is in his first year at Iowa State College.

Campbell and sons Bruce and Rodney

Helming

Edwin Helming
Woodbury County

Helming, 45, farms 300 acres in southern Woodbury County. On this 300 acres, Helming carries a large livestock program.

Last year he weaned 390 spring pigs and about 320 fall pigs. He has about 90 ewes. Right now he has 103 head of medium to good heifers and steers on feed. He kept a dairy herd until one year ago.

Hog pastures on the home farm are arranged so that water can be piped to all pastures as they are rotated. He is trying to keep cattle feeding costs at a minimum by putting into them cornstalks, grass silage and corn silage along with Purdue cattle supplement A.

Helming has a well-improved farm, including a modern house for his hired man. His is one of the rural electrification experimental farms. A useful building on his farm is the 26 x 90 machine shed that is used not only for machine storage, but also for straw and feed storage and for sheep at lambing time.

Helming has been president of the Woodbury County Farm Bureau. He is a county soil district commissioner. He has held offices in his church, school, 4-H, farm business association and has taught Sunday school. The Helmings have one child, Robert, nine.

John J. Moreland
Madison County

Moreland is 58, was raised in town. After service in World War I, he rented, then bought a quarter section. He has been on his present farm 29 years.

Moreland owed $100 an acre on his farm during 1932 but held onto his farm during the depression. One of his mainstays during this period was his milking herd. In 1942, Moreland had 62 head of cows, heifers and calves on his 160 acres. By using silage he produced all feed needed for the dairy herd.

When Moreland's son went to World War II, the dairy herd was sold for lack of labor. Moreland's son, Dorrence, now operates the farm with his father.

The farm is handled according to a Soil Conservation Service farm plan. All fields are

Moreland

worked on the contour.

Moreland's community activities include director of the local school district, vice-president and secretary-treasurer of the county AAA, township director and vice-president of the county Farm Bureau, chairman of the rural fire district, chairman of official church board, superintendent of Sunday school and adult class teacher.

The Morelands have one daughter, one son, and three grandchildren.

Walter McConohy
Clinton County

McConohy is 43, started farming in 1931. Now he operates 260 acres of his own and rents 220 acres belonging to his father. The land is rolling to rough.

McConohy's main livestock enterprises are hogs and a 45-cow beef herd. He feeds out the calves as well as buying feeders.

Probably McConohy's outstanding accomplishment is building up the farm he now owns.

Using an all-out soil conservation program including good rotations, liming, fertilizer and contouring, McConohy has built up his farm's productivity. He was one of the first men in Clinton County to use grass silage and to build terraces.

Community activities include offices in the county Farm Bureau and community fire association. He is a member of the farm business association, serves on local church committees, has been township assessor and township AAA chairman. He helped organize and is a commissioner of the Clinton County soil conservation district.

Walter McConohy and son Dale

The McConohys have five children, two girls, three boys. The two oldest children are in college.

Paul G. Williams
Page County

Williams, 48, is another farmer who has done an outstanding job with a rough farm. He owns 510 acres, rents an additional 160.

Williams built his first terraces in 1933. They are still in use. He has about 20 miles of terraces. All waterways are grassed.

The livestock specialty is hogs. About 40 sows farrow in February and March. Usually that many farrow in the fall. A flock of 100 ewes and a 30-cow beef herd complete the livestock program.

The Williams have four sons. The oldest, Robert, is preparing for the ministry.

Williams has served on the township school board as director and president. He has been director, vice-president, and president of the local REA and is a director of the district REA. He has been a county Farm Bureau director and a member of the State Farm Bureau nominating committee.

He has been a Sunday school teacher for 25 years. Williams will be one of the five delegates from the Iowa Methodist Conference to the General Conference of the Methodist Church.

Paul Williams has a 30-cow beef herd on his 510-acre farm

William Yungclas
Hamilton County

Yungclas is 53, has a wide range of public service. He has been president of the Hamilton County Farm Bureau. He is on the board of the Farmers Grain Dealers Association. He was an early commissioner of the soil conservation district in Hamilton County.

He is president of the locally-owned Production Credit Association. He is a past president of the Iowa Swine Producers Association and the American Pork Producers Association.

Yungclas farms 600 acres with his oldest son, Bruce. Yungclas owns all but 80 acres. The farm is operated un-

William Yungclas

der a soil conservation service plan. Main livestock enterprise is hogs. Right now 44 head of steers are on feed.

Mr. and Mrs. Yungclas have always tried to operate their farm without hired help. So in 1947, after a family conference, they retired while sons Bruce and Tom went to college.

After Bruce was graduated from Iowa State, Yungclas returned to active farming again in 1951.

Don, the second son, is preparing for the ministry. Two girls, Virginia and Gretchen, and two younger boys, Kreg and William Robert, complete the family.

1952
IOWA MASTER FARMERS
~
April 18, 1953

Shown here are the eight men who won the Iowa Master Farmer awards for 1952. They were honored by *Wallaces' Farmer and Iowa Homestead* April 15 at the annual Master Farmer luncheon in Des Moines.

These men were nominated for the award by friends or neighbors. Then editors of *Wallaces' Farmer and Iowa Homestead* visited their farms and submitted reports to the judges.

Barber

Judges for the 1952 contest were Donald R. Murphy, editor of *Wallaces' Farmer and Iowa Homestead*; Clyde Spry, Iowa Secretary of Agriculture; Dr. William G. Murray, head of the department of agricultural economics, Iowa State College; and J. J. Boatman, president of the Iowa Master Farmer Club.

S. A. Barber
Hancock County
At 69, Sam Barber no longer operates his farm. But he lives on his farm and takes an active interest in its management.

But Barber has not retired from community service. He is a district soil conservation commissioner and is on the Hancock County board of supervisors. He is president of the North Iowa Experimental Association.

As a member of the Kanawha Methodist Church, Barber has served as a steward for more than 20 years. He teaches the adult Bible class, sings in the choir, is on the board of trustees.

Barber was on the county PMA committee four years, has been a school board director, helped arrange for the Clarion-Webster experimental farm near Kanawha, and helped organize the original Farm Bureau in Hancock County.

Frank Christensen
Boone County
Frank Christensen is now semi-retired. One of his sons lives in a tenant house on Christensen's farm and operates the farm on a livestock-share basis. A second son rents a nearby farm.

Christensen

Greaser

Christensen, who is 63, helps his two sons with the chores and lighter farm work.

Christensen had the first soil conservation farm plan developed in Boone County. He has been a soil conservation commissioner since the district was established as well as serving as treasurer and vice-chairman. Christensen has been township Farm Bureau director and county Farm Bureau treasurer.

Christensen has often provided plots to state and county Extension workers to test new crop varieties.

"Tops morally, as a farmer, and as a community leader" was how Christensen was described by a man who has known him for 40 years.

Lewis Greaser
Benton County

Greaser is 59, owns 380 acres of Benton County land, farms 200. He feeds cattle every year, raises market hogs.

On his better land, Greaser uses a four-year rotation; on more rolling land, a five- year rotation. Sloping fields are contoured. Greaser was one of the first two men in Benton County to produce hybrid seed corn.

Greaser's community activities are many and varied. He has been local assessor, was state representative from Benton County for two years. He has served as soil conservation group leader, was on the county PMA committee four years, has been director of the Vinton State Bureau for 10 years, and is a director of the Eden Mutual Fire Insurance Company. He has been voting delegate, secretary, and president of the Benton County Farm Bureau.

The Greasers have two children: Marion, 11; and Frances, nine.

Orville N. Kalsem
Story County

Kalsem is 45, farms 380 acres, raises 300 hogs per year, feeds about 200 head of cattle per year. Yards, buildings, and equipment are designed to make handling of livestock easier.

Kalsem's list of community activities includes serving on the county boys 4-H committee, the county fair board, the county central committee for the fund drive for the state 4-H camp, president of the local Community Club, chairman of the Huxley horse show, on the organization committee and first president of the Story County Beef Producers' Association. Kalsem is a member of the church

Kalsem

council where he attends.

The Kalsems have two sons, one in the army, one in high school. While at home, the boys have definite areas of responsibility in the farm work. David, in high school, is the "hog-man," keeps the records of the Kalsem hog operations. Yet Kalsem has "tried to teach them (his sons) that there is something to farming besides hard work."

L. G. Stevens
Worth County

Stevens is 43, has been farming in Nebraska and Iowa since he was 19 years old. He has been on his present farm eight years. Stevens owns and operates 160, rents another 80.

Stevens raises from 900 to 1,000 hogs per year, has an efficient hog production setup. In addition to the large market hog program, he keeps a small herd of purebred Angus.

He has been a member of the local school board, has been a director and is now vice-president of the Worth County Farm Bureau, was on the official board of his church, and is chairman of the 4-H boys county committee.

Stevens

The Stevens have four children: a daughter who is a graduate nurse, two boys at Iowa State and a third son in high school.

Clarence Pellett
Cass County

Pellet, 63, has a long record of community service in Cass County. He was on the local

Pellett

school board eight years, chairman four years. Pellett has been township assessor, chairman of the cooperative telephone line for 20 years, was first chairman of the Cass County soil district commissioners, is president of the Cass County Fire Insurance Association, was a charter member and served on the county Farm Bureau board five years with two years as president.

Now semi-retired, Pellett has always been willing to try new farm practices. He first sowed alfalfa in 1908, sweet clover in 1910.

Pellett is a member of the board of trustees of his church. The Pelletts have five sons, all of whom attended college.

C. B. Schager
Franklin County

Schager is 47, rents the 320-acre farm he lives on, owns and operates another 320. Last year, Schager farrowed and marketed about 850 head of hogs, fed out 146 yearling steers.

Schager has been voc-ag advisory council chairman at Dows for two years, is a member of the Dows Cooperative elevator board, served two terms as director of the Central

Iowa Farm Business Association, was township Farm Bureau director, county Farm Bureau vice-president two years, and county president two years. He served on the board of deacons of his church and is now chairman of the board of trustees.

Schager was recently elected to the Franklin County Board of Education. Previously he had served on the township school board for 12 years. The Schagers have four children.

George K. Welty
Fremont County

Welty is 42, owns 451 acres, rents 914, manages seven farms for other people. Welty has an improvement program for every farm that he owns, rents, or manages. He has built terraces at his own expense on rented farms.

Leases with tenants on farms Welty manages have provisions for compensation for unexhausted improvements.

Welty has a long list of community activities including: chairman of the Fremont County soil district commissioners eight years; board of directors of the Nishna Val-

Welty

ley Flood Control Association; REA board two years; secretary and treasurer of cooperative oil and supply association seven years as well as president one year and now vice-president; school board director; and more than 20 years continuous leadership in 4-H.

Welty has been a Sunday school teacher for 13 years and is now chairman of the board of trustees of his church.

Welty was recently elected to the board of directors of Consumers Cooperative of Kansas City. He has won the national plow terracing contest.

Schager

IOWA MASTER FARMERS

1953

~ April 17, 1954

Here are the seven winners of the 1953 Iowa Master Farmer Award. The award is made each year to several of Iowa's outstanding farmers. It is sponsored by *Wallaces' Farmer and Iowa Homestead*.

Winners were honored April 14th at a luncheon in Des Moines. They were selected on the basis of nominations by friends and neighbors and reports by *Wallaces' Farmer and Iowa Homestead* editors who visited their farms.

Judges were Donald R. Murphy, editor; Clyde Spry, Iowa Secretary of Agriculture; Dr. W.G. Murray, Iowa State College, and Herman Franzenburg, Master Farmer Club president.

James. D. Helmick
Louisa County

Helmick is 61, owns and operates 313 acres in partnership with his son. Helmick has been a soil conservation district commissioner nine years. He has been director of the local Farm Service Company, director of the Louisa County National Bank, director of the fair board, town-

James D. Helmick, right, with son James B.

ship Farm Bureau director and school director.

For many years, Helmick has been Sunday school superintendent at the Methodist Church in Columbus City, is now a trustee and teacher of the adult Bible class for men, and has served on the church board for 20 years.

Helmick was one of the first in his area to use limestone and to put in terraces.

The Helmicks have two children, both of them graduated from college.

Doyce Miller
Clarke County

Miller is 47, owns and operates 523 acres. His main livestock operation is a herd of Angus beef cows and some hogs. Miller has been on the school board, township trustee member, past president and present secretary of the county fair board, township PMA committeeman, boys county 4-H chairman, secretary and vice-president of the Clarke County Farm Bureau.

Rolling fields on the Miller farm are farmed on the contour.

He has installed terraces on some fields. He has planted multiflora rose hedges as contour fences.

The Millers have three children: Jack, married and farming for himself; Lyle, married and farming with his father; and Lorna, attending college.

Lyle V. Ormston
Bremer County

At 51, Ormston has a long record of community service. He has served on the school board for nine years, leader of the local 4-H club for 27 years, a township trustee nine years, has been director, secretary and president of the Bremer County Farm Bureau.

Ormston has been township PMA chairman for 12 years, served on the creamery board for nine years, is president of the local telephone company, is county DHIA secretary. He has served as Sunday school teacher and assistant Sunday school superintendent, has been president of his church's brotherhood organization, was county draft board chairman, county fair secretary for 10 years, and on-the-farm veteran's instructor.

All grain raised on Ormston's 169-acre farm is fed. He keeps a herd of Holsteins and raises about 150 head of pigs each year.

The Ormstons have seven children, three boys and four girls.

Miller

Ormston

Donald Pullin
Black Hawk County

In a county with many top-notch farmers, Pullin is described as "one of the best farmers in the county." Pullin is 45, owns and operates 100 acres, operates 160 acres owned by his mother.

Main farm enterprises are purebred sheep and dairying. Pullin gives a registered Hampshire bred ewe to Black Hawk County's outstanding 4-H sheep club member each year.

Pullin has a long list of community activities including nine years of service on the school board, township chairman and county Farm Bureau executive committee, president of Iowa Sheep and Wool Growers Association, president of the Iowa State Sheep Association, on the board of directors of the American Hampshire Sheep Association and the American Oxford Down Record Association.

He is secretary of the Cedar Valley Co-op Milk Association and the Hudson Co-op elevator.

In recent years, Pullin has judged sheep at livestock shows including the International and leading state fairs.

The Pullins have two sons, two daughters.

Lawrence Reis
Adair County

In 1932, Lawrence Reis started farming under a livestock-share lease on the farm which he now owns. Neighbors say the farm was pretty well run down. Seven years later, Reis bought the 220-acre farm with one of the first tenant-purchase loans made in Adair County by the Farm Security Administration.

Now the Reis farm is one of the outstanding farms in the community. It has been used as a demonstration place for soil conservation projects and for planting demonstration plots.

Reis, at 45, has been president of the school board eight years, director of the school district 10 years, was AAA committeeman six years, chairman of the soil conservation district, secretary of the cooperative creamery 10 years, 4-H club leader two years, was on the FSA advisory board one term, has been trustee in his church, and secretary and vice-president of the Adair County Farm Bureau.

Mr. and Mrs. Reis have three children.

Reis raises about 40 litters of pigs each year and keeps a herd of 30 Angus cows.

Merle Travis
Taylor County

At 43, Travis is one of the younger Master Farmers. But despite his comparative youth, Travis has a long list of community activities.

He has been a school director for five years, county Farm Bureau director 10 years and is on the legislative and crops and soils committees, is president of the Taylor County fair board, is a PMA township committeeman, has been a 4-H club leader, has been chairman of the Taylor County soil conservation district commissioners for seven years and commissioner 14 years, is a director of the Midwest Feeders Association and is president of the Iowa Association of Soil Conservation District Commissioners.

Travis is on his church's official board. Main livestock enterprises are hogs and beef cattle. He owns 82 acres, rents 220 acres.

Mr. and Mrs. Travis have two sons: Mike, 15; and Jimmy, nine.

Travis

G. Donald Trenary
Pocahontas County

Trenary is 49, owns and operates 200 acres in Pocahontas County, rents an additional 120. He has 168 head of cattle on feed now and in addition raises hogs. He raises and feeds large amounts of roughage.

Trenary at one time had a herd of 70 beef cows but switched to feeding operations only three years ago.

Trenary has been on the township AAA

Trenary

committee and served as advisor to the Farm Security Administration. He is one of the soil conservation district commissioners. He has been president of the Pocahontas County Farm Bureau for five years and was organization director for seven years. He is one the board of stewards of his church.

The Trenarys have two daughters: Donolyn, 18, who is in college; and Betty, 13. Both have been active in 4-H club work.

The Don Pullin family of Black Hawk County in a family business conference

IOWA MASTER FARMERS

~ April 16, 1955

Meet seven good Iowa farmers. All are winners of the 1954 Iowa Master Farmer Award.

All the new Master Farmers have sound farming operations. They are good managers. But just as important, each one has given generously of his time and energy in community service.

In March, 1926, *Wallaces' Farmer* started the program of honoring Iowa farmers for their achievements in agriculture and good citizenship. Since then, 150 men and one woman have been recognized for their "Good Farming, Clear Thinking, Right Living."

To be considered for the Master Farmer Award, a man must be nominated by friends or neighbors. Editors then visit the nominee's farm, talk with his neighbors and business associates and file a report to the committee of judges.

Judges for the 1954 group were Clyde Spry, Iowa Secretary of Agriculture; Dr. William G. Murray, head, department of agricultural economics at Iowa State College; A. R. Clause, Grand Junction, Iowa, president of the Iowa Master Farmer Club; and Donald R. Murphy, editor of *Wallaces' Farmer and Iowa Homestead*.

Keith

Wayne Keith
Kossuth County

Keith is 46, has lived on his present farm 26 years. He owns 533 acres, rents 160. His farm is operated under a soil conservation plan.

From 500 to 600 hogs are marketed each year from the Keith farm. In addition, he feeds out 50 to 60 cattle and milks 15 cows. A 500-hen laying flock and 50 ewes are kept.

Keith served as president of the Kossuth County Farm Bureau six years, has been voting delegate many years, is a director of the Iowa Farm Bureau, and is a member of the American Farm Bureau Poultry commodity committee. He is a director of the Tri-County Drying Plant, has been president and director of the local creamery, is a soil conservation district commissioner, and is on the Burt Community School Board. He is a trustee is his church.

The Keiths have four children.

Dallas McGrew
Mills County

Dallas McGrew is now 64. In partnership with two sons, he operates 776 acres of Mills County land.

McGrew is a progressive farmer, keeps up with the latest experiment station results. He feeds sheep, raises hogs and Shorthorns.

In community service, McGrew has a long record. He has been director or secretary of the local school board for more than 30 years. He has served on the county school board, as township trustee, chairman of the local soil conservation district, which supervises the Mule Creek Watershed, director of the Pottawattamie Mutual Insurance Association.

McGrew helped organize the Farm Bureau in Mills County and was its first president. He has been president twice since. In his church, McGrew has been treasurer, steward, trustee, and Sunday school superintendent.

The McGrews have three children—two sons and one daughter—all of whom graduated from Iowa State College.

Sterling B. Martin
Monroe County

Martin is 64, operates the 358-acre family farm. He keeps a small herd of Angus and feeds out the steers raised. He raises about 200 hogs each year.

A charter Farm Bureau member, Martin has served as voting dele-

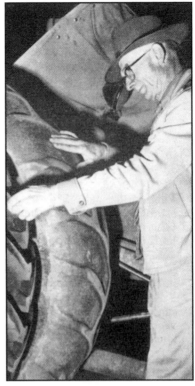

McGrew

gate, board member, and county president. He helped organize the Monroe County Soil Conservation District, was commissioner 10 years, and alternate regional director four years. He was township clerk four years and president of a local shipping association 12 years.

Martin has been president of the local school board, on the county board of education six years, and is on the State Board of Public Instruction. He was county agent in Lucas County for nine years. He was state representative from Monroe County in the 54th Iowa General Assembly.

In his church, Martin has been a steward, Sunday school superintendent, and Sunday school teacher.

The Martins raised five children, four of whom are now living. They have 12 grandchildren.

S. T. Rogers
Pottawattamie County

Sam Rogers is 72 and has been farming for 40 years. He operates a 160-acre farm in eastern Pottawattamie County. Rogers used to feed several hundred lambs each year and beef cattle. Now he has cut back his livestock operations to hog raising. All inter-tilled crops

Martin

Rogers

fed last year. They raised 300 hogs last year.

Community activities include serving as president and secretary of the Sioux County Farm Bureau, soil district commissioner, president of the Northwest Iowa Farm Business Association, REA board secretary, vice president of the Sioux City Producers' Commission Association, and president of the local co-op elevator board.

In addition, Pennings has served on the FHA committee, township AAA committee, school director 16 years, and elder and vice president of his church board. He has taught Sunday school for 40 years.

The Pennings have three children, seven grandchildren.

on the farm are contoured.

During his 40 years of farming, Rogers has compiled a long list of community activities. He was township Farm Bureau director seven years, county Farm Bureau treasurer three terms, school director 12 years, township AAA committeeman 11 years, and last month finished 20 years as director of the Farmers Co-op Creamery at Avoca.

Rogers served two terms on the Iowa Dairy Industry Commission and is now serving his third term on the county FHA advisory committee.

The Rogers have two sons.

William Pennings
Sioux County

The Pennings farm has been in the family for four generations now. At 66, Pennings no longer lives on the farm himself. He moved to nearby Orange City and operates the farm in partnership with a son.

The Pennings father and son team operate 300 acres. More than 300 heavy steers were

Pennings

Clarence S. Hill
Dallas County

Clarence Hill, at 53, has farmed for 29 years. He owns 410 acres, 260 of it tillable, and rents an additional 50. Crops raised on the farm are fed to livestock. Major livestock enterprise is cattle feeding, with only sufficient hogs raised or bought to follow the cattle. Lambs were formerly fed but sheep enterprise is now confined to a 70-ewe flock. His sons assume much of the care of the sheep and are accumulating flocks of their own.

He pioneered in use of grass silage and surface silos.

Hill, as a young man, served on the school board, including its presidency, was Dallas County Farm Bureau president, and has served several terms as director of the Iowa Sheep and Wool Growers Cooperative. He has a long record of service on his local church board and has taught a Sunday school class for 28 years. The Hills have four sons and one daughter.

Moreland

Elmer Moreland
Guthrie County

Soil conservation is not just a slogan for Elmer Moreland of Guthrie County. He has made it pay by controlling erosion on rundown, gullied land and building up its fertility.

Moreland is 53, owns and operates 360 acres. He raises sheep, hogs and purebred Herefords.

On Moreland's list of community activities, you'll find service as county voting delegate for Farm Bureau. He has also been county secretary, county president and township chairman. Moreland has been president of the Rural Fire Truck Association for seven years, president of the Guthrie Center PTA, is a soil commissioner, helped organize the Wolf Creek Watershed, helped organize and served as secretary of the Seeley Mutual Telephone Company, has been township clerk and assistant boy's 4-H club leader, has served on the township school board.

Moreland is an elder in his church, has been Sunday school superintendent and now teaches the men's Sunday school class.

The Morelands have four daughters.

Hill and two of his four sons

1955 IOWA MASTER FARMERS
~
April 7, 1956

Five men have received the Master Farmer award for 1955.

This year, the judges were Clyde Spry, Iowa Secretary of Agriculture; Dr. William G. Murray, department of agricultural economics, Iowa State College; G.D. Bellman, Indianola, president of the Iowa Master Farmer Club, and Arthur T. Thompson, editor of *Wallaces' Farmer and Iowa Homestead*.

Whitfield Adamson
Cherokee County

At 55, Adamson has been farming about 30 years. He owns 1,200 acres in Cherokee County, though he operates only 720.

Adamson feeds 200-300 steers each year and 400-600 lambs. He raises from 400-500 hogs a year.

Community activities of Adamson include serving as township Farm Bureau director, as FHA director, on the board of the Northwest Iowa Experimental Farm, and in various offices in the Cherokee County Farm Bureau. He helped organize the Cherokee Rural Fire Protection Association and has served as secretary and director.

The Adamsons have three children.

Alvin Christiansen
Mitchell County

Like several of the other Master Farmers for 1955, Alvin Christiansen started out as a hired man. Now he is 51 and has been farming 28 years. He owns 520 acres, operates 360.

Christiansen usually feeds about 150 calves each year. He raises from 275 to 300 hogs yearly.

Among Christiansen's community activities are service as a county supervisor, township Farm Bureau director, county Farm Bureau president, director and president of the county swine improvement association, president of the Mitchell County fair and 17 years as a 4-H club leader.

In his church, Christiansen has served as a trustee and Sunday school teacher.

The Christiansens have two children.

Whitfield Adamson, left, with son Darrell

Wayne E. Norman
Washington County

Wayne Norman is another of the new Master Farmers who started out as a hired man. Now at 54, he owns 329 acres and operates a total of 409 acres. Norman, his married son William, and a married hired hand operate the 409 acres.

Norman usually feeds about 100 head of cattle and raises about 450 hogs each year.

Norman's community activities include serving as township committeeman on the original AAA program, four years on the county AAA with three years as chairman, school board for 10 years, township Farm Bureau director, township trustee, 4-H club leader, six years on the county 4-H committee, township Republican chairman and chairman of the Washington County Republicans.

The Normans have two sons.

Harold Opsand
Clayton County

Opsand came to Clayton County in 1908 as an immigrant youth from Norway. For four years, he worked as a hired hand in the community where he now lives. In 1912, he started farming for himself. In 1917, he bought a 168-acre farm.

Norman

Opsand is now 65. He lives in a house on an acre of his farm. He sold the other 167 acres to a son-in-law several years ago.

Through the years, Opsand developed an outstanding Holstein herd. Dairy cattle and hogs were his main source of income.

Opsand has been director of his local school board, member of the board and president of the Gunder Cheese Factory, president of the Elgin Farmers Cooperative, DHIA director and an officer in the local telephone company.

Christiansen

In the local Lutheran Church, Opsand has served as trustee and president of the congregation.

Mr. Opsand has five daughters.

Ivan Slater
Webster County

At 58, Ivan Slater is semi-retired. His son, Daniel, is now operating the farm in partnership with his father. Slater farmed for about 35 years. Main livestock enterprises were cattle and hogs.

Slater came from Indiana to Iowa in 1915 and worked as a hired hand in the Dayton community for the next six years. He started farming for himself in 1921.

Slater has a long list of community activities. He has been county Farm Bureau president, county PMA chairman, FHA director, and soil conservation district commissioner. He has served on the local co-op elevator board, on the county 4-H committee, has been a bank director for about 15 years and has been active in his church.

The Slaters have one son.

Adamson

Opsand

Norman

1955

Slater

Opsand

MASTER FARMERS

Christiansen

Slater

1956 IOWA MASTER FARMERS
~
April 6, 1957

Meet six good farmers—typical of Iowa's best. All are winners of the 1956 Iowa Master Farmer Award.

All of these men have sound farming operations. They're good farm managers. Added to that, their neighbors respect them as good citizens, good family men and able community leaders.

They were selected by a committee of judges including Dr. W.G. Murray of Iowa State College; Clyde Spry, Iowa Secretary of Agriculture; W.E. Goodhue, president of the Iowa Master Farmer Club, and Art Thompson, editor of *Wallaces' Farmer and Iowa Homestead.*

A total of 168 men and one woman have received the Iowa Master Farmer Award since this program of recognition was started by *Wallaces' Farmer* in 1926. That includes the six 1956 award winners.

Mr. and Mrs. Ned E. Perrin

Ned E. Perrin
Monona County

At 45, Perrin is the first World War II veteran to receive the Iowa Master Farmer Award. During the war, he leased his farm to a tenant and served three years in the U.S. Navy, including duty in the Pacific theater.

Perrin owns and operates 345 acres. He carries about 200 western ewes, markets about 400 hogs per year and sometimes fattens cattle.

An Iowa State College graduate in agricultural engineering, Perrin spent five years with the U.S. Soil Conservation Service.

He has been a leader in affairs of his local school board, county Farm Bureau, county fair board, county Extension, planning committee, 4-H clubs, soil conservation district, Iowa Sheep and Wool Growers Association, county civil defense and the one-time Monona County Tenant Purchase Committee.

Sunde

Perrin has served as chairman of his church board and as a superintendent and teacher in his Sunday school.

The Perrins have two children.

Elvin L. Sunde
Emmet County

At 47, Sunde now owns and operates 480 acres near the Iowa-Minnesota line. He feeds 100 beef cattle per year, raises 350 to 400 hogs, fattens about 1,000 lambs and maintains a herd of 20 registered milking Shorthorns.

Sunde has taken a leading part in local school affairs, has served as a 4-H club leader, AAA committeeman, county Extension council member, county Farm Bureau official, National Farm Loan Association director, head of the local telephone co-operative, president of the Emmet County Artificial Breeders Association and Emmet-Palo Alto Farm Service Company director.

Both Mr. and Mrs. Sunde have held offices in their church and Sunday school.

The Sundes have four children.

Russell Eldred
Jones County

At 46, Eldred has worked up through 25 years of farming to a current owner-operation of 418 acres. Good land management and a soil conservation program enabled him to re-build a "run-down" farm.

Eldred is a Master Swine Producer and raises 800 to 900 hogs each year. He also feeds about 100 head of cattle.

Community activities include extensive service on the Morley school board, the Farmers' Co-op Elevator board, Jones County Farm Service Company board, FHA county board, county ASC committee and county and state Farm Bureau.

In addition, Eldred is now in his second term in the Iowa House of Representatives.

The Eldreds have two children.

Eldred

Donald W. Pratt
Carroll County

Donald Pratt started farming in the 1930s with a loan from the Farm Security Administration.

Today, he owns 210 acres and rents an additional 80 acres. The mainstay of his livestock operation is a 20-cow herd of Guernseys. Pratt's DHIA average last year was 439 pounds of butterfat per cow. He raises 250 to 300 hogs per year.

Pratt has served with the Carroll County Farm Bureau, Carroll Milk Producers' Association, Carroll County DHIA, Glidden consolidated school board, Cal-Car Service Company, PMA township committee and his Guernsey Breeders' Association.

Pratt is a trustee and elder of his church.

Pratt, now 47, is a graduate of Iowa State College.

The Pratts have three children.

Pratt

C. Raymond Fisher
Greene County

After nearly 30 years of running his own set-up, Raymond Fisher became a "partnership" farmer. That is, he worked out a share deal with his two sons, Roger and Tom, and then shifted residence to town. However, he's only 49 and still active in the operation of the two places, totaling 475 acres.

The Fishers specialize on beef feeding and hog production.

Fisher has been an elder of his church for 15 years. Other community activities include leadership in the direction of federal farm

C. Raymond Fisher, right, with sons Roger (left) and Tom (center)

programs at the county level, 4-H clubs, adult evening school, rural electric cooperative, Farmers Home Administration, Clarion-Webster experimental farm, local soil conservation district, county Farm Bureau, Greene County Beef Producers' Association and Central Iowa Farm Business Association.

Lowell Hall
Cass County

Another 1956 Master Farmer who used soil conservation methods to get ahead is Lowell Hall. When he bought his 583-acre farm 13 years ago, it was in poor shape. Since then, he has boosted its productive worth through wise application of recommended practices. He has won several awards for his outstanding farm renovations record.

During the years before he became an owner, Hall was regarded as an exceptional tenant. He feeds 150 head of cattle per year and about 200 hogs.

Now 51, Hall has been local school director, county Farm Bureau officer, member of the county Extension advisory council, 4-H club leader, Farmers Home Administration committeeman and on the council of the Griswold adult evening school.

The Halls have two sons.

Hall

1957 IOWA MASTER FARMERS
~
April 5, 1958

Otto Schaper of Emmet County feeds part of his 400-hen flock

Ten Iowa farmers are being recognized as winners of the 1957 Iowa Master Farmer awards.

The committee of judges naming the winners includes: Dr. W.G. Murray, Iowa State College; Clyde Spry, Iowa Secretary of Agriculture; C.B. Schager, president of the Iowa Master Farmer Club; and Richard Albrecht, editor of *Wallaces' Farmer*.

Ray Mitchell
Floyd County

Ray Mitchell owns 130 acres and rents 290 acres of cropland near Charles City, Iowa.

Mitchell was named a Master Corn Grower in 1954. He maintains a 65-cow herd of purebred Shorthorn cattle, raises 40 litters of hogs each year and keeps a flock of 500 hens.

Some activities in the community include 10 years service to 4-H, president of the county Farm Bureau, vice president of the county fair board, school board member and Charles City Chamber of Commerce member.

Mitchell, who is the father of 10 children, was

Mitchell

Siglin

Long

named Charles City's "Father of the Year" in 1954. The Mitchell family is active in church work.

Otto Schaper
Emmet County

Otto Schaper, who owns 160 acres south of Estherville, produces hybrid boars and hatchery eggs.

In addition, Schaper raises about 150 hogs a year, keeps a 400-hen flock and maintains a 20-cow beef herd. He is a leader in the community with soil conservation and land-use practices.

Community activities include service as township trustee, REA director, chairman of soil conservation district, past township director of Farm Bureau and a member of the Izaak Walton League.

His hobby is cabinet working. The Schapers have three children and are active in church work.

Amos Siglin
Appanoose County

Amos Siglin, who lives southwest of Centerville, farms 640 acres. His land is farmed according to a soil conservation plan.

Siglin, in partnership with his son, feeds 160 cattle and raises 400 hogs a year.

Some community activities include service as chairman of the County Farmers' Home Administration Committee, member of the Extension planning committee, president of county Farm Bureau, president of Lions Club and member of the Governor's Drought Committee in 1956.

The Siglins, who have four children, are active in their church.

Blahauvietz

Ralph Long
Ringgold County

Ralph Long owns and operates 150 acres north and west of Mt. Ayr, Iowa.

He has been particularly successful with his work in soil conservation. Long purchased his farm in a run-down condition, but a good soil conservation and fertility program has built the farm into a highly productive unit.

He raises 120 hogs a year and keeps a beef herd of 24 cows.

Community activities include service on the county Farmers' Home Administration, soil conservation district commissioner, adult night school planning committee, farm record association and Extension planning committee on crops and soils.

Mr. and Mrs. Long and their three children are active workers in their church.

William Blahauvietz
Osceola County

William Blahauvietz owns 312 acres east of Harris, Iowa, and farms in partnership with his son, Wayne.

Blahauvietz specializes in raising hogs and feeding cattle. He handles 400 hogs and 150 cattle each year.

Recognized as a community leader, some of his activities include service as a member and chairman of the Osceola County Soil Conservation District Commissioners, past member and chairman of the Harris school board, and past director and vice-president of the Osceola County National Farm Loan Association.

He has also been director and vice-president of the county Farm Bureau board, member of the county fair board, chairman of the county ASC committee, member of the Northwest Iowa Farm Business Association and township clerk.

Mr. and Mrs. Blahauvietz are active in their church. A second son is now serving in the Air Force.

William Darbyshire
Calhoun County

William Darbyshire, 49, owns and operates 280 acres near Rockwell City, Iowa.

Darbyshire raises about 300 hogs and feeds 150 cattle each year. His up-to-date farming methods give him top efficiency and management.

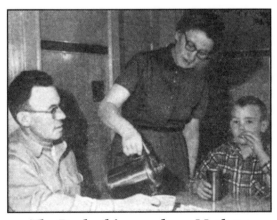
The Darbyshires and son Mathew

This Master Farmer was graduated from Iowa State College in 1928. He worked for Swift and Company before accepting a position as Extension director in Calhoun County.

After 10 years of Extension work, Darbyshire purchased a 160-acre farm. He has been farming for 20 years now.

Some community

activities include service on the county board of education, cooperative elevator board, county Farmers Home Administration advisory committee, dean's advisory committee in the Division of Agriculture at Iowa State College and as chairman of the Calhoun Soil Conservation District and state soil committee.

Mr. and Mrs. Darbyshire, and their five children, are active in church and school activities.

Oswell Fisher
Hardin County

Oswell Fisher, a former farm manager in Kansas, now owns 160 acres near Hubbard, Iowa. His intensive and efficient management makes this farm operation superior.

Fisher rents an additional 170 acres cropland and will be raising over 200 litters of pigs this year.

The land, run down at the time of purchase, has been built up to a highly productive level by Fisher.

Some community activities include Farm Bureau National Policy Committee, county Extension Farm and Home Development

Fisher with grandson Stephen

Committee, 4-H club leader, director of the Central Iowa Farm Business Association and director of the Hardin County REA board.

The Fishers are active church workers. They have four children. Two sons are in partnership with their father.

Marion J. Steddom
Polk County

Marion Steddom, 56, is known over the state for his work with swine. He owns 400 acres north of Grimes, Iowa, and raises 1,000 hogs a year.

Steddom has been particularly active in swine organizations.

He has been director, vice president and is now president of the Iowa Swine Producers Association, director and member of the executive council of the National Swine Growers Council, member of the National Meat Promotion Committee and director of the Iowa Livestock Council.

Steddom's other activities include work with Farm Bureau, school board and Iowa

Steddom

Foutch

Donald Foutch
Harrison County

Donald Foutch began working as a hired man 20 years ago. Now he owns 500 acres near Woodbine, Iowa.

Foutch feeds 800 head of cattle and raises 500 hogs each year. His sloping land is terraced and contoured.

Community activities for Foutch include service as a member of the county Extension council, Beef Producers' Association, past president of the Dunlap Farmers Cooperative and a board member of the Picayune watershed organization.

Foutch is one of the founders of the beef association and the cooperative. The family is active in the church.

Mr. and Mrs. Foutch have two children, both in college.

State College Division of Agriculture Dean's Advisory Committee. Steddom has also been named a Master Swine Producer.

The Steddoms, who have a son in college, are active in their church.

Ray Webber
Van Buren County

Ray Webber, who owns 320 acres near Stockport, is recognized in his community for general farming but his greatest interest is dairying.

Webber, in partnership with two sons, rents an additional 200 acres and keeps a milking string of 45 purebred Jerseys. In addition, he farrows from 25 to 30 litters of pigs a year and keeps 60 ewes.

Community activities include service as director of the school district, county supervisor, director and president of Keosauqua Cooperative Creamery, and work in Farm Bureau, 4-H and soil conservation.

The Webbers, who have four children, hold offices in their church.

Webber

1958

IOWA MASTER FARMERS

~
April 4, 1959

The four men who received the 1958 Master Farmer award from *Wallaces Farmer* represent the many outstanding farm folks who make up Iowa's strong farm leadership. The four new Master Farmers were nominated by neighbors, and chosen for achievements in family living, community service and farm operation and management.

The men received the award for achievements made through "Good Farming—Clear Thinking—Right Living."

The committee of judges that named the winners includes: Dr. W.G. Murray, Iowa State College; Clyde Spry, Iowa Secretary of Agriculture; William Yungclas, president of the Iowa Master Farmer Club; and Richard Albrecht, editor of *Wallaces Farmer*.

Christy

J. Merrill Anderson
Jasper County

J. Merrill Anderson turned down a promising banking career to start farming in 1947.

He now operates 400 acres north of Newton. He feeds about 150 head of cattle and 200 hogs per year. He keeps a 600 bird flock to produce hatching eggs.

He was general chairman of the 1956 National Field Days and Plowing matches. He has been master of the local Grange, president of the local school board, chairman of the Jasper County Soil Conservation District Commissioners and a director of the Iowa Wool Growers Association.

Anderson has also been chairman of the state Extension advisory committee and a member of the Iowa State College alumni executive committee.

He has held many Farm Bureau positions and is now a state director. He is also on the county FHA advisory committee and county fair association.

The Andersons have two daughters.

Glenn Christy
Benton County

Glenn Christy owns 160 acres and operates it according to a soil conservation plan. He raises about 300 hogs and feeds 75 to 100 cattle per year.

He is a township trustee, vice president of the local rural electric cooperative and director of a mutual insurance company. He is on the county fair board and has served as superintendent of the crops division.

He takes an active part in county Extension work and in Farm Bureau.

Christy has been a director of the county FHA, director of a cooperative creamery and soil conservation district commissioner.

He has served on the local school board and is active in politics.

He's been on the official board of his church and held many other church positions.

The Christys have two sons and a daughter.

Alvin Schnack
Shelby County

Alvin Schnack owns and operates 165 acres. He raises 30 to 40 litters of pigs a year. He also keeps a dairy herd and sells grade A milk.

Community service for Schnack centers around the young folks of his community. He's been a 4-H club leader and is now on the county boys' 4-H committee. He was also co-manager of a junior baseball club.

He and Mrs. Schnack have served as consulting couple for Farm Bureau young people.

Schnack has been on the Shelby County board of education for 10 years. He also served on the study committee for the Harlan school reorganization.

He has been a deacon in his church and has served on many different church committees.

Schnack is active in Farm Bureau and is a trustee of Myrtue Memorial Hospital.

The Schnacks have three sons and a daughter.

Schnack

Harold Neill with his grandson

Harold Neill
Adams County

Harold Neill farms in partnership with his older son, Tom. The younger son, Ralph, expects to join the partnership after his graduation from Purdue University.

The Neills have been feeding about 500 head of cattle and 2,000 hogs per year.

Community service for Neill shows many long-term activities. He's been a school board member for 30 years and on the county fair board for 20 years.

He helped organize the Adams County Rural Electric Cooperative and served as one of its first board members. He also helped start the Midwest Livestock Feeders Association.

Neill has been a Sunday school teacher, township trustee, Master Mason and member of the community development committee of the Corning Chamber of Commerce.

His hobby is flying. He's former treasurer and president of the Flying Farmers of Iowa.

Anderson

Christy

Schnack

Neill

1959

IOWA MASTER FARMERS

~
April 2, 1960

Six outstanding Iowa farmers are given special recognition in this issue of *Wallaces Farmer*. Five of them were presented with Master Farmer awards. The sixth, Lawrence Cain, received the new Master Farmer Exceptional Service award.

Cain's outstanding service as steward of the Cerro Gordo County farm includes farm management and, even more important, responsibility for the welfare of 101 residents. His devoted, thoughtful care of the county farm residents has earned for him the admiration of the entire county.

Judges for the contest included Richard Albrecht, editor of *Wallaces Farmer*; Herbert Howell, Iowa State University agricultural economist; Wayne Norman, president of the Iowa Master Farmer Club; and Clyde Spry, Iowa Secretary of Agriculture.

George

Bernard Collins
Wright County

Bernard Collins farms 440 acres in partnership with his father. Ten years ago, they changed from general livestock to a specialized swine operation. Since that time Collins has become well-known in swine circles.

He is now chairman of the Iowa Swine Producers boar testing station at Ames and vice president of the Iowa Swine Producers Association.

Other activities include serving as a member of the Iowa Agricultural Marketing Board and member of the dean's agricultural advisory committee at Iowa State University.

Collins is also treasurer of the Board of Trustees of the local Methodist Church.

Collins has two daughters: Christie Lou (15), a sophomore in high school; and Mary Anita (12), in 7th grade.

Ervin J. J. Koos
Pottawattamie County

Koos conducts a general livestock operation on the 160 acres he owns and 200 rented acres. The rolling fields are terraced and farmed on the contour.

Koos' interest in soil conservation resulted in his election as commissioner in the county conservation district. He is chairman of the county Agricultural Coordinating Council and committeeman for ASC.

Koos played a big part in the school reorganization program and is now president of the Board of Education of the Avoca Community School District.

He helped organize the drive to get the Federal Crop Insurance into the county.

He is active in his local Lutheran Church and has served on the church council and other committees.

Koos has three children: David, teaching in Albia High School; Karen, in college; and Kathleen, in the 5th grade.

Collins

Koos

Floyd N. George
Black Hawk County

Floyd George owns and farms in partnership with his son, Neal. George has a long list of community activities. He is a township trustee and has served on the Janesville consolidated school board. He is also on the board of the rural fire department.

He has been active in Extension service, farm business association, local politics, and Farm Bureau.

George is chairman of the Cedar Falls Federal Land Bank Association and president of the Cooperative Service Company.

Floyd George is an active member of Janesville Methodist Church.

George has two children: Neal, in partnership with his father; and Beverly (Mrs. Larry Everett), a farm homemaker living near New Sharon.

Donald Johnson
Jefferson County

Johnson owns 350 acres and rents an additional 200. He keeps a flock of 2,400 layers and follows a varied livestock program.

When Johnson bought his farm, it was badly run down. He has filled gullies, built ponds and planted about 4,000 Christmas trees.

Johnson

As a result of this special interest in conservation, he was elected as soil conservation district commissioner and serves as secretary. He is also regional director and state secretary for the Iowa Association of Soil Conservation District Commissioners.

He also has many other community activities. In the First Lutheran Church in Fairfield, Johnson has served as Sunday school teacher, assistant Sunday school superintendent, secretary of the church council and trustee.

The Johnsons have three children: Dian, 14, in the 9th grade; Douglas, 12, in the 7th grade; and Delores, 7, in the first grade.

Thomas Herbert Newell
Louisa County

Newell owns and operates 185 acres as general livestock farm and rents 80 acres to his younger son, Joe, who started farming a couple years ago.

He is now looking after Joe's farming operation while Joe is spending six months in

Newell

122

military service.

Newell has served as soil conservation district commissioner, member of the school board and township commissioner.

He spends considerable time working for the Pleasant Grove Bethel Church of God. He has been a Sunday school teacher, superintendent of the Sunday school and on the finance board.

The Newells have three children: Noel, working in Des Moines; and Joe and Marianne, in the 8th grade.

Exceptional Service Award

Once in a while, someone nominated for the Master Farmer award richly deserves recognition but does not exactly fit the Master Farmer classification. It was for such situations that the Master Farmer Exceptional Service award was created this year.

Lawrence Cain
Cerro Gordo County

Though neither a farm owner nor renter, Lawrence Cain has earned a reputation as an outstanding farmer. As steward of the Cerro Gordo County farm, he is responsible for farming 400 acres, raising 700 to 800 hogs a year and managing a 50-cow dairy herd.

An unusual degree of care and maintenance has made the farm a place of beauty.

Even more important, he has responsibility for the welfare of 101 patients at the county farm. This demanding and challenging task he, with Mrs. Cain's help, has handled with understanding and skill that brought sincere admiration from Cerro Gordo farm leaders.

Though the job of county farm steward is a 24-hour-a-day task, he has found time to serve as a director of the county Swine Producers Association, director and president of the county DHIA.

He is also past president of the Iowa Steward's and Matron's Association and sings in the choir at St. Joseph's Catholic Church in Mason City.

EXCEPTIONAL SERVICE AWARD

Cain

1959

CHAPTER 4
~
1960 - 1969: Stability & Growth

The Triple A – Agriculture Adjustment Act of 1938 – formalized federal farm programs. In the 1960s, another triple A combination boosted farm productivity. That combination was anhydrous ammonia and Atrazine.

For centuries, crops grown on the farm fed the livestock. Manure produced on the farm fertilized the crops. Farmers hoped to withdraw enough meat and grain from that closed system to turn a profit.

Anhydrous ammonia brought low-cost nitrogen fertilizer to the farm. The amount of manure available no longer limited corn yields or acreage. Specialized livestock and cash-grain-only operations began replacing diversified crop and livestock farms.

Atrazine, an early grass herbicide, eliminated quack grass, a pesky cool-season grass, from corn almost overnight. Atrazine added grass management to broadleaf weed control offered by 2,4-D. These and other herbicides freed farmers from growing-season cultivation as their primary means to control weeds.

Chemical weed control set the stage for a tillage revolution. Moldboard plowing gave way to a plethora of conservation tillage techniques – chisel plowing, ridge till, minimum till and no-till are a few. These technologies hiked yields, thereby lowering per unit production costs.

Technology treadmill

The industrialization of agriculture following World War II put U.S. farmers on what University of Minnesota economist Willard Cochrane described as the "technological treadmill."

In an oversimplification, the process is as follows:

* A new technology arises that lowers per unit cost or boosts yields, and ideally does both.

* Better yields and higher production help early adopters of the technology capture profits.

* Farm product prices fall, squeezing margins and setting farmers up to need the next new technology.

If it's any consolation, this phenomenon is not unique to agriculture. Your home computer can perform hundreds of times more functions in a fraction of the time at a fraction of the cost of mainframe computers of just 10 or 20 years ago.

Insatiable thirst for power

During a tour of Deere's Waterloo Works in the mid-1950s, some farmers heard speculation that John Deere's 70 diesel tractor would have as much power as any farmer would ever need. That notion didn't last long. In the 1960s, all tractor manufacturers introduced models with much more horsepower.

A host of factors drove the push for more power. A short list includes:

* Low prices pushed farmers to up volume to earn more revenue.

* Farming more acres spread fixed costs over more units of output, driving per unit costs lower.

* Some tax laws favored substituting capital for labor.

* Farming was becoming more management intensive.

Better managers earned higher returns for their superior management. Higher incomes helped better managers improve their lifestyle, expand their operations and adopt new technologies. Some technologies carried high price tags, but promised to trim per unit costs.

School consolidation

First the horse, then the automobile, and later the school bus meant children no longer had to walk to school or ride a horse. Improving financial conditions on the farm had more parents seeking better educational opportunities for their children.

The industrial revolution demonstrated the need for better education. Some people pushed for broader curricular offerings in schools. Both the race to explore outer space and the Cold War raised concerns that small high schools were not developing the kind of human capital needed to promote national security.

These forces, plus the trend toward fewer farmers farming the land—mostly the latter—precipitated consolidations of many small rural schools. Consolidations, and controversy, over them continue today.

Seeds of inflation

In the mid-1960s, President Lyndon B. Johnson launched the Great Society program to fight poverty and racial inequality. The war in Vietnam to contain communism was escalating.

The humanitarian programs cost money. The war cost money. Government efforts to finance them fueled inflation. As the 1960s drew to a close, no one could foresee that inflation, and efforts to fight it, would leave indelible scars on farmers and agriculture over the next 15 years. Nor could anyone know that the early 1970s would bring one of the most significant opportunities to make money that U.S. grain farmers had ever seen.

1960 Iowa Farm Facts

FARMS & INCOME

Number of Iowa farms	183,000
Crop production value	$498 million
Livestock production value	$1.9 billion
Iowa net farm income	$611 million

LIVESTOCK

	Inventory	Average price
Cattle and calves	6.7 million head	$22.98/cwt (beef)
Hogs and pigs	12.4 million head	$15.40/cwt
	Production	Inventory
Chickens (Layers)	4.8 billion eggs	21.8 million birds
Milk	5.9 billion lbs.	

CROPS

	Harvested acres	Yield	Production	Avg price
All Hay	3.5 million	2.32 tons/acre	8.1 million tons	$14.5/ton
Corn	12.2 million	63.5 bu./acre	773 million bu.	$0.97/bu.
Soybeans	2.6 million	25.5 bu./acre	66.2 million bu.	$2.13/bu.
Oats	4.1 million	42 bu./acre	172 million bu.	$0.60/bu.
Wheat	119,000	25 bu./acre	2.9 million bu.	$1.77/bu.

IOWA MASTER FARMERS
~
April 1, 1961

Five outstanding Iowa farmers—nominated by friends and neighbors for achievements in farm operation, family living and community service—received the 1960 Master Farmer award.

Judges for the contest included Clyde Spry, Iowa Secretary of Agriculture; Herbert Howell, Iowa State University agricultural economist; Russell Eldred, president of the Iowa Master Farmer Club; and Dick Albrecht, editor of *Wallaces Farmer.*

Herb Cline
Marion County

Cline feeds hogs and keeps a herd of purebred Angus on his 280 acres. Rolling fields are contoured and terraced.

One of his major interests has been the 4-H program. Last year, he received a state alumni award for outstanding contribution to 4-H club work.

He is a di-rector of the American Aberdeen Angus Association and has managed county and state Angus sales.

Other community service includes soil conservation district, Extension service, school board, Farm Bureau and church.

Mr. and Mrs. Cline have two children: Carolyn, 19, attending Simpson College, and Joe, 15, sophomore in high school.

Ralph Fox
Howard County

Fox feeds 200 cattle and raises 8,500 turkeys on his 481 acres. His cropping program includes permanent pasture and continuous corn.

Much of his community service time has centered around local schools. He has been president of the township district, on the county board of education and is vice-chairman of the community district.

Other ac-

Cline

Fox

tivities include Farm Bureau, township trustee, church and Extension council.

Mr. and Mrs. Fox have seven children: Carol, 16, junior in high school; Mike, 15, sophomore in high school; Gary, 13, in 7th grade; Jack, 10, in 5th grade; Jane, 6, in first grade; Susan, 4; and Sarah, 3.

Elmer Hamann
Scott County

Hamann keeps a dairy herd and raises hogs on his 160-acre farm. He started farming as a hired man, became a tenant operator and then bought his present farm where he developed his high-producing dairy herd.

He has served as president of the community school district.

Other community service includes FHA committee, DHIA, Extension service, Farm Bureau, bank director and church.

Mr. and Mrs. Hamann have three children: Carol, now teaching school at Durant; Dale, 18, attending Iowa State University; and Wynee, 9, in 4th grade.

Don Kruse
Floyd County

Kruse follows a general cropping and livestock program on his 280 acres. Livestock includes hogs, beef and poultry. Contoured row crops and grass waterways keep soil erosion under control.

His community service activities include Extension service, 4-H clubs, soil conservation district commissioner, county livestock groups, FHA committee, Farm Bureau, co-op elevator board and Kiwanis.

He has been chairman of trustees and chairman of a building committee for his

Hamann

church. He is a long-time member and director of the Northeast Iowa Farm Business Association.

Mr. and Mrs. Kruse have two daughters: Sharon, now Mrs. Dale Chestek, on a farm nearby; and Nancy, working in the Floyd County social welfare office.

Ferd Schmidt
Clinton County

Schmidt farms 480 acres in partnership with his son, Owen. They feed 300 cattle and farrow 15 sows four times a year. They also keep a herd of 100 purebred Angus cows.

Schmidt has judged at the National Western Stock Show at Denver and at the feeder show in Chicago several times and is president of the Iowa Beef Producers Association.

Other community service includes Eastern Iowa Angus Breeders Association, community hospital, school board, 4-H clubs and volunteer fire department.

Schmidt has three children: Owen; Adena, a nurse; and Ruth, 16, sophomore in high school.

Kruse

Ferd Schmidt, right, with son Owen

1961
IOWA MASTER FARMERS
~
April 7, 1962

Five Iowa farmers have been awarded the title Master Farmer for achievements in farm operation and community service.

Judges who selected the group included L.B. Liddy, Iowa Secretary of Agriculture; Herbert Howell, Iowa State University farm management specialist; L.G. Stevens of Northwood, president of the Iowa Master Farmer Club; and Richard Albrecht, editor of *Wallaces Farmer*.

Chester Shirer
Lucas County

Shirer farms his 280-acre Pine Knoll farm with the help of his grandson, Bill. They keep a herd of about 50 purebred Angus cows and 20 to 30 purebred Poland China gilts.

Shirer has been township trustee and township assessor. He has also been a member of the county FHA committee, old AAA committee and reorganized school board. He helped organize a rural fire association. He is a charter member and has been president of the county Farm Bureau.

The Shirers have one son, Bob, of Fort Worth, Texas.

Roy Olson
Dickinson County

Olson has been feeding 300 to 500 cattle and 400 to 500 hogs on 1,280 acres. Breeding herds include about 100 beef cows and 250 ewes. This year, son Don took over part of the operation, though machinery and equipment are owned jointly.

Olson has been active in church, politics, beef producer groups and Farm Bureau. He is now a director of the D.E.K. Rural Electric Cooperative.

The Olsons have three sons; Don; Larry, in the bank at Royal, Iowa; and Scott, a freshman at Iowa State University.

Chester Shirer, left, with grandson Bill

Pellett

Wendell C. Pellett
Cass County

Pellett built up a run-down 250 acres to high productivity. His was the first farm in Cass County to have a conservation farm plan and parallel terraces. He feeds out about 80 cattle and raises about 300 hogs a year.

Much of his community service time has been spent encouraging conservation. He's a member of the state soil conservation committee and a soil conservation district commissioner.

He has also been active in politics, Lions Club and church where he has served 23 years on the official board.

The Pelletts have a daughter, Karen, 14, and a son, Ricky, 9.

Edmund Groomes
Guthrie County

Groomes feeds out about 100 head of cattle and 500 hogs a year on his 206 acres.

He has been active in politics, church and public speaking. He has been president and is now director of the Iowa Association of School Boards. He's been president and is now director of radio for the Iowa Council for Better Education.

He has participated in many education conferences, including a White House Conference on Education.

Mr. and Mrs. Groomes have four daughters: Marilyn, now Mrs. Thomas McDonald of Fort Worth, Texas; Gwen, doing research at Johns Hopkins University; Joyce, now Mrs. Howard Gilman of Stuart; and Genelle, age 12.

Olson (on previous page)

William F. Imlau
Worth County

Imlau keeps a herd of 42 purebred Angus cows on Willene Angus Farm. He also feeds 50 to 80 head of cattle and raises 30 litters of pigs per year on the 320 acres.

He worked as field man for the Iowa Beef Producers Association and as Assistant Secretary of Agriculture for Iowa before starting to farm. He's now a director of the Beef Producers and active in Angus groups. He frequently judges beef shows with emphasis on carcass quality.

He's also active in his church, politics and school affairs.

The Imlaus have five children: Mary Ellen, 11; Carolyn, 9; Barbara, 6; Elaine, 3; and William Allen, 5 months.

Groomes

Imlau

IOWA MASTER FARMERS

~
April 20, 1963

Iowa has four new Master Farmers. They were selected by a board of judges from nominations made by neighbors and friends. Selection is made on the basis of long records of achievement in farm operation and management, family living and community service.

This makes a total of 201 men and one woman who have received the award from *Wallaces Farmer* since the program began in 1926.

Ervin Schmuecker
Iowa County

Ervin Schmuecker farms 160 acres known as Pinehurst Angus Farm northeast of Marengo in Iowa County. His son Tom operates another 160 acres nearby.

He purchased his farm in a rundown condition. Since then, he has reconstructed or replaced the entire farmstead, installed conservation practices, and doubled the productive capacity.

His major livestock interest lies in a herd of about 110 purebred Angus beef cows. Grand champion loads at many major feeder cattle shows have been sired by Schmuecker's Pinehurst bulls.

His interest in beef cattle led naturally to many of his activities. He helped organize and was first president of the Iowa County Beef Producers, the Hawkeye Angus Association and the Iowa Beef Improvement Association.

Schmuecker has also been active in the county 4-H committee, Extension council, Farm & Home Advisory Committee, cooperative telephone company, school reorganization committee, adult night school council, county fair board and as 4-H club leader.

Mr. and Mrs. Schmuecker have three children. Tom, 28, is farming nearby. James, 24, is with the University of Missouri Extension Service in Maryville, Mo. Kathryn, 22, now Mrs. Darryl Dochterman, attends the University of South Dakota.

Schmuecker

132

Walter Hagen
Allamakee County

Walter Hagen farms 530 acres near Waterville in Allamakee County. Following a basic plan developed by the Allamakee Soil Conservation Service, he uses terraces and strip cropping on rolling fields. In addition, he has built ponds and planted 25,000 trees. His farm was the 20th tree farm in the state.

One spring-fed pond has been developed into a recreation area widely used by church and civic groups.

Hagen

His present livestock operation includes hogs and beef cattle. He developed a purebred herd of Holsteins (averaging 500 pounds butterfat) which was dispersed in 1956. He was named Master Swine Producer in 1942.

Hagen is now serving his second term in the Iowa legislature and is chairman of the Fish and Game Committee. He is chairman of the Allamakee Soil Conservation District Commissioners and of National Foresters Association.

He has been active in Farm Service Company, local telephone company, Farm Bureau, Northeast Farm Management Association, school reorganization and building committees, Kiwanis, Izaak Walton and Masonic Lodge.

The Hagens have two children. They are Russell, 14, in 9th grade, and Sandra, 11, in 5th grade.

Harvey Moeckly
Polk County

Harvey Moeckly farms 580 acres near Polk City in Polk County. His livestock operation includes 40 head of milk cows plus 15 heifers, 600 chickens, 400 hogs and 40 head of beef cattle.

His modern, attractive farm has been visited by 40 diplomats and representatives from numerous foreign countries in recent years.

Moeckly is president of the Des Moines Cooperative Dairy and of the county DHIA. He has also been a director of the Polk County Beef Producers Association.

He's held county and state positions in Farm Bureau and the Farm Supply Company.

Moeckly has also been active in the local telephone company, rural fire department, Polk City grain company, county ASCS committee, Masonic Lodge (Master), Kiwanis (Lt. District Governor), and numerous fund-raising efforts.

Mr. and Mrs. Moeckly have one son, Maurice, 20, who has attended McPherson College in McPherson, Kansas, and Grand View College in Des Moines.

Moeckly

Joseph O'Hara
Page County

Joseph C. O'Hara farms 712 acres east of Shenandoah in Page County. He feeds out 150 to 200 steers, raises 800 to 900 hogs, and keeps 25 to 30 Shorthorn beef cows.

O'Hara's interest in soil and water conservation led to wide recognition. He has been a commissioner in the Page Soil Conservation District for 22 years. One of the organizers of the Soil Conservation District Commissioners Association of Iowa, he has served as director, vice president and is now in his third term as president. He also represents Iowa on the council of the national association.

He has also been township trustee, precinct political chairman, vice president of Izaak Walton League, secretary of the local school

O'Hara

board, on the adult evening school council, boys' 4-H leader, and a member of numerous Extension committees.

Mr. and Mrs. O'Hara have two children. They are James, 21, studying farm management at Iowa State, and Mary Ann, 16, sophomore in high school.

IOWA MASTER FARMERS

~
April 4, 1964

Five outstanding Iowa farmers have been selected for the Master Farmer award. They were nominated by friends and neighbors and then chosen by a panel of judges.

Long records of achievement in farm operation and management and in family living are the first requirements. Then heavy emphasis is placed on community service, recognizing that the citizenship responsibilities of a farmer extend beyond the bounds of his own acres.

This new group makes a total of 206 men and one woman who have received the Master Farmer award from *Wallaces Farmer* since the program was started in 1926.

Here is a brief summary of the nominating report for each of the Master Farmers.

Bert Ballou
Jones County

Bert Ballou farms 537 acres near Monticello in Jones County in partnership with his eldest son. They marketed 1,015 fed cattle and 525 hogs last year. While the land is cropped intensively, there is a conservation plan and sound fertility program.

He was president of the Monticello Community School Board last year and is now chairman of the personnel committee.

Ballou

Ballou is serving his second three-year term as a director of the Federal Land Bank Association of Cedar Rapids and his second year as president of that three-county association.

He has been active in the Iowa Livestock Feeders Association, the Jones County Beef Producers, Farm Bureau, Rotary, Masons and his political party.

He served many years as member of the official board of St. Luke's Methodist Church and was a 4-H leader.

His interest in foreign affairs led to a People-to-People tour of Europe. Last year the Ballous were hosts to an American Field Service exchange student from the Philippines.

The 1960 state corn-picking contest was held on his farm.

The Ballous have five children. Bill, an agribusiness graduate of Iowa State University, is in partnership on the farm; Susan is a senior at Iowa State; JoAnn is a freshman at ISU; Andrew is a senior in high school; and Bobby is in 6th grade.

Glenn R. Brown
Grundy County

Glenn Brown keeps a herd of 60 purebred Angus cows on his 80-acre farm near Grundy Center. He sells breeding stock and feeds the remaining animals for market. He also raises about 250 head of hogs per year in confinement. Except for extra labor during haying, he does all his own farm work.

He holds a bachelor of science degree from Iowa State University where he was elected to membership in Alpha Zeta and Gamma Sigma Delta.

He takes an active interest in the youth of his community. He has been a 4-H leader for 20 years and is on the county 4-H committee. He was on the local school board and served seven years as president. During this time he played an active part in county school reorganization.

Brown helped form the Grundy Soil Conservation District. He has been on the board of directors for his cooperative elevator for 18 years and is now its president.

He has been chairman of the official board of his church and has been active in district church affairs.

His interest in Angus cattle has led to considerable traveling. He has visited herds in many different states, Canada and in Scotland.

However, the visit to Scotland was part of a European trip to see his younger daughter, Mrs. Larry Eslinger, who is still with her husband in Germany. The older daughter is Mrs. Carroll Austin of Mabel, Minnesota.

Elvie Dreeszen
Ida County

Elvie Dreeszen manages his 240 acres as a balanced livestock and grain production unit. It is near Cushing in Ida County.

Brown

Dreeszen

He keeps a small Angus cow herd and feeds 200 to 400 head of cattle and 600 feeder pigs per year. Farm management records indicate a high return from each dollar of feed fed. The same records also show excellent crop production efficiency, emphasizing corn grown on the contour.

He's been active in school reorganization.

The Federal Land Bank Association directors recognized his contribution in the farm credit field by making him the youngest member of their national advisory committee.

He's been active in the Livestock Feeders Association and in Farm Bureau, including the state resolutions committee. He's a member of the County Rural Areas Development Committee. He has served on numerous Extension committees, REC committees and the local school board.

He has held a number of responsible church positions and teaches Sunday school.

The Dreeszens have four children: Roger, 17, junior in high school; Lanyce, 15, sophomore in high school; Randall, 12, in 6th grade; and Carolyn, 9, in 3rd grade.

Willis McAlpin
Montgomery County

Willis McAlpin, in partnership with sons, Tom and Dave, operates 676 acres near Villisca in Montgomery County. Together they milk 90 registered Holsteins. This herd has been on official test since 1935 and now has a production record of 13,700 pounds of milk. In addition they

McAlpin

farrow and feed out 800 to 900 hogs.

Interest in dairying led to many of McAlpin's activities. He is now president of the Iowa Dairy Industry Commission and the American Dairy Association of Iowa. He is a director of Iowa State Dairy Association. He is also president of the local DHIA, district director of the Iowa Breeders' Co-op, and director of the Iowa Holstein Breeders' Association.

He's been on the school board and the county board of supervisors, a soil conservation district commissioner, and past member of the Lion's Club. He's been active in Farm Bureau.

He's taken an extensive role in church activities, serving many years as Sunday school teacher.

The McAlpins have five children. Tom and David are farming in partnership with their father. Dale is also farming near Waterloo, Iowa. Dale and David are twins. So are Margaret, now Mrs. Cecil Aborr of Des Moines, and Marjorie, now Mrs. Glenn Bush of Misenheimer, N.C.

Les McGohan
Henry County

Les McGohan emphasizes quality pork production on the 290 acres he farms near Swedesburg in Henry County. He raises 1,100 to 1,200 hogs per year in a pasture confinement system. Purchase of tested boars insures continued improvement of his herd. His ef-

forts in the area were recognized when he was named Master Swine Producer in 1954.

He also concentrates on corn production.

His major interest has been cooperatives. He served 11 years on the board of Supply Co-op, Inc., including six as president and four as secretary. He is a past president of the Southeast Iowa Council of Cooperatives, and is now vice president of the Mt. Pleasant Farmers Cooperative Elevator board.

McGohan worked extensively on school reorganization and served as reorganization committee chairman in the present WACO Community School district.

He is an active member of the Finley Methodist Church and has served as chairman of numerous church committees.

The McGohans have two children. Bill majored in farm operations at Iowa State University for two years and is now farming an adjoining farm. Betty is attending the University of Iowa majoring in art education.

McGohan

137

1965
IOWA MASTER FARMERS
~
April 17, 1965

Five outstanding Iowa farmers have been added to a long list of Iowa Master Farmers from previous years. Each of these five men has a long record of achievement in farm management and operation. Each also has demonstrated effective community leadership over many years.

Judges for this year were C. Raymond Fisher, Greene County farmer and president of the Iowa Master Farmer Club; Prof. Herb Howell, Extension farm management specialist at Iowa State University; Kenneth Owen, Iowa Secretary of Agriculture; and Richard Albrecht, editor of *Wallaces Farmer*.

Wallaces Farmer has presented awards through the years in an effort to direct public attention to the thousands of excellent managers and community leaders found on farms all over the state of Iowa.

Harold Ryon
Pocahontas County

The home farm of 239 acres on the edge of Laurens in Pocahontas County is only part of the land owned by Harold Ryon. He owns and rents out two other nearby farms.

Ryon follows a general crop and livestock program. A three-breed cross is used to produce 200 to 300 head of market hogs. He also feeds about 25 cattle and keeps 35 ewes to use pasture. His operation is guided by a set of detailed records he's kept since 1936.

Mr. and Mrs. Ryon have four children. Dale, an Iowa State University graduate, is now renting one of Ryon's farms. June, now Mrs. Richard Buhr, lives near Tripoli, Iowa. Roger is a junior at Iowa State. Lois is a junior in high school.

Ryon

Wright

James W. Wright
Story County

Central Iowa Farm Business Association records have been important to James W. Wright. He is in his third term as president of that group and has served as state president.

Wright now is farming 420 acres near Collins in Story County. Row crops are concentrated on the more level land. Permanent pasture has been renovated with birdsfoot trefoil. Some rough land has been planted to trees.

Wright's livestock operation includes about 70 litters of pigs and feeding 200 to 300 head of cattle. He has just installed an automatic feeding system in order to get by without full-time hired help. He did much of the design and installation himself.

The Wrights have three children: Rebecca Jo, 13, in 7th grade; Thomas, 10, 5th grade; and James, Jr., 6, kindergarten.

J. Gordon Hollis
Black Hawk County

From hired man to renter to owner to Master Farmer—that's the story of J. Gordon Hollis. He started farming in 1938 with $400 he saved from work as a farmhand and with a hardware firm.

Hollis farms 360 acres near Waterloo in Black Hawk County. He raises 600 to 700 head of hogs in confinement, but his herd of 80 mostly purebred Guernseys are a major interest. Production records show over 11,000 pounds of milk and 540 pounds of fat, near the top among the state's Guernsey herds.

Mr. and Mrs. Hollis have three children. Sheryl is teaching school in Mt. Hope, Kansas. Curtis, 19, is a sophomore in dairy science at ISU. Joyce, 17, is a senior in high school.

H. M. Black
Kossuth County

Black Acres, Inc., is the name given to the 480-acre incorporated family farm operated by H. M. Black. It is near Algona in Kossuth County.

Black's cropping program is a rotation of corn, beans and meadow. He harvests corn

Hollis

with a picker-sheller and dries it for storage.

Black has sold his Ayrshire milking herd, but still has 32 heifers. He is shifting his livestock enterprise to more hogs and beef cattle in order to reduce labor requirements of the operation. SPF gilts have been purchased to establish the sow herd.

Mr. and Mrs. Black have three children: Louise, 7, in 2nd grade; Jim, 5; and Carolyn, 4 months.

Black

Leon Haahr
Buena Vista County

Accurate and detailed records play a major role in the farm business operated by Leon Haahr. He has been a member of the Northwest Iowa Farm Business Association since he started to farm.

In this activity, he follows in the footsteps of his father who was a charter member. Leon

Haahr has twice been elected president of the association, first in 1955 and again this year.

Haahr farms 400 acres near Newell in Buena Vista County. Part of his corn acreage is used to produce hybrid seed corn.

His livestock program includes 80 litters of pigs and feeding 300 to 350 head of cattle. An automated feeding setup is used to lighten the labor load.

Mr. and Mrs. Haahr have three sons: Dennis, 18, senior in high school; Dana, 16, sophomore; and Ronald, 11, in 6th grade.

IOWA MASTER FARMERS
~
April 9, 1966

Four outstanding Iowa farmers have been named Master Farmers. They are Norman Barker of Plymouth County, Roy B. Keppy of Scott County, Paul McNutt of Johnson County, and Gaylord Stadlman of Sac County.

Wallaces Farmer has presented Master Farmer awards since 1926 to call attention to the excellent managers and community leaders found on Iowa farms. In the past 40 years, 215 men and one woman have been named Master Farmers.

Norman Barker
Plymouth County

Norman Barker owns 60 acres and rents 240 acres in northwestern Plymouth County. All his crops are planted on the contour, and the entire cropping system is aimed at conservation of moisture.

The land he farms has 6.3 miles of terraces and 5 acres of grass waterways. The farm has been an award winner in the Sioux City permanent agriculture program.

Barker is a member of the Northwest Farm

Barker

Business Association. Marvin Polzien, association field man, says, "Barker's farm records show an unusual ability to pull a large income off an average-size farm in an area with below-average rainfall." Barker feeds about 70 head of cattle each year and is developing an expanded cattle-feeding setup. He has been farrowing about 60 or more litters of pigs per year. He has a new farrowing and confinement house started and is doing much of the actual construction himself.

Barker has been active in school, church and many other community affairs.

Mr. and Mrs. Barker have four children: Carolyn, 13; Joann, 11; James, 9; and Jean, 7. All attend LeMars Community School.

Roy B. Keppy
Scott County

Roy B. Keppy owns and operates 320 acres northwest of Davenport in Scott County. Widely known for raising prize-winning crossbred hogs, Keppy operates largely as a general livestock and

Keppy

grain farmer. In addition to 175 litters of hogs, he feeds about 200 calves and yearlings each year.

Keppy exhibited the first crossbred grand champions at the International Livestock Exposition in both barrow and truckload competition. He also had the first crossbred load to receive similar honors at the National Barrow Show. Additional winnings have been numerous.

To maintain herd quality, Keppy usually buys two boars each year. But the boar doesn't earn his place in the herd until his offspring have proven out in both feedlot and in the packing plant.

Keppy, a Master Swine Producer, was named "Businessman of the Year" by the Davenport Chamber of Commerce. Other honors include the Ford Farm Efficiency Award and the National Hog Farmer Award. Along with numerous church and community activities, Keppy is a director of the National Pork Producers Council and a member of the state Ex-

tension advisory committee.

Mr. and Mrs. Keppy have four children: Glenn, 18, senior in high school; Dale, 16, junior in high school; Annette, 11, 6th grade; and Ila Jean, 6, in kindergarten.

Gaylord Stadlman
Sac County

Gaylord Stadlman owns 120 acres and rents additional land about 4 miles north of Sac City in Sac County. He has a general farming operation with emphasis on swine and beef. He feeds out about 600 head of cattle—part calves and part yearlings—and farrows 100 to 125 litters of hogs per year.

The new farmstead he's building on his home farm includes a beef feeding setup with fenceline bunks, holding facilities and scales. He has designed the facilities to handle a sizable volume of cattle with minimum labor but without high per-head investment.

Stadlman has been active in school affairs and has spent 27 years as boys' 4-H leader or on the county boys' 4-H committee.

Stadlman

He served as chairman of a group which established a direct line telephone market news service for cattle and hogs for several counties in northwest Iowa.

Stadlman received the state 4-H Alumni Achievement award, is a Master Swine Producer, and has received the Ford Farm Efficiency award.

Mr. and Mrs. Stadlman have two sons: Neil, 20, former state FFA president and now a junior at ISU; and Evan, 13, 8th grade.

Paul McNutt
Johnson County

Paul McNutt owns 313 acres and rents an additional 153 acres in Johnson County. His livestock operation centers on raising about 1,300 head of hogs

McNutt

per year, but also includes about 70 purebred Angus cows. His hogs are crossbred with emphasis on carcass quality and are marketed grade and yield.

McNutt is a member of the Mississippi Valley Farm Business Association and was recently elected president of the Iowa Swine Producers Association. He has also served on the National Pork Council. He takes an active part in Farm Bureau, church and other community affairs.

Other honors include Master Swine Producer and 4-H Alumni Achievement awards.

Mr. and Mrs. McNutt have three children: Jim, 20, at Iowa State University prepping to study veterinary medicine; Martha, 16, junior at West-Branch Community High School; and John, 14, in junior high.

IOWA MASTER FARMERS

~ May 27, 1967

Five outstanding Iowa farmers have been named Master Farmers.

Wallaces Farmer has been presenting Master Farmer awards since 1926. The new group brings the total to 220 men and one woman who have received the award.

Nominations are made by friends, neighbors and co-workers. Then selection is made on the basis of farm management and outstanding community service.

The Master Farmer award program is designed both to honor individual farmers and their families and to call widespread attention to the excellent management and unselfish community leadership found among farmers all through the state.

Horace Autenrieth
O'Brien County

Horace Autenrieth raises 600 to 700 head of hogs. Crates are used for winter farrowing, pasture for summer farrowing. Litter average usually ranges from 8½ to 10 pigs.

He weans pigs as they reach 15 pounds, with weight rather than age the determining factor. Sanitation to prevent spread of disease is an important part of his management program.

Autenrieth feeds out 180 head of calves and 70 yearlings.

He owns 120 acres and rents

Autenrieth

another 360 acres of rolling land, which is farmed on the contour.

He aims for 17,000 final plant population on his 225 acres of corn. Phosphate is plowed down with nitrogen applied as anhydrous ammonia in fall or spring.

He has served on the policy determining board of Scattergood School, West Branch, Iowa, for 17 years.

Autenrieth is chairman of O'Brien County Extension's long-time planning committee, a member of northwest Iowa area agronomy advisory committee, treasurer of the local Farmers Cooperative Elevator, and a member and past president of the Northwest Iowa Farm Business Association. He is also a member of the Paullina Lions Club.

He is past chairman of the soil conservation district and was a Register and Tribune Sweepstakes award winner in 1965. He was also on the executive committee for the Northwest Iowa Experimental Farm when it was established in 1955.

Autenrieth has been treasurer of the Society of Friends meeting near Paullina, where he taught Sunday school for 10 years. He is serving on the Midwest Regional Board of the American Friends Service Committee, and is chairman of the Paullina chapter of the American Field Service.

Mr. and Mrs. Autenrieth have

two children: Aline Ann, 15, a Scattergood School freshman; and Greg, 13, in 8th grade at Paullina Community School.

Herbert Hinkhouse
Cedar County

Herbert Hinkhouse feeds 750 to 800 head of cattle per year. Most of these are calves. His feeding program includes high-moisture ear corn and corn silage.

Fenceline bunks and a self-unloading mixing wagon are used to handle feed. He is installing scales for weighing live animals and feed, and for crop-yield checks.

Hinkhouse owns 275 acres and rents an additional 760 acres. Landowners have offered to rent still more land to him, but he has declined.

He has about 700 acres of corn, all in 30-inch rows this year. He figures a 5-bushel yield increase will pay for the changeover in one year, especially since he needed a new planter.

He aims for a final stand of 20,000 to 24,000 plants per acre.

The operation includes one hired man, and two sons, one in high school, and one in 6th grade.

Hinkhouse is currently on the advisory council for the vo-ag adult farmer night school and the agricultural committee for the Area 10 Vocational Education Technical School. He has been vice president of the county Extension council and president of the local school board.

He is a director of the Iowa City Federal Land Bank Association and is a member of the advisory committee for the Omaha district.

Hinkhouse uses the Farm Bureau record-keeping service and is anxious to have analysis and comparisons added to the service. Hinkhouse is a Farm Bureau member and has held county offices and served on state committees. He is also a member of the National Livestock Feeders Association.

He and his family are active members of the Friends Church.

Mr. and Mrs. Hinkhouse have five children: Richard, 21, in service; H. Clifford, 19, attending Iowa State University; Glen, 16, in high school; Stanley, 12, in 6th grade; and Hilda Marie, 5.

Keith McAllister
Henry County

Keith McAllister operates a grain and livestock farm in partnership with his brother and son. They employ one hired man.

They farm a total of 1,040 acres with 700 in corn and 200 in soybeans. They also feed out 300 steers, both yearlings and calves, and 2,500 hogs a year.

They plant both corn and soybeans in 30-inch rows and try to get a final stand of 21,000 plants per acre. Their fertilizer program includes plow-down phosphate and potash plus 200 pounds of nitrogen before planting and 100 pounds of 8-32-16 as starter.

Insecticides are used to control soil insects and corn borers. In the past four years, they have used herbicides to control weeds on their entire acreage of corn and soybeans.

In 1960, McAllister designed and built facilities to dry and store

Hinkhouse

McAllister

Winslow (next page)

Schmidt

shelled corn. He has also designed and built a bunker silo, which doubles as a feed floor when empty. He has remodeled two barns into slotted-floor finishing facilities for feeder pigs with liquid manure pits underneath.

McAllister was a board member of the Winfield-Mount Union School board for 12 years. He was also state board member of Iowa Association of School Boards for two years.

He has been a member of the board of the Mount Union Co-op Elevator for 14 years. He has been township chairman of Farm Bureau and is presently an NFO member.

He has also been very active in the Mount Union Methodist Church where he is chairman of the official board. He is chairman of the building committee that recently completed an addition to the church.

Mr. and Mrs. McAllister have three children. They are Kenny, 21, who attended the winter quarter at Iowa State University and now is at home; Pamela, 10; in 4th grade; and Tim, 6, in primary in the Mount Union School.

George Schmidt
Clinton County

George Schmidt farms in partnership with his son, Robert, and son-in-law, Paul Hinck. This partnership farms 630 acres, feeds about 400 cattle, and raises about 400 head of hogs.

The home-raised calves are fed out for market, with the exception of 15 replacement heifers that are registered. The best-quality larger heifers are kept for replacements. All home-raised calves are ear tagged and tattooed.

Calves are creep fed. At weaning time, the steer calves are put with 100 head of steer calves purchased in Nebraska. Heifers are fed separately.

In spring, the cattle go on rolled-shelled corn and limited pasture until September 1. They are then finished in drylots.

About 100 head of 650-700 pound steers are purchased in May and fed for January and February market.

The cows run in stalk fields and are wintered on hay without corn.

About 100 head of Montana calves are fed on one farm. Two 14- by 40-foot silos on that farm are filled with high-moisture ear corn ground at 24% to 27% moisture.

Farrowing stalls are used four times a year for 12 sows each time. Second litter sows average 10 pigs and gilts average nine.

Schmidt served 12 years on the Delmar school board, six years as a member of the county board of education, 21 years as 4-H club leader, and 12 years as a director of the county 4-H club show.

He has been active in Farm Bureau, beef producer groups and Clinton County 100-Bushel Corn Club. Schmidt and his brother have shown grand champion cattle six times at the International.

Schmidt is a longtime treasurer and trustee of Delmar Methodist Church.

Mr. and Mrs. Schmidt have two children, Robert and Joan, both married.

Francis Winslow
Grundy County

Francis Winslow operates a grain and dairy farm. He sells Grade A milk from about 30 registered Holstein cows. His production records have topped 16,000 pounds of milk per cow.

He plans to disperse his dairy herd this fall after 35 years as a dairyman and adopt some livestock program requiring less labor.

His interest in dairying has extended to numerous organizations. He has been president of the Iowa Purebred Dairy Cattle Council, Cedar Valley Milk Producers Association and Grundy County DHIA.

He has also served as a director of the Iowa State Dairy Association, the United Dairy Cooperative and Iowa Holstein Breeders Association.

Winslow has received the Progressive Breeder award from the National Holstein Association eight times. He was in the first group presented the Iowa Distinguished Dairyman award.

He was named Iowa Master Swine Producer in 1942. He closed out his hog operation in 1960 when he decided to operate the farm without any extra help.

Winslow owns 120 acres and rents another 120. On his 90 acres of corn, he used the Iowa State University fertilizer recommendation for 150-bushel yields. Last year, the average was 140.

Winslow has been 4-H leader, chairman of the county 4-H committee, secretary and director of the Morrison Cooperative and president of the fair board.

He is a longtime member and past director of the Cedar Valley Farm Business Association.

Winslow is chairman of the newly-organized zoning commission of Grundy County.

He has been Sunday school superintendent and on numerous committees in the Grundy Center Methodist Church.

Mr. and Mrs. Winslow have two daughters. Francene, now Mrs. Lee Gruenhaupt, lives in Waukon. Carolyn, now Mrs. Loren Miller, lives in Tipton.

Cover of May 27, 1967 award issue

Master Farmer Exceptional Service Award

Dr. C.R. Weber, breeder of the new Amsoy and Hark soybean varieties, has been presented the Master Farmer Exceptional Service award.

While *Wallaces Farmer* has been presenting Master Farmer awards to outstanding Iowa farmers since 1926, this is only the second Exceptional Service award. The first went to Larry Cain, manager of the Cerro Gordo County farm, in 1959.

Dr. Weber earned advanced degrees from the University of Illinois and Iowa State University. He was leader of the USDA and Agricultural Experiment Station Cooperative Soybean Research Project from 1942 until April 1967. At that time, he joined Peterson Seed Company as director of research.

In 1963, he was made honorary life member of the American Soybean Association.

In 1964, he was selected Fellow, American Society of Agronomy. The citation said, "Dr. Weber has pursued the profession of crop breeding with unlimited energy and enthusiasm. High standards, inquisitive approach to research problems, and ambitious nature have made him inspirational to and a leader among his colleagues and graduate student associates. Through his understanding of the basic problems of crop breeding, he has contributed much to the development and understanding of crop service."

He represented the United States at the World Agricultural Fair in New Delhi, India, in 1959-60. In 1965, he went to Japan at the invitation of Kyoto Prefectural University to study soybean food uses as related to soybean improvement.

Most of his work in the Department of Agronomy at Iowa State University has been on research problems related to soybean breeding and production. He is author and co-author of more than 70 scientific papers and numerous articles. He served as major professor for 18 graduate students.

Weber

Dr. Weber has assisted in the development of more than 40 superior soybean varieties, with 15 varieties of his own.

He played a big part in the development of improved varieties such as Hawkeye, Clark, Ford, Adams and Blackhawk.

His more recent soybean selections include Amsoy and Hark. These are what he calls "thin-line" varieties that perform best in narrow rows with high plant population.

Amsoy is adapted to most of Iowa—all except the southern two rows of counties and part of northeast Iowa. Of course, its adaptation extends into states to the east and west of this belt.

It has the potential of increasing yields by perhaps 8% on millions of acres of soybeans.

While a limited amount of seed is available this year, it will be generally available in 1968.

The Hark variety is best-adapted to the northern three rows of counties in the state, but does well all through the northern half of the state. Its area of adaptation also extends into southern Minnesota. Hark seed will be available for extensive planting in 1968.

This variety has the potential of increasing yields by about 10% in its area of adaptation.

Obviously, the increased yields of Amsoy and Hark will provide important economic gains for Iowa soybean growers and for the state as a whole. Of course, the benefit is not to Iowa alone since other states can obtain yield increases, too.

When economic benefits derived from other varieties on which Dr. Weber has played a big part are included, his contribution to soybean growers is truly outstanding.

1968

IOWA MASTER FARMERS
~
February 10, 1968

Seven outstanding Iowa farmers have been named Master Farmers.

Wallaces Farmer has been presenting Master Farmers awards since 1926. The new group brings the total to 227 men and one woman who have received the award. Nominations are made by friends, neighbors and co-workers. Then selection is made on the basis of farm management and outstanding community service.

The Master Farmer award program is designed both to honor individual farmers and their families and to call widespread attention to the excellent management and unselfish community leadership found among farmers all through the state.

Louis Byrnes
Howard County

Louis Byrnes operates a dairy farm in partnership with his son, Robert. He sells Grade A milk from a herd of 99 registered Holsteins, and has pushed his herd to a five- year average of 14,335 pounds of milk and 530 pounds of fat.

The feeding program looks like this: Hay silage is fed with hay as soon as it's available in the summer. As soon as corn silage is ready, it replaces the hay silage. Ear corn and oats make up the grain portion. This is balanced

Byrnes

to 16% protein ration. Replacements are heifers from the best cows in the herd. These heifers are expected to produce 450 pounds of fat during their first lactation.

The cows are milked in a modern milking parlor and housed in a 120-foot barn equipped with free stalls. An auger setup distributes the feed.

Byrnes was named Iowa Distinguished Dairyman in 1967.

The operation also includes 175 acres of corn, 55 acres of oats and 80 acres hay. The corn averages about 100 bushels per acre, the oats 80 bushels. Another 240-acre farm he owns is rented out on a 50-50 basis. This farm has a 40-cow dairy herd.

Fertilizer rates are based on soil tests. Application is plow down, followed by sidedressing with the planter on corn ground.

A balanced fertilizer is used to increase oat yields and gives the alfalfa stand a boost.

Byrnes is a former county DHIA president, is president of the Farmers Co-op Creamery, president of the Howard County Agricultural Association, and president of the Howard County Holstein Association.

Byrnes is a member of the Assumption Catholic Church in Cresco and has served on various church committees.

Mr. and Mrs. Byrnes have three children. Robert is in partnership with Louis. John is in the military service. Betty Lou Moen is a housewife in Cresco.

Ralph Calmer
Calhoun County

Ralph Calmer operates a diversified grain and livestock farm.

The farm consists of 200 acres owned and 400 acres rented. He feeds out about 350 head of feeder cattle per year and 850 head of hogs.

His beef-feeding program is to start heavy cattle on corn silage and switch to a full feed of corn and concentrate to finish them. He buys cattle at about 800 pounds and finishes them to 1,200 pounds.

Calmer uses top-notch breeding stock, high level management including limited feeding, and lots of experience to come up with eight to nine good pigs per litter average from gilts. His sows average 10 pigs per litter. This type of management ability brought him the Master Swine Producer Award in 1960.

Despite close attention to the livestock, crop yields stack up well. Calmer reports corn yield of about 100 bushels per acre, a little above the average for that area.

About 80 acres of the farm are devoted to hay and oats. The rest is in corn and soybeans, with about 40 acres of corn harvested as silage.

Calmer has been active in his community and county. He served on and is past president of his local school board. He is a member of the township trustee committee, member of the county fair board, and a past

Calmer

member of the county Extension council.

He is also president of the co-op elevator board and has served 30 years on the county ASCS committee.

Calmer plays an active role in the Farm Bureau, Calhoun County Beef Producers Association and Calhoun County Swine Producers Association.

He is an active member of the American Lutheran Church in Manson.

The Calmers have two daughters. Gwen (Mrs. John) Ewing lives in Manson. Gail is a high school senior at Manson.

John D. Morris
Louisa County

John Morris specializes in hogs and corn production.

All phases of pork production are carried out in controlled-environment confinement facilities. Rations are formulated, ground and mixed on the farm.

It was on this farm that tethering sows on slotted floors was developed. Artificial insemination is used to maintain a closed herd physically, but to open it up genetically.

Four years of work stomach-tubing pigs has led to development of a new technique for saving most problem pigs.

Pneumatic feed handling is another innovation. That is, ground feed is blown through galvanized pipe.

He operates one 200-acre farm. Another 180-acre farm is operated under a partnership arrangement.

Continuous corn is grown on nearly all 380 acres. A chisel plow used in the fall substitutes

Morris

for plowing and places fertilizer 8 to 10 inches deep in the soil.

Morris has developed a management-training program designed to help young men establish their own environmentally controlled pork production systems. At present, he is training two young Japanese men.

He is chairman of the Iowa and a member of the national Hog Cholera Eradication Committee. He spearheaded a drive that collected more than $80,000 for swine-disease research.

Morris has served as chairman of the Iowa Swine Disease Research Committee, Swine Specialists Seminar, Mississippi Valley and Iowa Farm Business Association Councils and County Extension Council. He has also been active in Farm Bureau.

Morris is a graduate of Iowa State University. He is an elder in the Presbyterian Church.

Mr. and Mrs. Morris have two children. David, an ISU graduate, is employed by Dallas County State Bank. Marilyn, Mrs. George Max, is attending graduate school at Kansas State University.

Herbert Pike
Monona County

Herbert Pike operates a large farm in the Missouri River valley near Whiting. He employs three full-time men.

An intensive corn-soybean cropping system is supplemented with a 100-litter hog project, 200 head of feeder cattle, a beef cow herd and a ewe flock.

Hogs are farrowed in February, July and August, and December. Summer pigs are raised on pasture and winter pigs in semi-confinement—open sheds with a deep, narrow gutter.

Cows and calves glean 500 acres of cornstalks. Then, the Angus cows are carried on chopped hay through the winter until pastures are ready.

Several hundred acres of heavy clay soil on the farm have been put to grade in a land-shaping project to improve drainage.

Pike is a 1933 graduate in agriculture from Iowa State University. He earned a master's degree there in 1939.

He now serves as chairman of the board of trustees of the ISU Agricultural Foundation that operates demonstration farms.

Pike was a member of the agricultural delegation to the Soviet Union in 1955. He is active in the Farm Bureau and is serving on its state Farm Management Committee.

He has appeared on numerous farm programs, including the Omaha National Livestock Conference, the Swine Institute and the National Farm Institute.

Pike

Pike is president of the Whiting Cooperative. He is a member of the National Advisory Committee for the Federal Land Bank Association and a director of its Sioux City branch.

The Pikes are members of the United Church of Christ (Congregational) where Herb is a trustee.

They have two children, both attending Iowa State University. Julia, Mrs. Howard McLeod, is a senior, majoring in journalism. Charles is a freshman in farm operation.

Clifford Stille
Pottawattamie County

Clifford Stille feeds out 1,500 feeder pigs per year, mostly in complete confinement. He gets Wisconsin pigs in at about 40 pounds and feeds them to market at 240 pounds.

The confinement setup is a 29-pen unit. There is space for 280 feeder pigs and 270 head of market hogs. Before going to confinement, feed conversion was 367 pounds of feed per

100 pounds of pork. Stille reports he is using less feed now.

A stress ration of corn, oats, supplement and antibiotics is fed the first two weeks. Then he changes to corn, soybean meal and a vitamin

Stille

and mineral-antibiotic premix.

Hogs marketed from this building are yielding 2.5% over standard yield and are grading better than hogs on self-feeders in his other lots.

Several years ago, Stille and his hired men built a 17-bin, 25,000 bushel elevator. It headquarters grinding and mixing facilities. Augers transfer rations to the feeding areas.

Soil conservation gets top billing on Stille's farm. Since 1957, over 13 miles of terraces have been added to the farm. Land-shaping cut out 43 acres of wasteland.

Major crops on the farm are corn, milo and soybeans.

Stille has served seven years on local school boards. He is serving on the SCS Farm Advisory Committee for the Clarinda State Experiment farm.

He served four years as soil conservation assistant commissioner in East Pottawattamie County. He is chairman of the Macedonia Watershed Board and has served on county Extension councils.

The Stilles are members of the Methodist Church at Macedonia. He has served as chairman of the board, layman leader and is serving on the board of trustees.

Mr. and Mrs. Stille have two daughters: Sandra, Mrs. Brent Krantz; and Carol, Mrs. Douglas Carley. Both are registered nurses living in Omaha.

Ed Hanrahan & Gene Dunphy
Union County

Ed Hanrahan and Gene Dunphy operate under one of the most unusual and successful farm partnerships in Iowa. They operate 1,200 acres in Iowa's southern "beef cow area." The operation focuses on general crop and livestock farming.

The unusual thing is that the two brothers-in-law have no formal division of the property. And while it has worked for them for 30 years, even they do not recommend the practice for others. They see less risk in formal and written agreements.

They farrow 35 to 40 litters of pigs per year.

A three-way cross—Duroc, Spotted Poland, Hampshire—is used. Farrowing is planned for January, March and September. They run a 150-head beef cow herd. Production tested bulls from Iowa State University are used.

Cows are wintered on roughages and range cubes. Calves are creep-fed, carried on pasture and sold as feeders in the fall.

Hanrahan

Their fertilizer program for corn is fall plow-down. Herbicides are used for both corn and beans. Corn yields top 100 bushels per acre. Beans run 35-40 bushels per acre. Oats yield 70 bushels.

The farm is the site for one of the Iowa Crop Improvement Corn Yield Tests.

Dunphy's list of activities includes 15 years as secretary of the co-op elevator board and a member of the rules committee of the Farmland Industries. In 1967, he was one of 15 selected for a Farmers Regional Co-op Farm county tour. He also serves on the resolutions committee of the Farmers Union Marketing Association.

Dunphy is a charter member of Creston Lions Club and has served as president. He is also a member of the Knights of Columbus and past Grand Knight.

The Dunphys are members of St. Malachy's Catho-

Dunphy

lic Church at Creston and Gene has been a church trustee.

Mr. and Mrs. Dunphy have four children. Ron, 25, lives in Maryville, Mo. Sharon, 23, lives in Denver, Colo. Tom, 20, is a junior at Atchison, Kansas College. Mary, 14, is a student at Maryville Catholic School.

Ed Hanrahan's list of activities includes president of the Farm Service Company for 10 years. He's also a member of the Union County Beef Production Board and a member of the Beef Production Sales Committee.

He is a member of the Lions Club and has served as secretary for two years. He is a member of the Knights of Columbus and has served as deputy Grand Knight for two years. Hanrahan has also been Union County Farm Bureau president, voting delegate, and a member of the State Farm Bureau Resolutions Committee. He is also a Farm Service voting delegate.

He has taken an active part in 4-H work, has been a 4-H leader for nine years and a member of the 4-H County Club Committee for three years. He is also an honorary 4-H member.

He received the Civic Service Award presented by Eagles and the KSIB Farm Family award in 1951. Hanrahan is a member of St. Malachy's Catholic Church in Creston and is serving as a trustee.

Mr. and Mrs. Hanrahan have two children. Jack is 30 years old and lives in Kansas City, Mo. Theresa is 21 and a senior at Iowa State University.

IOWA MASTER FARMERS

~

February 8, 1969

New Master Farmers

SIX OUTSTANDING Iowa farmers have been named Master Farmers.

Wallaces Farmer has been presenting Master Farmers awards since 1926. The new group brings the total to 232 men and one woman who have received the award.

Nominations are made by friends, neighbors, and co-workers. Then selection is based on farm management and outstanding community service.

The Master Farmer award program is designed to honor individual farmers and their families and to call widespread attention to the excellent management and unselfish community leadership found among farmers all thru the state.

Donald F. Doolittle
Hamilton County

Donald F. Doolittle takes a strong business approach to farming. His 720-acre corn-soybean rotation brings high yields.

He also raises about 1,000 head of hogs and finishes 125 head of feeder cattle.

A unique farrowing system follows the free stall idea. Pens 6-feet-square are formed with foot boards set on edge so sows can easily walk out of pens. Feed and water are provided outside the building. A big advantage is that the pens stay clean.

While this system works

Doolittle

well in his case, Doolittle doesn't recommend it for everyone. He maintains an eight to nine pig average litter size.

Doolittle puts heavy emphasis on records. In 1967, he showed a $161 return per $100 worth of feed fed on his farm.

Doolittle received a R.S.C. degree from the University of Iowa. He served on the county school board and is now chairman of the new

Tri-County school district.

He is a member and secretary of the Blairsburg co-op elevator board, was on the conservation district board six years with two years as chairman and is a past member of the board of the Central Iowa Farm Business Association.

Doolittle is active in the Farm Bureau. He has served as township director and on several committees. This year, he is a county Farm Bureau voting delegate. He is also a member of the Lions and the Elks Clubs.

In 1948, Doolittle and his father were named Master Swine Producers.

Doolittle is an active member of the Catholic church in Williams. He has served as a church trustee, has taken part in lay formation classes and is a member of the Knights of Columbus.

Mr. and Mrs. Doolittle have two sons. Dennis, 24, has completed three years at Iowa State University and has just returned from Vietnam. Royal, 17, is a senior at Northeast Hamilton High School.

Paul Griffith
Decatur County

Paul Griffith manages a 360-acre farm following a corn-soybean rotation. He also has a large livestock operation, with 950 hogs, a few cattle and a small poultry flock.

His specialty is hogs. Farrowing is done in small, portable houses. Goals are to produce 80 hogs per month for market.

A confinement finishing house highlights the operation. He designed and constructed it himself. The unit has automatic feeding and watering, plus slotted floors with a lagoon for manure disposal.

The building was designed for 320 hogs. Griffith pushes the hogs from 30 pounds to over 200 pounds in four months.

Griffith

Griffith is on the school board at Lamoni and served on a school reorganization study committee prior to reorganization. He also was on the Decatur County board of education for 11 years.

He served as township trustee two years, township clerk four years, is a member of the election board and was a delegate to the 1968 state political convention.

Griffith is a member of the Ringgold Mutual Insurance board, served on the Farmers Co-op Elevator board, was on the county Farm Bureau board of directors, and has been a member and president of the Decatur County fair board. He also served three years as a 4-H leader and was a member and president of the Lamoni Co-op Creamery board.

A member of the Reorganized Church of Jesus Christ of Latter Day Saints, Griffith is an ordained member of priesthood holding the office of teacher.

Last year, the Griffiths were hosts to an IFYE delegate from Japan for three weeks.

The Griffiths have five children. They are Nancy (Mrs. Ray Powell), Creston; Gene, married and a territory manager with John Deere Company in Akron, Ohio; Barry, married and a junior at the University of Iowa; Janet, a freshman at Graceland College; and Laurel, in the 8th grade.

Irvin Harvey
Mahaska County

Irvin Harvey farms 210 acres specializing in a 1,200-head hog operation.

A modern, slatted floor confinement hog setup highlights his operation.

His sights are set on developing a sow herd with the mothering ability to produce large litters of disease free, fast growing pigs. These sows are crossed with meaty boars from tested herds. Grade and yield selling is the payoff.

Grade and yield results are coupled with breeding, farrowing and feed records to point the direction of his hog program.

In addition to the hog operation, Harvey has 50 Angus cows that are in the IBIA on-the-farm performance testing program.

Harvey is a firm believer in accurate farm records and is a member of the Farm Bureau computer records program.

Harvey

The crop portion of Harvey's operation is 100 acres of corn, with the rest as hay and pasture.

Harvey is a 1943 graduate of Iowa State University with a major in agricultural education. He taught vo-ag at West Branch and worked in Extension in Franklin County. He served on the salary study committee for the Oskaloosa schools in 1968.

Harvey is a member of the Mahaska County Pork Producers Association and a former member of the board of directors. He has served as county Farm Bureau director and treasurer and is now secretary.

Harvey has also served as a 4-H leader for three years. The Harveys are now hosting their second Japanese farm trainee. He terms it "a tremendous experience in international understanding."

The Harveys are members of the Central United Methodist Church where he serves as a Sunday school teacher, is on the official board and served eight years on the membership arid evangelism commission.

Mr. and Mrs. Harvey have two children, both at home: Stephen is 15, and Joan is 6.

Newhouse

Maynard Newhouse
Winneshiek County

Maynard Newhouse puts special emphasis on dairy and hogs. He milks 44 top-quality registered Holsteins and farrows and markets 400 to 500 hogs.

The current DHIA rolling herd average is 12,608 pounds milk and 468 pounds fat. This is a boost of about 1,670 pounds milk and 84 pounds fat in the last three years.

One cow from his herd has produced over 1,000 pounds of fat in each of its last few lactations. The herd is kept in a stanchion barn equipped with a barn cleaner and semi-automatic feeding.

Newhouse keeps most of his heifers for herd replacements. Steers are grown to 800 pounds, mainly on forages.

Cropping on his 500-acre farm is guided by conservation.

A graduate of the University of Northern Iowa, Newhouse taught school before farming. He now serves on school planning and study committees and is a member of a Tri-County board of education.

A WWII veteran, Newhouse served in the infantry in Italy where he received the Purple Heart and Cluster.

Newhouse is president and a board member of the Northeast Farm Service Company and has served on the REA board.

He has also been active in Farm Bureau and has served eight years on the county 4-H committee. He has served as chairman of the county DHIA board and is active in the county Holstein Breeders Association.

An enthusiastic sportsman

and former coach, Newhouse actively promotes the county 4-H sports festival. He also golfs and bowls.

Newhouse is a member of the Burr Oak Lutheran Church, has served on the church council and many church committees.

Mr. and Mrs. Newhouse have seven children. Nancy is a school librarian at Madison, Wis.; Craig is in the U.S. Army; Gail is a junior at the University of Northern Iowa; Faith, Jean, Keith, and Bruce are at home.

William H. Stillman
Palo Alto County

William H. Stillman feeds 200 to 300 head of cattle and 400 feeder pigs. He also keeps about 50 ewes.

His cropping program is 320 acres of corn, 320 of soybeans and 30 of alfalfa. He also allots 100 acres of his corn acreage to seed corn production.

The idea behind feeder pigs is to ease the labor situation. Stillman also has a partnership agreement with his full-time employee in another hog setup. The man lives on a separate farm using the facilities for a farrowing and feeding operation. Stillman likes this arrangement. It makes for a better working relationship, plus serving as an excellent bonus plan.

Cattle feeding is completely automated. Stillman buys plain- to good-grade steers weighing about 600 pounds. He feeds hay-lage, corn silage and high-moisture shelled corn.

Active in his community, Stillman serves on the Emmetsburg Board of Ed-

Stillman

ucation and is a member of the school booster club. He is on the board of directors of the Farmers Mutual Insurance Association, a past Farm Service Company board member and an ASCS committeeman.

Stillman is a past president of the Palo Alto County Farm Bureau. He is on the board of directors of National Corn Growers Association and a past member of the Iowa Crop Improvement Association's corn yield test committee. He is also a member of the county Beef and Pork Producers' Associations.

He has served as a 4-H leader and member of the county 4-H club committee and county fair board. He has received the county 4-H alumni award.

Stillman is a member of the St. Thomas Catholic Church at Emmetsburg, Knights of Columbus and has served on various church committees.

The Stillmans have two sons. Jim, 20, is a sophomore at Emmetsburg Community College; and Jeff, 12, is in 6th grade.

Harlan A. Tonderum
Jackson County

Harlan A. Tonderum operates a diversified farm including corn, hogs and feeder cattle.

Of his 775 acres, 500 are in corn. Livestock consists of 500 hogs and 600 feeder cattle.

Tonderum is described as one of the do-it-yourself farmers. He designed and constructed much of the farm's feeding network. Last fall, he installed a corn-drying setup.

He also remodeled an old barn to fit his hog op-

Tonderum

Mr. and Mrs. Donald F. Doolittle

eration. It has automatic grinding and feeding facilities which use the haymow for grain, bulk supplement and prepared ration storage.

Cattle feeding is a combination of an auger bunk system and self feeders. Tonderum designed it for optimum use of present facilities. The two-auger feeding setup will handle 250 cattle at a time.

Choice 500 pound calves make up about 75% of the feeders purchased. Tonderum's records show rate of gain averaging 2.5 to 3.5 pounds per day.

This winter, Tonderum plans to put in cattle scales to improve his record keeping.

Beef rations shift from high silage to high corn during the feeding period.

Tonderum is active in his community as an ASC township committeeman, member of the Federal Land Bank Association at DeWitt, chairman of the Federal Land Bank advisory committee of Omaha, and secretary of the hospital trustee board. He has also served as Jackson County Farm Bureau president and was on the executive board for five years. He is a member of the Jackson County Pork Producers, Beef Producers and the 100-Bushel Corn Club. In 1965, he was in the top 20 in the 200-Bushel Corn Club.

As a member of the Methodist Church, he has served on the official board and is chairman of the building committee.

Mr. and Mrs. Tonderum have two children. Lynn is 14 and Paul is 11.

CHAPTER 5
~
1970 - 1979:
Farming Becomes A Business

Events of the 1960s set up dramatic growth and opportunities in the 1970s, but also spawned uncertainty and inflation.

The United States was engaged in a war in Vietnam that would expand into other parts of Southeast Asia including Laos and Cambodia. Political leaders contended that by defeating communism on foreign shores, we would avoid fighting the communists here at home.

President Lyndon Johnson launched the Great Society program in the mid-1960s. Its goals included:
 * Providing abundance and liberty for all
 * Ending poverty and racial injustice

The money spent on these programs and on the war in Vietnam led to new spending outpacing federal tax revenues. The U.S. government chose to monetize the debt. Oversimplified, that involves increasing the money supply. More money chasing the same amount of goods lets inflation creep in. The value of the currency erodes, allowing the government to pay down the debt with cheaper dollars.

Soviets fuel export boom

By the early 1970s, inflation had gained a strong toe hold. Then our Cold War adversary, the Soviet Union, found buying power to offset their drought-reduced crop yields by selling their gold reserves. The Soviets also changed policies to strive to feed their people better. Soviet buying triggered the grain export boom of the early 1970s. Farmers geared up to plant fence-row to fence-row.

Grain prices began marching higher. Cash corn ran in a $0.95 to $1.40 per bushel range for most of the 1960s. In 1970 widespread northern corn leaf blight, eventually linked to a technological change in good corn production methods, shortened the 1970 crop. In March 1971 corn was selling for $1.10 per bushel. Then a wet 1974 planting season plus an early frost combined with strong demand to boost the monthly average corn price to $3.37 in August 1974. Soybeans, meanwhile, had advanced from $2.85 a bushel in May 1971 to a record $8.99 in August 1973.

Booming exports pushed Iowa net farm incomes higher. Inflation coupled with soaring net farm incomes ratcheted land values higher. Farmers, and others, developed an attitude that "we need to buy today because it will cost more tomorrow." That became a self-fulfilling prophecy. For a time, the inflation rate topped the interest rate, enticing people to borrow to buy.

President Richard Nixon tried a Phase I, Phase II, Phase III approach to slow inflation. President Gerald Ford followed with his Whip Inflation Now effort. Both approaches were to no avail.

In the 1970s, Iowa State University economist Bill Murray strongly cautioned farmers about the hazards of buying overpriced land. Too many farmers ignored that advice.

The October 1973 Yom Kippur War between

Israel, on one side with Egypt and Syria on the other, brought an inflationary oil price shock. World economic growth stagnated under higher world energy prices. But inflation continued, resulting in a period called stagflation.

Bigger, more specialized farms

Structural changes were at work as well. In 1970, Iowa had 145,000 farms with 34,400,000 acres in production. In 1979, the number of farms had dropped to 121,000 with 33,800,000 acres in production. In 2006, Iowa reported 88,600 farms with 31,500,000 acres in production.

High feed costs and reduced demand for red meat squeezed profits for livestock producers leading to herd liquidation. The U.S. cattle herd peaked at 133.7 million head as of July 1, 1976. The cattle inventory skidded to 94.9 million on January 1, 2004. It subsequently recovered to 105.2 million as of July 1, 2006.

No longer did most farms grow grain crops, hay and raise hogs plus beef cattle, milk cows and sometimes both, plus a few chickens. Most diversified farms cut back on the number of livestock enterprises and worked to become more efficient with the remaining enterprises. Broiler and egg production shifted to the southeastern states. Iowa's dominant position in cattle feeding declined as feedlot cattle shifted to large feedlots in the southwest. Farms growing only cash grain became more numerous.

1970 Iowa Farm Facts

FARMS & INCOME

Number of Iowa farms	145,000
Crop production value	$1.1 billion
Livestock production value	$2.9 billion
Iowa net farm income	$1.1 billion

LIVESTOCK

	Inventory	Average price
Cattle and calves	7.5 million head	$28.14/cwt (beef)
Hogs and pigs	16.1 million head	$21.78/cwt
	Production	Inventory
Chickens (Layers)	2.5 billion eggs	11 million birds
Milk	4.7 billion lbs.	

CROPS

	Harvested acres	Yield	Production	Avg price
All Hay	2.5 million	2.77 tons/acre	6.8 million tons	$20/ton
Corn	10.1 million	86 bu./acre	867 million bu.	$1.25/bu.
Soybeans	5.7 million	32.5 bu./acre	185 million bu.	$2.82/bu.
Oats	1.7 million	55 bu./acre	94.1 million bu.	$0.64/bu.
Wheat	40,000	35 bu./acre	1.4 million bu.	$1.25/bu.

1970 IOWA MASTER FARMERS

~
January 24, 1970

Five outstanding Iowa farm operators have been named Master Farmers for 1970. Brief descriptions of their operations and community activities are listed here.

The Master Farmer award program was begun in Iowa in 1926. *Wallaces Farmer* has sponsored the program since its inception.

A select few farmers and their families are honored each year at the award luncheon. The ultimate goal of the program is broader: to call widespread public attention to the high level of management abilities and accomplishments found on farms and to honor these rural leaders for unselfishly devoting part of their valuable time to community leadership roles of all kinds.

Master Farmers are selected by a qualified panel of judges from nominations made by friends, neighbors, and rural leaders. The 1970 selections bring the total to 237 men and one woman who have received the award.

Judges for 1970 were Elvie Dreeszen, president of the Iowa Master Farmer Club; Herbert Hinkhouse, vice president of the Master Farmer Club; Herb Howell, Iowa State University farm management specialist; and Al Bull, editor of *Wallaces Farmer*.

Robert W. Bell
Linn County

Robert W. Bell has a herd of 70 dairy cows and farrows 350 pigs per year on his 460-acre farm.

Records play a big part in decision making. Bell is a member of the Cedar Valley Farm Business Association and uses computerized DHIA records.

Bell

The rolling herd average is 14,682 pounds of milk and 537 pounds of fat. The best cow on the record shows $890 above feed cost for one lactation.

In shooting for higher production, Bell is trying a unique idea of piping water to the feed boxes in the milking parlor to wet the cows' grain mix. This helps them eat faster and gets more energy to high producers.

Bell is president of the Linn-Jones Holstein Association, a director of the district Holstein Association; and has served several terms on the DHIA board and as its president. He is also a member of the Mid-America Dairy Co-op.

A 1943 graduate of Iowa State University, he was a school board member for 13 years and is past president of the Quarterback Club of North Linn High School.

Bell has been a soil district commissioner for 6 years and uses terraces and grass waterways.

He is a past board member and county treasurer of the Farm Bureau, has been a board member of the Carrington-Clyde Experiment Farm Association, and is a 4-H Club leader.

In 1956, he was named Linn County Outstanding Young Farmer and in 1967 received the Provider of Plenty medallion from the Federal Land Bank.

As a member of the Spring Grove United Methodist Church, Bell has served as Sunday school superintendent and chairman of the board of trustees.

The Bells have four children. Mildred is a senior at ISU. Marilyn (Mrs. Phil Hanna) is a sophomore at ISU. Richard is a high school senior at North Linn and Michele Christine, 4, is at home.

Leo Dunn
Marshall County

Leo Dunn operates a 740-acre farm with prime emphasis on corn and cattle.

His 650 acres of corn is planted in 36-inch rows. Part of the crop is dried and the rest is used as high moisture corn to fit his cattle-feeding program.

About 700 steer calves, weighing 450-500 pounds are put on feed in the fall. They are fed to a high choice grade at 1,200 pounds.

An automated auger system highlights the feeding operation. Dunn constructed it himself, using such things as a corncrib converted to shelled corn and an old furnace stoker to meter in supplement.

Dunn is active in his community. He served on the board of education of the Liberty Consolidated School and was

Dunn

one of the original members of the West Marshall School board at State Center.

He is a past township trustee, past director of the Lawn Hill cooperative at New Providence and past president of the Clemons Mutual Telephone Company.

Presently he is a director of the Minerva Valley Telephone Company and the Marshall County Beef Producers. He is also a member of the State Center Lions Club.

In 1967, the Federal Land Bank awarded Dunn one of its Golden Anniversary medallions for his outstanding contributions to American agriculture.

As an active member of the Sacred Heart Catholic Church in St. Anthony, Dunn has served as a trustee.

The Dunns have five children. So far, four have graduated from Iowa State University.

Francis is married and farms with his father. Kenneth is married and is county supervisor for the Farmers Home Administration in Cedar, Jones and Clinton counties. Phyllis teaches home economics in the Fort Dodge school system. Maurice is presently on active duty in the National Guard in Georgia. Karen is a junior at West Marshall High School at State Center.

Jack M. Elliot
Ringgold County

Jack M. Elliot manages a large operation with a strong business approach to farming.

The 1,300-acre farm is operated by Elliott in partnership with father-in-law, O.G. Dixon, who is retired. Of this, 600 acres is in corn and soybeans. He also farrows and finishes 1,600 hogs, feeds 550 head of yearling steers

Elliot

and has 100 beef cows.

Elliott has compiled an enviable hired labor record. His two men have been with him 10 and 21 years. Another retired after 30 years on the farm.

A combination of automatic and bunk feeding is used in the operation. Feed and cattle are weighed to give accurate cost and gain figures.

In his 125 sow herd, farrowing is scheduled to fit available labor. A 10 pig-per-litter average helped Elliott earn the Master Swine Producer's award in 1967.

Elliott is a member of the Mount Ayr Community School Board, has been a 4-H leader for nine years and was a member of the county Extension council. In 1965, the Elliotts hosted an IFYE delegate from India.

Many acres of terraces, contours and pasture improvement helped earn Elliott the Iowa Soil Conservation District Award in 1965.

Elliott is also a member of the Masons, the Order of the Eastern Star and the advisory board of the Rainbow for girls. He is a director of the Mount Ayr Golf and Country club, a member of the Lions Club and is an Iowa State University Cyclone Century Club member. He is also chairman of the Ringgold County Republican Central Committee.

As a member of the Mount Ayr United Methodist Church, he has served on the official board and is on the Pastoral Relations Committee.

The Elliotts have four children. Craig is married and a senior at ISU. Dick is a University of Northern Iowa freshman. Twins Karen and Kirk are in the 8th grade.

Rasmussen

Schuiteman

Harry Rasmussen
Sac County

Harry Rasmussen specializes in dairy and hog farming. Automation and two hired men complete his labor force.

He sells Grade A milk from 55-grade Holstein cows with a herd average of 13,000 pounds milk and 485 pounds fat.

Facilities consist of a dairy parlor with four gate-type stalls built in a U-shape. A milk line runs directly into a bulk tank. Feed grain is stored overhead and metered to the cows through an auger. Automatic equipment helps out with silage and hay feeding. He also has a 64-unit free stall barn.

Rasmussen feeds about 1,200 head of hogs and farms 700 acres of land with 550 acres of row crops.

About 25 sows are farrowed every two months in a combination of confinement and pasture facilities.

Rasmussen was a member of the Crestland community school board for 6 years. He was the first president of the Sac County Handicapped Children's School, organized to aid handicapped children in the county before special education was offered in the public school. This group rented an abandoned country school and hired their own teacher. The Rasmussens' son, Randy, attended this school.

In farm service, he is a past president and board member of the county DHIA, is a past president and board member of the Northwest Farm Business Association and serves on the Sac County Extension council.

He also served on a committee for the 1969 Newell

Centennial and is a member of the Nemaha Boosters Club that sponsors local and charitable activities.

As a member of the Methodist church at Nemaha, he has served on the official board and has been lay leader.

The Rasmussens have four children. The two oldest are Randy, 25, and Diane, 23, who teaches second grade at Rockford, Ill. Ann, 12, and Kathleen, 10, are at home.

Art J. Schuiteman
Sioux County

Art J. Schuiteman farms 460 acres specializing in a 2,500-head hog operation. He takes advantage of remodeled buildings and labor saving equipment to trim costs.

About 55 sows are farrowed every eight weeks in a converted chicken house and a remodeled dairy barn. Finishing facilities consist of two remodeled dairy barns with sloping floors and gutters. Bulk trucks from a local elevator deliver feed to these units, saving farm labor.

Cattle are another big part of the operation. Schuiteman feeds 350 head now, with plans to go to 600 head next year. Cattle are fed from a silo with grain bins built next to it. A 150-foot precast concrete bunk with a trolley type conveyor for feeding is another labor saver.

Till planting has become the exclusive way of planting corn on the Schuiteman farm. He figures the reduced tillage helps conserve moisture in his "dry" part of the state.

Schuiteman is another Master Farmer who takes a strong business approach to farming. He is a member of the Northwest Iowa Farm Business Association. He is also a soil conservation district cooperator, a Co-op member and is active in Sioux Center community affairs.

As a Farm Bureau member, he has served on the local board.

With a keen interest in youth, Schuiteman has been a 4-H leader for five years, has been active in county fair work, and gives much assistance to the Future Farmers of America in his community.

Schuiteman is a member of the First Reformed Church of Sioux Center where he serves on the consistory as a deacon.

Mr. and Mrs. Schuiteman have eight children. They are: Jan Philip and Leon, students at Iowa State University; Mark, a junior; Kirk, in 5th grade; Kim, in fourth grade; and Kay, in third grade, all at Sioux Center Community School. Kyle, 4, and Shonna, 1, are at home.

Seed ad from 1970 Master Farmer award issue

164

1971
IOWA MASTER FARMERS
~
March 13, 1971

These outstanding farmers have been named Iowa Master Farmers for 1971.

Harvey C. Bolte
Mills County

Harvey Bolte has built an excellent pure-bred hog business by banking on reputation. Success can be measured by repeat customers. Some are third generation customers.

Bolte is described as starting from nothing during the depression and building an outstanding farming operation.

Along with the 500 head of pure-bred Chester White hogs he farrows, Bolte keeps a 70-cow beef herd. He owns 400 acres with 270 acres in row crops. Last year he sold 176 boars.

"Selection is the biggest key to success in the hog business," says Bolte. "If there is any doubt about a hog, I scratch him."

A leader in conservation, Bolte has over 16 miles of terraces on his farm.

He won the Iowa Soil Conservation district award in 1965.

He is a conservation district cooperator, has served on the ASCS township committee and is a township trustee.

Each year, he gives a pig to a 4-H'er for a project. He has also been county fair swine superintendent for 10 years and has been recognized as an outstanding 4-H leader, serving 10 years as a leader.

Bolte has also served as chairman of the Glenwood Community School reorganization committee and has been a township representative on the Extension council.

As an active member of the Silver City United Methodist Church, Bolte is a member of the church board and recently worked to get a new parsonage built. The Boltes also sponsor a young marriage group of the church.

The Boltes have one daughter. Waunita is married to Dwayne Reinert,

Donald Hood (next page)

165

a purebred Hampshire breeder who farms near Silver City. They have four children.

The Boltes also helped raise his brother, Richard L. Bolte. He is county supervisor for the Farmers Home Administration in Bremer, Black Hawk and Butler counties.

Donald Hood
Humboldt County

Donald Hood ranks high in livestock production. He feeds out 300 head of cattle and markets 800-1,000 head of hogs per year.

Bolte

The 260-acre farm he lives on is rented on crop and livestock shares. Another 70 acres is rented on crop shares.

All pigs are farrowed on the farm and finished in an open front building he designed. Recently, 20 sows farrowed an average 14 pigs per litter, saving 12 pigs per litter. Hood earned the Master Swine Producer title several years ago.

Cattle are grown on a high silage ration and finished on self feeders.

"I've been real happy with self feeders," says Hood. "They save labor and packers like the cattle."

Community activities rank high with Hood. He has served as township political committeeman, was county treasurer of the Republican Central Committee and helped raise funds for the Humboldt County Memorial Hospital.

In farm organizations, Hood is on the Farm Service Advisory board, is a past ASCS committeeman, served as a soil commissioner for 7 years—four years as chairman—and is on the FHA county board. He has also been on the county Farm Bureau board, serves on the Farm Bureau national policy committee, and has represented the Farm Bureau in Washington, D.C.

Hood

Hood is vice chairman of his county Swine Producers Association and a board member of the Central Iowa Farm Business Association. He was chosen as Humboldt County's Outstanding Young Farmer several years ago.

He is also a member and secretary of the Odd Fellows Lodge.

The Hood family is active in the Rutland United Methodist Church. Don serves as a lay leader, a Sunday school teacher, is on the administrative board, does lay speaking, and is a member of the district council. He and his wife have been delegates to the National Family Life Conference.

The Hoods have three children: Kenneth, a junior; Linda, a freshman; and Elaine, in sixth grade, all at Twin Rivers of Bode schools.

Edward Ladd
Lyon County

Edward Ladd feeds 200 head of cattle, has a 126-cow beef herd and raises 350 head of hogs per year. He also owns 480 acres and rents another 160 acres.

"Beef cows best fit the hilly land I have," says Ladd. Most of his pasture land has been renovated. And these pastures are arranged around a corral and working area so he can give the animals first class care. He feels quick identification and ease of handling are essential.

As a member of the northwest Iowa Farm Business Association, records help Ladd keep an eye on costs. He trims his machinery budget by sharing some equipment with a neighbor. That explains his low machinery cost of $20.46 per rotated acre.

Minimum tillage is important on his farm in a dry part of Iowa. He also has at least 4 miles of parallel terraces.

Ladd serves his community as a member of the newly organized county zoning board, on the township election board and is active in his political party.

He is a past master of the Masons and past worthy patron of the Order of Eastern Star. He is also a member of the VFW.

In farm organizations, Ladd served 12 years as a soil conservation district commissioner and was named Outstanding Commissioner in 1966. He is a director of the Farmers Co-op Elevator and is vice president of a newly formed rural water system.

Ladd

Ladd is also a farm member of the advisory council for Rock Rapids, a member of the Farm Bureau, an ASCS township committeeman and has served on the Extension council. He also worked seven years as a 4-H leader.

He is secretary of the Lyon County Livestock Feeders Association, a member of the Swine Producers Association and a member of the Iowa Beef Improvement Association.

The Ladds are members of the United Church of Christ—Congregationalist, where he serves on various boards, and on the newly formed parish council.

They have two children. Robert is a junior at Iowa State University, and Barbara is a senior at Rock Rapids High School.

Ken Showalter
Franklin County

Ken Showalter is an all-around livestock man and community leader. He markets 600 to 800 head of hogs a year, feeds 80 head of cattle and has a herd of 80 Holstein dairy cows.

He and his brother, Charles, share some machinery and labor in crop production. Showalter farms about 600 acres.

"This year, I also hope to save labor and machinery cost by not plowing where soybeans were grown last year," reports Showalter.

Cattle feeding consists of feeding out Holstein steers. "The past few years, I've made more money feeding these than I used to when I fed beef breeds," he explains.

Records play a big part in this operation with 50 of his cows on DHIA test. Milk average is about 13,000 pounds per cow and butter fat average is about 500 pounds. Showalter uses AI on his dairy herd.

He is also a member of the Central Iowa Farm Business Association, where he has served as a director.

In school work, Showalter served on the reorganization committee and on promotion of a new high school building. He is a member of the Tri-County Board of Education.

He is also president of the Hampton Federal Land Bank Association, was president of the Hampton Farmers Co-op board and has been a county DHIA officer.

Showalter was Franklin County fair secretary for 15 years, has been on the county FHA committee, and served three years on the county estate appraisal committee.

He is also a Farm Bureau member, has served as township CROP drive chairman, and has been honored for 15 years of leadership in county 4-H work.

The Showalters are active in the Hampton Trinity Lutheran Church. Ken is a member of the planning board and has served as a trustee.

Showalter

The Showalters have four children: Mary (Mrs. Lyn DeSotel) of Hampton, is a graduate of UNI as a Spanish major and is now teaching; John is a sophomore at Iowa State University; Christine is in seventh grade; and James is in third grade in the Hampton Community School.

IOWA MASTER FARMERS

~
March 11, 1972

Five outstanding Iowa farmers have been named Master Farmers for 1972. Brief descriptions of their operations and community activities are listed here.

An awards luncheon was held at the Fort Des Moines Hotel in Des Moines, March 9, to honor these men.

The Master Farmer award program was begun in Iowa in 1926. *Wallaces Farmer* has sponsored the program since its inception.

A select few farmers and their families are honored each year at the award luncheon. The ultimate goal of the program is broader: To call widespread public attention to the high level of management abilities and accomplishments found on farms, and to honor these rural leaders for unselfishly devoting part of their valuable time to community leadership roles of all kinds.

Master Farmers are selected by a qualified panel of judges from nominations made by friends, neighbors and rural leaders. The 1972 selections bring the total to 246 men and one woman who have received the award.

Judges for 1972 were Roy Olson, president of the Iowa Master Farmer Club; Leon Haahr, vice president of the Master Farmer Club; Herb Howell and Everett Stoneberg, Iowa State University farm management specialists; and Al Bull, editor of *Wallaces Farmer*.

Marlowe Feldman
Buena Vista County

Marlowe Feldman is described by neighbors as an innovator, trying new ideas even with the risk of slightly lower yields if he can save soil. He farms 480 acres, farrows and

Feldman

finishes 100 litters of pigs and feeds out 250 head of calves.

"It really bothers me to see soil blow and water run," is a typical Feldman comment. He's trying minimum tillage with a till planter. "Yields are cut when the herbicide doesn't work," he explains. "And you're more vulnerable to weeds when you don't work the seedbed as much. But we have to try new techniques to keep the soil. John Q. Public demands it."

Shop work is one of Feldman's cost cutters. He has built several pieces of machinery and a bunk feeder-mixer truck from scrap parts.

As a member of the Northwest Iowa Farm Business Association, Feldman has served two years on the board and one year as president. "A good set of records with year-end analysis is the best farming tool I have," he adds.

Active in his community, this leader has

served as an ASCS township committeeman, a soil conservation district cooperator, and on the county Extension council. He has won the *Sioux City Journal's* Soil Conservation Award and the county Outstanding Young Farmer Award.

He is also secretary of the Farmers Co-op Elevator board and a director of the county REC. He has been secretary and county president of Farm Bureau and serves as a voting delegate.

Feldman is precinct committeeman and a member of his political party's central committee. He has represented Farm Bureau and the REC at the legislature in Des Moines and Congress in Washington.

The Feldmans are active in Our Saviour's Lutheran Church at Albert City. Feldman teaches Sunday school, is chairman of the church council and sings in the choir.

The Feldmans have two children: Kirk, 12; and Jayne, 8.

Delbert L. Grafft
Jones County

Delbert L. Grafft is noted as a top livestock man. He has a 160-head ewe flock, and feeds out 10,000 head of lambs and 350 head of cattle. He owns and operates 575 acres.

Conducting on-farm tests with feed companies has helped him move to high grain sheep rations. This saves time, makes a carcass that "the packet loves," and puts gains on faster.

Grafft likes the sheep and beef feeding combination. "It lets us start harvesting corn early in the fall as silage, then move on to high-moisture corn harvest. By that time, the rest of the corn is ready to shell and dry. And we end up with the right kind of feed supply for our livestock program."

In community service, Grafft has served as

Grafft

president of the Olin PTA; seven years on the Olin Board of Education, four as president; and has been on the Jones County Board of Education the past four years.

He is on the Jones County conference board, is vice chairman of the Maquoketa Valley REC board and serves on the Linn-Jones FS board. Grafft is also a soil conservation district cooperator.

Record keeping is through the Cedar Valley Farm Business Association where he is a director.

Active in Farm Bureau, Grafft has served on county livestock and sheep legislative committees.

In service clubs, Grafft is a director of the Anamosa Rotary Club, is past chancellor of the Anamosa KP Lodge and has served on the Jones County OEO advisory committee.

Grafft is a 1965 Master Lamb Producer and recently received the Ford Foundation award for excellency in sheep production.

The Graffts support the Antioch Community Church and the Olin United Methodist Church.

The Graffts have three children. Tani (Mrs. Ned Strain) of Wilmette, Ill., has a masters degree in psychology. Gayle (Mrs. Gary Catlette) is a farm wife at Center Junction, Iowa. La Mar is a junior in animal science at Iowa State University.

Garland C. Hanson
Webster County

Garland C. Hanson goes crops all the way in his farming operation. He is also a leader in community service.

Hanson owns 240 acres and rents another 520. Last year, he grew 425 acres of corn and 247 acres of soybeans.

Records tell Hanson a lot about his operation. He has even fed records through a computer analysis as a double check. He belongs to the Central Iowa Farm Business Association.

"I'm really sold on timeliness," he explains. "My records show that bigger equipment is saving me costly trips over the field."

Like many farmers, Hanson has a head bookkeeper—his wife. He explains that this saves time for him and keeps his wife up to date on the farm business.

Strong in community activities, Hanson has served on the Prairie Community School board for the last eight years.

Hanson is also past president of the Central Iowa Farm Business Association and a director of the Iowa Farm Business Association. He is chairman of the Webster County Soybean Association and was a state delegate to the American Soybean Association meeting.

He has served as crop project leader for 4-H, has worked with the county Farm Bureau, has served as chairman of a community fund drive and is on the county drainage committee.

Hanson also served as director of the Farnhamville Co-op Elevator and a member of the Webster County Extension council.

In 1968, Hanson was part of a people-to-people tour to South America. He also finds time for golfing and bowling.

The Hansons are active in Our Saviour's Lutheran Church at Callender. Hanson has served on the building committee for a new church, has been on the church council, and the Hansons have served as advisors to a young people's group.

Hanson

Livingston

The Hansons have three boys. David farms and attends community college at Fort Dodge. Daniel is a sophomore, and James is in eighth grade at Prairie Community school.

John R. Livingston
Taylor County

John R. Livingston sees good pasture production and beef cows going hand in hand to make southern Iowa farms profitable. He has 870 acres with 400 in pasture and another 100 ready for renovation.

This farm handles 200 beef cows and a 500-head hog operation.

In renovating pastures, Livingston clears the brush, then plants to corn for a year or two to get it ready for seeding. This way, the corn crop pays the renovation bill.

An old 20 x 50-foot cattle shed serves as his hog-finishing unit. It is completely enclosed and has a deep-gutter liquid manure system that uses sloping floors as a cleaning tool. Total cost was $1,700. It houses 250 head at a time.

Improved breeding and pasture improvement have helped Livingston move up to a $50-per-cow return on his beef herd, not including labor and cow investment. Labor is less than five hours per cow. He plans to expand to a 300-cow herd.

Active in service work, Livingston is a township trustee, helped organize and was a director of the Southwest Iowa Farm Business Association and is on the ASCS township committee.

He has also served on the county FHA committee, is chairman of the Co-op Elevator board, and is a Farm Bureau director serving on the commodity and marketing committees.

Livingston is a member of the Iowa Beef Producers Association and has served on Vo-Ag and Extension committees.

The Livingstons are members of the Bedford United Methodist Church. John serves as chairman of the pastor-parish relations committee and is on the official board. He has taught Sunday school and has worked with the youth group. The Livingstons also help supervise at a new youth center in Bedford.

Mr. and Mrs. Livingston have three children. Diana is taking accounting in Omaha, Nebraska. Rena is a junior and Marilyn is in eighth grade at Bedford Community School.

Wesley J. Shafer
Jefferson County

Wesley J. Shafer puts his farming talents to work in a large hog operation. He farrows and finishes 1,100 head of hogs a year in low-cost facilities. He also farms 310 acres, feeds 25 head of cattle and has a 40-cow beef herd.

This cost-trimming, farrowing setup consists of a pull-together house with seven stalls. Sows stay in the stalls only three days, then go to buildings in groups of five or six sows. Average litter size is 10.5 pigs with an average 9.5 marketed.

Here may be the key to big litters: "We equalize litter size—both in number and in physical size," explains Shafer. "Sometimes a sow will end up with all the smaller pigs from five or six litters and none of her own. This cuts down on the number of runts and increases the number of pigs saved."

The local draft board still has a hold on Shafer. He serves as its chairman. He has also been a township committeeman for 20 years.

Shafer served on a citizens committee for

Shafer

better schools that was aimed at helping pass a bond issue for a new school. He was treasurer.

In farm groups, Shafer has worked on public relations and membership committees for Farm Bureau, is a member of the supply co-op, the REC and is a soil conservation district cooperator and has won awards for conservation work.

He is also on his political party's central committee and was co-chairman of "Farmers for Schwengel" during the last election.

Record keeping is through the Mississippi Valley Farm Business Association where Shafer serves as a director.

The Shafers are active in the Lutheran church where Shafer teaches an adult Sunday school class and has served on the church council.

The Shafers have two daughters. Sarah Beth, 16, is a sophomore at Fairfield Community High School. Melissa Ann, 14, is an eighth grader at Fairfield Community Junior High.

Dr. E.P. "Dutch" Sylwester
Master Farmer Exceptional
Service Award

Dr. E.P. "Dutch" Sylwester, Iowa's well-known weed and herbicide specialist, has been selected to receive the Master Farmer Exceptional Service Award.

Wallaces Farmer has presented Master Farmer awards to outstanding Iowa farmers since 1926. But Dr. Sylwester is only the third person to be honored for exceptional service to the state's farmers.

The first such award went to Larry Cain, manager of the Cerro Gordo County farm in 1959. The second was presented to Dr. C. R. Weber, an Iowa State University agronomist and breeder of Amsoy and Hark soybean varieties in 1967.

Widely known as "Dutch,'" Dr. Sylwester was born and raised on a farm near Gaylord, Minn. He earned his degree from St. Olaf College in Minnesota and his advanced degrees from Iowa State College. He came to Iowa State in 1930 and has been in charge of Extension weed control work in Iowa since 1935. That's long enough to earn him the title of "Iowa's chief weed puller."

In his years of service, "Dutch" has conducted countless weed identification and control meetings. In these presentations, he explains the seriousness of weed problems; profits lost because of weeds; and effective, economical, safe, and easier methods of control.

He is a strong advocate of both chemical and cultural methods of weed control. "Use one to supplement the other," is his familiar statement.

Known and respected by thousands of Iowa farmers, his crusade against weeds and brush has been a major contribution in reducing crop losses.

It's impossible to put a dollar value on the effect he has had on farm profits during his more than 36 years of service. But farmers have seen the benefits in fewer weeds and high yields.

Dr. Sylwester was chairman of the Extension committee of the North Central Weed Control Conference from 1944 to 1950, then served as president of the North Central Weed Control Conference in 1950. In 1952-53, he was national chairman of the Association of Regional Weed Control Conferences, the forerunner of today's Weed Society of America. He was named honorary member of the North Central Weed Control Conference in 1964 and the Weed Science Society of America in 1969.

Among his long list of awards is the Superior Service Award from the United States Department of Agriculture, citing Dr. Sylwester for meritorious service in fostering educational and action campaigns for the control of noxious weeds. He also received the Epsilon Sigma Phi award for Outstanding Extension Work in Iowa, and a Distinguished Service to Agriculture Award from the Iowa Grain Dealers Association.

Sylwester

IOWA MASTER FARMERS
~
March 10, 1973

Six top Iowa farmers were named Master Farmers for 1973 at an awards luncheon at the Holiday Inn in Des Moines, March 8.

Judges were Leon Haahr, president of the Master Farmer Club; Walter Hagen, vice president of the Master Farmer Club; Herb Howell and Everett Stoneberg, Iowa State University farm management specialists; and Al Bull, editor of *Wallaces Farmer*.

George H. Busch
Butler County

George H. Busch farms about 600 acres in partnership with a son. He also has a 150-cow beef herd, feeds out about 75 head of cattle and produces 800 to 900 head of hogs.

Busch emphasizes performance testing in his beef operation. "We buy performance tested bulls that weigh at least 1,000 lb. at 365 days," he says. "Yearling weight is highly hereditary and we feel we can get much heavier calves by using such a bull."

As well as managing a purebred Angus herd, Busch also has a planned crossbreeding program.

"Crossbreeding is kind of a shortcut to bigger calves," he says. "You can get better calves without crossbreeding, but it takes quite a bit longer. "We bought some half Holstein, half Hereford heifers and crossed them with a production tested Angus bull," he explains. "And we got some real good calves."

The Busch farm was the second farm in Butler County to practice contour farming many years ago and his conservation practices have constantly improved. Now he has about 14, 710 feet of grass backsloped terraces on the farm and has 46,467 feet of tile.

Busch keeps records with the Butler County Farm Bureau. His community service includes being a member of the Allison-Bristow School board. He is a district soil commissioner and has been a member of farm service board and FHA board. Active in Farm Bureau, Busch has served as Butler County secretary-treasurer.

A strong believer in youth, Busch has served as 4-H leader and on 4-H and youth county committees. He joined a people-to-people tour to South America in 1968.

The Busches are members of

Buddy Jorgenson plays checkers with daughter Judi

Trinity Reform Church at Allison where George has served as Sunday school teacher, member of the church board, and is currently on the church's planning and development committee.

Mr. and Mrs. Busch have four children: Wayne is a research scientist for Swift & Company; Lois Stauffer lives near Charles City; Wendell works for the Chamberlain Corp. at Waterloo as a safety engineer; and Maurice farms with his father.

Busch

Glenn H. Freese
Crawford County

Glenn H. Freese farms 400 acres and has a 38-cow grade-A Holstein dairy herd.

He uses his DHIA records to come up with a strict culling program. Here are some of his guidelines:

•A cow should return about $1 above her feed cost for every pound of butterfat she produces.

•If she's a first calf heifer, she will be producing about 70% of what she will produce in her second or third lactation. If that's not up to par, she goes.

•He also compares the difference in production between each cow and her herd mates in deciding whether to cull.

This has added up to about 15% of the cows culled per year. This resulted in a 14,672-pound milk and 543-pound butterfat average in December. That's about 2,600 pounds milk and 89 pounds fat above the state average of Holstein cows on test.

Freese is also active in his community. He is chairman of the Crawford County soil conservation district and an FHA committeeman. He is president of the Carroll County DHIA cooperative delegate to Mid-America Milk Cooperative's annual meeting, a member of the Midwest Breeders cooperative and a member of the Iowa Holstein Breeders Association.

Freese

As a Farm Bureau member, he has been chairman of the farm record committee, chairman of environmental resources committee, chairman of the public relations committee and has served on the resolutions committee. He has also been a township director, secretary of the board of directors and chairman of the dairy section on livestock.

Freese is also a member of the county Pork Producers Association, a member of the community club at Vail, and serves as dairy superintendent at the Crawford County fair.

Mr. and Mrs. Freese have five children: Kevin is married and a student at Western Iowa Tech at Sioux City; Beth is a secretary in Carroll; Kary is a freshman; Barbara is in third grade; and Kurt is in first grade at Ar-We-Va schools.

Frank A. Hasenclever
Lee County

Frank A. Hasenclever was a dairyman who switched to beef cows. He looked at feeder cattle prices last fall and started considering expanding his 30-cow beef herd to 100 head.

"We had the silos from when we used to milk," he explains. "So we decided to feed alfalfa and grass silage and then refill the silos with corn silage for the cow herd.

"This way, the cows are going to come to me at least once a day so I can see them," adds Hasenclever. "That will save some labor."

Frank started farming in partnership with his father and now farms with his brother, Bob. They also operate about 600 acres together and feed about 850 head of hogs in confinement.

"We tried to buy Western cows from the Sandhills," explains Frank. "We looked for a good stretchy cow that could take the weather. And since we were buying heifers, we looked for a bigger cow that was bred to a smaller breed bull."

Hasenclever

On their timberland soil, the Hasenclevers are giving chisel plowing a try this year. Their corn averages about 120 bushels per acre and soybeans average about 40 bushels per acre.

In his community, Frank has worked on a school bond issue study. He has been an ASCS township committeeman, is a township trustee, a Farm Service member and an REA member. While dairying, he served on several dairy boards and co-ops.

Hasenclever is past president and a voting delegate for Lee County Farm Bureau. He has also served as a 4-H leader.

The Hasenclevers are members of the Denmark Congregational United Church of Christ. Frank has been a trustee in the church and has served as chairman of God's Portion Day. He and his wife have served as youth leaders.

The Hasenclevers have four children: Sandra is a teacher; Debra is a sophomore at Iowa State University; Randy is a junior at Fort Madison; and Elaine is in eighth grade.

Buddy E. Jorgenson
Fremont County

Buddy E. Jorgenson farms about 800 acres, produces about 1,200 head of hogs per year, and feeds out about 200 head of cattle. He employs one full-time hired man.

Strong emphasis is put on marketing livestock in this operation.

"We're using a closer-to-home market than we used to," reports Jorgenson. "They're paying a good price for top-quality hogs because they keep a record of how each one dresses out. Recently, they paid 25 cents more than their advertised top.

"Most packers still aren't paying enough premium for top-quality hogs," believes Jorgenson. "They're still buying too much on weight alone."

For hog production, he makes use of older buildings that have been remodeled with farrowing stalls. Litter size averages about nine pigs at weaning.

Jorgenson keeps records through the Southwest Iowa Farm Business Association. "These records encourage you to keep your books up," he says. "And it helps tell you if it's the right time to buy new equipment. It's also a great help in getting your taxes prefigured before the end of the year."

A number of terraces have been built on the farm. Jorgenson finds they help control drainage water from washing over his low land.

In his community, Jorgenson has served on the school board and is secretary-treasurer of the Fremont County Cattlemen's Association that is just getting started.

He is an SCS cooperator, trustee and secretary of the Walnut Creek drainage district, a township ASCS committeeman and served on the fair board for a number of years.

He is a Farm Bureau member and has been on the board. And he is a member of the legion post.

The Jorgensons are members of St. Mary's Catholic Church in Shenandoah. Buddy serves on the finance committee.

Mr. and Mrs. Jorgenson have three children: Jerry teaches Vo-Ag at Williamsburg; Christel is an apprentice architect in Switzerland; and Juli is in third grade.

Edward Klodt
Wapello County

Edward Klodt feeds "pickled" milk to his dairy replacement calves, and they are thriving on it. He has a 60-cow Holstein herd.

Pickled milk is simply the colostrum milk the first few days after calving. He puts it in plastic garbage cans and keeps it in the barn where the temperature is about 45 degrees. The garbage can lid is the cap and it keeps for about six weeks while he's feeding it.

Another unique feature is a feeding setup consisting of three silos. One contains high moisture corn, one an alfalfa grass mixture and the other corn silage. When the feed reaches the bunk, it is completely mixed and supplemented. Klodt says it takes only about 20 minutes a day to feed with this system.

The total operation consists of about 450 acres and 900 head of hogs in a father-son partnership. They use Farm Business Association and Dairy Herd Improvement Association records.

Their dairy herd averages 13,700 pounds milk and 520 pounds butterfat.

In community service, Klodt worked on the Walsh Catholic School committee for building a new high school and he provides school tours on his farm. Other past and present activities are: county Extension council, ASCS member, Wapello County dairy board of directors, Wapello County water association member, soil conservation district commissioner and regional director, Des Moines Milk Marketing Co-op member, DHIA board member, and Livestock Producers Association member.

He has also been a Wapello County 4-H leader. As a Farm Bureau member, he has served on the board and environmental committee. He cooperates with the agricultural committee of the Ottumwa Chamber of Commerce.

The Klodts are members of St. Mary's Catholic Church where Edward has served as chairman of the finance committee and is a member of the parish council.

Mr. and Mrs. Klodt have five children and one foster child: William farms with his father; Leo is a veterinarian at Perry; Richard is a farmer and elevator operator; Gerald is a college student; Johan Nelson teaches in Iowa City; and Shirley Donahue works at the First National Bank in Ottumwa.

Jorgenson

Klodt

Courtney Siglin
Wayne County

Courtney Siglin puts action into his belief in saving the soil. He recently cleared about 30 acres of rough bottomland that was "practically worthless." It's good corn-producing ground now.

"It was really rough land," he says. "Covered with big trees and brush. I don't think the 30 acres would have supported more than a few cows."

Siglin figures clearing the land has increased its value about six times. He's had it in corn the past few years and is getting "real good corn," he says.

Siglin farms about 750 acres and keeps his farm records through a computerized system at his bank.

Siglin also produces about 500 head of hogs per year, feeds out 400 head of cattle, and has a 60-cow beef herd.

At present, he's feeding cattle in open lots, but says he's going to build a shed this year and maybe go to total confinement to get the cattle out of the mud.

"I sold some recently and got severely docked because of the mud," he says. "We are going to see more confinement units if cattle prices stay up around $40 per cwt., because you can afford it."

In his community, Siglin has served as the PTA representative on the school board and has served in the band parents program.

He is a past member of the county Extension council, is vice president of the fair board and beef superintendent of the Wayne County fair.

In county farm organizations, he is a Farm Bureau member and has been chairman of the commodity and marketing board. He is president of the Pork Producers Association and a member of the Beef Improvement Association.

Other activities include being a member of the Lions Club and a member of the Wayne County model county program.

The Siglins are members of the Corydon Methodist Church where Courtney serves as an usher and worship assistant.

Mr. and Mrs. Siglin have one child. Sandra is in high school.

Siglin

1974

IOWA MASTER FARMERS

~

March 9, 1974

DeVere Steffensen

Six Iowa farmers were named Master Farmers for 1974 at an awards luncheon at the Holiday Inn in Des Moines March 7. Brief descriptions of their operations and community activities are listed here.

The Master Farmer program was begun in Iowa in 1926. *Wallaces Farmer* sponsors the program.

The awards are aimed at calling attention to the high level of management these men demonstrate and to honor them for unselfishly devoting part of their time to community leadership roles. The 1974 selections bring the total to 258 men and one woman who have received the award since 1926.

Judges were Walter Hagen, president of the Master Farmer Club; Everett Stoneberg, Iowa State University farm management specialist; and Al Bull, editor of *Wallaces Farmer*.

David Flint
Keokuk County

David Flint farms 575 acres in Keokuk County. He produces 600 head of hogs, feeds 90 head of cattle and has a 40-cow beef herd.

Flint is conservation minded and has done a lot of work with minimum tillage and terracing on his farm. "One of the best things a man can do in this world is to leave his land in better condition than when he found it," he reasons.

Last year, he planted beans in stalk ground after chisel plowing. "It was late and the stalk had rotted so I thought I'd give it a try. We had some problems with the trash, but it wasn't too bad."

Most of Flint's farm is drained by tile outlet terraces. Cost runs somewhere around $100 per acre. "But these costs can be cut by making the back side of the terrace steeper and seeding it down," he says. "This means there's less dirt to haul in."

Flint

Jensen

Juelsgaard

Flint has helped organize a farmer-backed machinery dealership to provide parts, service, and new equipment for an area where the established dealer went out of business.

In community-farm activities, Flint has served as a county soil conservation district commissioner or assistant for five years and is vice chairman of the local soil conservation committee. He is a township Farm Bureau director and has served four years on the county legislative committee. He has been a member of the township ASCS committee.

In other community work, Flint has served as a member of the local school board for eight years, president for three. He also worked 10 years for school reorganization. Flint was also on the parade committee for the What Cheer centennial and worked on a fund drive to build a county hospital. He has been a crop reporter for more than 30 years.

The Flints are members of Gibson Presbyterian Church at Gibson where David was an active church elder for six years, has taught Sunday school more than 10 years and has served as a trustee.

The Flints have three children: Barry is a graduate of William Penn College and farms with his father; Rhonda is a student at Buena Vista College; and Shelby is in seventh grade at Tri-County Community Schools.

Roland Jensen
Ida County

Roland Jensen farms 320 acres in Ida County. He produces 200 head of hogs and feeds 600 head of cattle.

As a pioneer in minimum tillage, Jensen has used a till planter for the past six years and was one of the first in the area to use bench-type terraces.

He chops stalks, fertilizes, then

goes right in with a till planter. "You have to use a herbicide with this system," he points out. "But I'm getting along just fine by banding herbicides in the row at slightly less than the recommended rate."

Jensen's cattle-feeding facilities include two bunker silos, sunshades, mounds, and shelters. The silos are used for corn silage and cracked-shelled corn.

"A scale is probably the most important piece of equipment I have," says Jensen. "I use it to yield check each corn and soybean variety, and to see what effect varying plant populations and different fertilizer rates has on yields. Most value, though, is in weighing livestock."

Jensen is a member of the Farm Bureau public relations committee, the Pork Producers Association, the Cattlemen's Association, the Ida County Agricultural Council, and the Ida County 4-H committee. He has been a 4-H leader for five years.

Along with other community activities, Jensen is on the township ASCS committee and township election board, is president of the Ida County REC and was a vice president of a corporation formed to build the Horn Memorial Hospital.

The Jensens are members of St. Paul Lutheran Church at Ida Grove where Roland has served as an elder, Sunday school teacher and Sunday school secretary and superintendent.

The Jensens have three children: Rodney attended Iowa State University and works in Ames; Marilyn (Mrs. Terry) Lovett is a nurse at Horn Memorial Hospital in Ida Grove; and Richard is a student at Iowa State University in veterinary medicine.

Glen Juelsgaard
Audubon County

Glen Juelsgaard farms 840 acres in Audubon County. He produces about 1,500 head of hogs and feeds out about 600 head of cattle per year. Crops are about 300 acres of beans and 500 acres of corn. All crops are grown in 30-inch rows, half of which are planted by no-till method. All are harvested by combine.

The Juelsgaards mix some of yesterday with the modern. They keep a family milk cow and a small flock of laying hens. There are five riding horses for the family pleasure.

As with all large farming, good hired help is a requirement and Juelsgaard feels fortunate to have a young couple in his employ— both are college graduates. Glen remarked, "I'd like to see hired help get involved in the community because it makes them feel they are part of it."

Among his farm activities, Glen is a member of his county and state Cattlemen's Association, the Audubon County Pork Producers and Farmers Union.

He's also a boys' 4-H leader and was instrumental in getting a scholarship program initiated in the local FFA chapter in 1966. Glen helped start this program for the first two years through donating the crop of corn from a 5-acre plot on his farm. This program is being continued and awards a scholarship to the outstanding FFA member graduate each year.

He is the FFA honorary chapter farmer, has been awarded the Iowa Soil Conservation achievement award and Certificate of Merit award for soil conservation, and cooperates with Extension and SCS in encouraging conservation tillage.

He is president of Multi Pig, Inc., which was recently formed by a group of farmers in Audubon County and involves a 920-sow confinement-farrowing unit to be built this summer.

The Juelsgaards are members of St. Patrick's Catholic Church in Audubon, where Glen serves as a member of the parish council.

Mr. and Mrs. Juelsgaard have 10 children: Steven is a veterinarian; Barbara is a medical technologist in Ames; Nancy is a nurse in Ames; Eleanor and Mary attend Iowa State University; Ann, 17; Cathy, 16; John, 14; David, 12; and JoEllen, 9, attend Audubon Community School.

Marshall King
Boone County

Marshall King farms 1,040 acres in Boone County in partnership with his son. He feeds 700 head of hogs and 1,200 head of cattle.

"I use a scale to keep close tabs on shrink on both incoming and outgoing cattle," says King. "We've purchased nearly all our cattle directly from the same South Dakota ranches for the last 12 years. We send gain and carcass data back to the producers."

King

King markets cattle every two weeks to help average out prices.

In farm activities, King has been a longtime 4-H leader. He is a member of the Boone County fair board and is 4-H beef superintendent. He has served as a Farm Bureau board member, is a director of the Boone County Cattlemen's Association, is a member of the Pork Producers Association and is an SCS cooperator.

King is a member and director of the Central Iowa Farm Business Association and has served as treasurer in the Iowa Association.

He is a member of the Booster Club and serves as a board member for the United Mutual Insurance Company. He is active in the Masonic Lodge, DeMolay and Lions Club.

The Kings are members of the United Methodist Church in Boone, where he is an officer in the Methodist men's group, is a past lay leader, serves as a lay speaker and is chairman of the worship commission. King is also chairman of the Inter-Church Council of Laymen of the Boone area and the Kings have sponsored MYF groups.

Through his church, King has been especially active in the Heifer Project International that raises livestock to be sent to other countries to help them develop livestock programs. He's now raising two buffalo calves as a church project. He also spent a week last year working with Indians on a reservation in Oklahoma.

The Kings have five children: Randy is married and a banker at Minburn; Nancy works at the Iowa Highway Commission; Jon farms with his dad; Lori is a junior, and Kathy is in seventh grade at Boone Community School.

DeVere Steffensen
Winnebago County

DeVere Steffensen farms 240 acres in Winnebago County. He feeds out 500 head of cattle per year.

"A number of years ago, I wasn't making enough money feeding cattle," says Steffensen. "So I started keeping records."

Steffensen

As a result, he became a pioneer in feedlot record keeping and use of performance tested cattle. This went to the point where western ranchers started asking him to feed out their cattle because he could supply the kind of feedlot gain and carcass records they wanted for breeding purposes.

The Steffensens have served as the host family for an International Foreign Youth Exchange student from Germany.

Farm activities include being a member of the national, state and local Cattlemen's Associations. He served as president of the Winnebago County Beef Producers for six years. He is a Farm Bureau member and is on the co-op elevator board. He also served six years on the Winnebago County 4-H youth committee, was a participant in the Iowa State University feeder cattle performance evaluation program, and was a member of an Iowa cattlemen's study tour.

Other service includes being a Lake Mills Community school board member and president for two years, serving as township trustee, secretary-

Zumbach

treasurer of the Winnebago Rural Electric Company, and a director of the Winnebago Rural Telephone Company.

The Steffensens are members of the Salem Lutheran Church at Lake Mills where DeVere has served on various committees.

Mr. and Mrs. Steffensen have six children: Lou Ann (Mrs. Richard) Mikes is a home economist for the State of Georgia Peanut Commission; Patricia (Mrs. Curtis) Nelson is a registered nurse at Lake Mills Nursing Home; Nancy (Mrs. David) Monson is associate director and a teacher at the Worth County development center; Julie is a registered nurse in Charles City; Rebecca (Mrs. Larry) Hill is a junior at Mankato State College in Mankato, Minnesota and DeRay is a freshman at Iowa State University.

moved to the finishing portion of the building with partial slats and dribble feeders.

His dairy operation is consistently one of the top producing herds in Delaware County and Iowa. Cows are averaging 17,400 pounds of milk and 640 pounds of butterfat. An ultra-modern grain handling and processing setup on the Zumbach farm features push button hog feeding. It consists of an elevator leg, dryer and electric mill. "It's a real labor saver," says Zumbach.

In farm service, Zumbach is a member of Iowa Farm Bureau dairy advisory council and state dairy advisory committee, the Delaware County Dairy Herd Improvement Association, and a former president of the county Pork Producers Association. He has also served as county Farm Bureau president, a member of the national policy committee and is on the state resolutions committee.

Earl Zumbach's total confinement unit

He has served his school on community study committees, is a member of the county Extension public affairs committee and chairman of the agricultural property rights association.

Past honors include Master Swine Producer, Master Corn Grower and Distinguished Dairyman.

The Zumbachs are members of Peace Lutheran Church in Ryan where Earl serves as a Sunday school teacher.

The Zumbachs have seven children: Doran farms in Delaware County; Judy is a college graduate; Marilyn attends Paris Beauty Academy; Jolean is a sophomore; Dorothea is in eighth grade; and Daniel and Denise are in seventh grade.

Earl Zumbach
Delaware County

Earl Zumbach farms 320 acres in Delaware County. He has a herd of 26 registered Holstein dairy cows and feeds out 1,500 head of hogs per year.

"You've got to keep sows happy to save pigs," says Zumbach. "We let sows out twice a day to eat and exercise. This also helps keep the pens clean."

He farrows in a modern house plus a converted chicken house.

Pigs are finished in a total confinement building. They're started on full slats with self-feeders. After they reach 80 pounds, they're

1975
IOWA MASTER FARMERS
~
March 22, 1975

Five top Iowa farmers were named Master Farmers for 1975 at an awards luncheon at the Holiday Inn in Des Moines, March 20. Brief descriptions of their operations and community activities are listed here.

The awards are aimed at calling attention to the high level of management these men demonstrate and to honor them for unselfishly devoting part of their time to community leadership roles.

The 1975 selections bring the total to 263 men and one woman who have received the award since 1926.

Judges were Clifford Stille, vice president of the Master Farmer Club; Marlowe Feldman, treasurer of the Master Farmer Club; Everett Stoneberg, Iowa State University farm management specialist; and Bob Dunaway, managing editor of *Wallaces Farmer*.

Dale Sorenson demonstrates his pig holder

Duane Boyd
Floyd County

Duane Boyd farms 440 acres. He handles 2,000 head of hogs a year in a total confinement farrow-to-finish operation and feeds out about 225 head of cattle.

Accurate feed records are a must, he says. A scale on his grinder-mixer tells him how his hogs are doing.

Automation has helped Boyd sidetrack labor problems. Pushing buttons lets him feed cattle in 15 to 20 minutes. Hog facilities are climatized with ventilation through the pits on time-controlled fans during cold weather. Both pit and forced air ventilation are used in the summer.

"Our hobby is pork promotion," says Boyd. "My wife and I have headed up barbecues of pork loins, helped in pork cooking schools, and many county and state pork promotions." The

Boyd

Boyds also joined a pork promotion tour to Boston, Mass., to promote pork in supermarkets.

In farm activities, Boyd has served on the farmer's night school council, is an honorary FFA member and has helped the local FFA chapter with their crops. He is a township trustee. He helped organize the Floyd County Pork Producers Association and served as president, has been a district director of the Iowa Pork Producers Association and served on the state executive board.

He is also chairman of the state Farm Bureau swine committee and represented Iowa on the American Farm Bureau swine committee. He has also served on the Iowa livestock council committee.

Boyd practices soil conservation on his farm with crop rotation.

In other community activities, Boyd is a member of the American Legion, served as a 4-H leader and is weighmaster at the county fair.

The Boyds are also active in the Trinity United Methodist Church at Charles City.

Mr. and Mrs. Boyd have two children. Karen (Mrs. Steven Rankin) is a college graduate and homemaker in Wisconsin. Leland is a graduate of North Iowa Community College and farms in partnership with Duane.

Wilbert H. Frye
Buchanan County

Wilbert H. (Bill) Frye, farms 900 acres in Buchanan County. He produces about 1,500 head of hogs, feeds out 75 head of cattle and has a 120-head beef cow herd.

Building and rebuilding his own machinery is one way he faces increasing farm costs. One example is a forklift to haul big bales. He describes it as being an 8-foot wide, 3-point lift with four long tines made out of I-beams. It will carry up to 2 tons.

"The bale handler cost about $100 less than I would have had to pay for one and it's built heavier," says Frye. "It can also be used to move lick tanks and about anything else."

Another project was to recondition a nitrogen applicator with hydraulic wings and electric controls.

All hogs are raised in confinement from farrowing to nursing to finishing.

Frye emphasizes conservation with all of his crops planted in 30-inch rows on contour or strips.

He is a member of the Northeast Iowa Farm Business Association and is president of the board. He has also helped plan adult vocational agriculture and Extension programs and has been a 4-H advisor.

He is a past president and board member of the county Pork Producers Association, was the first president for the reorganized county cattleman's association, and is a Farm Bureau member.

Frye served on the local school board for 12 years and on the Buchanan County school board for 12 years. He has been an officer of the Buchanan County Historical Society, is Cornell College area alumni president and was a director of the Carrington-Clyde experimental farm.

The Fryes are members of the Presbyterian church where Bill has been an active elder for nine years, is a Christian education board member, served on the new church building committee, and has taught church school with his wife for nine years. He is also a member of the Mariners.

The Fryes have two children. Richard attended Iowa State University and farms in partnership with his dad. Robert is an ISU farm operations graduate and is manager

Frye

Johnson

of a chemical and fertilizer plant in Nebraska.

Lester Johnson
Plymouth County

Lester Johnson farms 315 acres. He handles 800 to 900 hogs in a farrow-to-finish operation and feeds out 200 to 300 head of cattle.

Johnson's cattle feeding operation consists of upright silos, a cattle shed and automated feeding.

"I like the flexibility of silo storage," he says. "I can go to high-moisture ear corn, shelled corn or silage. Plus, I can harvest early and keep field loss to a minimum. And the feed is processed and ready to go to the bunk as it comes out of the silo."

Shelter pays, he says. His records show there's been no difference in rate of gain during hard winters, and he suffered no loss when last January's blizzard hit.

Johnson is strong on soil conservation practices. He is a member of the Floyd Valley Watershed Association and received the outstanding cooperator award in 1966. Conservation practices include four miles of terraces and contouring. He has recently started no-plow tillage using a disc and conventional planter.

He has also served on the Farmers Cooperative Elevator board in Craig, is president of the Plymouth Electric Co-operative, secretary of the Northwest Iowa Power Co-operative board, and is a member of the area committee on low-cost energy. He also serves on Farm Bureau committees.

Johnson keeps his own records. He got started through the Plymouth County Farm and Home program.

Johnson also served on local rural school boards, was a member of the study committee for reorganization and has served on the Plymouth County zoning board.

The Johnsons are members of St.

Kluver

John's Lutheran Church at Craig where Lester has served as president of the congregation for three years, worked as Sunday school treasurer and superintendent and has been on the Iowa district evangelism committee.

The Johnsons have three children. Gail (Mrs. Kent Jones) is a medical technologist in Colorado. Mary (Mrs. Verdayne Brandenburg) works for a bank in South Dakota. Both are Augustana College graduates. Kathy is a junior in the Le-Mars Community Schools.

Morris Kluver
Hancock County

Morris Kluver farms 480 acres. He feeds out 450 hogs and 200 head of cattle a year.

Minimum tillage has caught on in Kluver's operation. He started using just a heavy disc on soybean stubble 10 years ago, "back when it was lazy to trim back on tillage," he explains. He's trying to find a combination that leaves a third of the corn residue on top of the soil.

"I'm trying to adapt something to fall plow as rough as possible," he explains. "Heavy-discing stubble is now beyond a doubt an accepted practice."

In farm activities, Kluver has served on the Extension council and as chairman, has been on the county Farm Bureau board and is on the local affairs committee. He is in his 10th year as a 4-H leader.

He is a member of the Central Iowa Farm Business Association, a member and past vice president of the county Beef Producers Association and serves as an Iowa State University counselor.

Kluver has also served on the North Iowa Area Development (NIAD) ag committee, and was the Hancock County board of supervisors' representative on the North Iowa Community Action board. He also served as Hancock County chairman of the Iowa 2000 program.

Sorenson

A Korean War veteran, Kluver received the presidential unit citation and three bronze stars. He served on the Hancock County selective service board for 10 years.

Kluver is a member of the American Legion and has served as adjutant. He is also a member of the legion's honor guard. He has served on the Britt school board and has been a PTA chairman.

The Kluvers are members of the Crystal Lake Methodist Church where Morris has been a trustee, Sunday school teacher and lay leader.

The Kluvers have three children. James is a graduate of North Iowa Area Community College and is employed at Winnebago Industries. Kent is attending NIACC and will start farming with his dad this spring. Lynn is in sixth grade at Crystal Lake Community Schools.

Sorenson's fenceline hog feeding setup

Dale Sorensen
Shelby County

Dale Sorensen farms 500 acres. He handles about 1,500 head of hogs in a farrow-to-finish operation and feeds out 240 to 300 head of cattle.

Handy ideas are one of Sorensen's specialties. For example, he uses fenceline bunks for feeding his sows.

"When you limit-feed sows they get a little aggressive," he explains. "It's easier to feed them without going into the lot. It saves wear and tear on the operator. And there's little more expense than with the regular fence."

Another handy idea is a pig holder. It's simply a 2- by 2-foot square box that's 1-foot deep.

It will hold one litter. It uses an inner tube and a brick to hold pigs down so one man can handle a litter by himself. Sorenson says it works well until the pigs are two to three weeks old.

Sorensen is also a strong believer in farmers taking vacations. "We think it's a must to get away; it gives you a different outlook when you come back," he says.

Records on the Sorensen farm are kept through the Southwest Iowa Farm Business Association. Sorensen is secretary and a director of that association.

Conservation practices on the farm include all acres being terraced and contoured. He has served on the education committee of the local soil district.

Sorensen is a member and past director of the Shelby County Pork Producers Association, belongs to the Iowa and county Cattlemen's Association and has served as a 4-H club leader for seven years.

In other community activities, Sorensen was on a reorganization study committee for the Harlan Community School District.

The Sorensens are members of the First Baptist Church at Harlan where Dale has served as chairman of the pulpit committee, chairman of the board of deacons, chairman of the board of Christian education, and has been Sunday school superintendent and a trustee.

The Sorensens have four children. Arlin is a freshman at Iowa State University. Brenda is a junior, Bradley is a sophomore, and Jolene is in sixth grade in the Harlan Community Schools.

William H. Greiner
Exceptional Service Award

William H. Greiner, director of the Department of Soil Conservation for the state of Iowa, has been selected to receive the Iowa Master Farmer Exceptional Service Award.

Wallaces Farmer has presented Master Farmer awards to outstanding farmers since 1926. But Greiner is only the fourth person to be honored for exceptional service to the state's farmers.

The first of these awards went to Larry Cain, then manager of the Cerro Gordo County farm in 1959. The second was to Dr. C.R. Weber, an Iowa State University agronomist and breeder of Amsoy and Harksoy soybean varieties in 1967. The third was to Dr. E.P. "Dutch" Sylwester, Iowa's well-known weed and herbicide specialist, in 1972.

Greiner attended grade school in Farlin, Iowa and is a graduate of Jefferson High School and Iowa State University.

He worked as an Extension youth assistant during the summer while a student at ISU, taught at Jefferson High School, then farmed for three years near Jefferson.

Greiner was named assistant director of the state soil conservation committee (now the Department of Soil Conservation) of Iowa in 1956 and was named director in 1957.

In his years of service, Greiner has been a leader in soil conservation work. He works closely with all agencies interested in the conservation of natural resources, particularly with the 100 soil conservation districts of Iowa and the elected governing members of these districts. Farmers who have witnessed his efforts recommended him for this award.

During his time with the Department of Soil Conservation, state appropriations for soil conservation programs have more then tripled, now amounting to more than $3.6 million per year.

Known and respected by thousands of Iowa farmers, Greiner is often called on as a guest speaker.

With new emphasis being put on environment and conserving what we have, it's impossible to put a dollar value on the effect Greiner's work has had on Iowa farm profits. His efforts are partly responsible for the greatly increased number of terraces, contours and other soil conserving practices seen throughout the state.

Among the honors Greiner has received are honorary Iowa Farmer Award from the Future Farmers of America; soil conservation award from WMT radio and TV stations; honorary member of the Iowa Association of Soil Conservation District Commissioners; and fellow, Soil Conservation Society of America.

Greiner

186

IOWA MASTER FARMERS
~
March 27, 1976

Five top Iowa farmers were named Master Farmers for 1976 at an awards luncheon at the Holiday Inn in Des Moines, March 25.

The 1976 selections bring the total to 268 men and one woman who have received the award since 1926.

Judges were Clifford Stille, president of the Master Farmer Club; Marlowe Feldman, vice president of the Master Farmer Club; Everett Stoneberg, Iowa State University farm management specialist; and Al Bull, vice president and editorial director, Farm Progress Publications (former editor of *Wallaces Farmer*).

Ollie Kaldenberg
Monroe County

Ollie Kaldenberg farms 1,000 acres in partnership with his son, Tom. He produces about 250 head of hogs, feeds 175 head of cattle and maintains a 70-cow beef-breeding herd.

Adapting present machinery to fit new methods is one way he keeps machinery costs down. For example, with the help of Tom, he converted a four-row, 38-inch corn planter to a seven-row, 19-inch planter by adding another row on each side and one in the middle. This means all rows are 19 inches apart except the two behind the tractor wheels.

"We wanted to be able to go to narrow-row soybeans and still be able to cultivate," he says. "We don't plant in the tractor track with this system so we can still get through the beans. We used it for the first time last year and our yields were the best we've ever had," he adds.

Kaldenberg is a strong advocate of conservation. He is chairman of the Monroe County Soil Conservation District and has been involved in many of its activities. He has served as a district commissioner since 1964. Presently, he is serving as Region 9 director on the state board of Soil Conservation District Commissioners. He was a leader in the development of the Rathbun Regional Water Association's push for rural water. He is a former chairman and is presently executive board member of the Chariton Valley Resource Conservation and Development Association.

In church activities, Kaldenberg is

Kaldenberg

a member of the administrative board and council of ministries for the Trinity United Methodist Church. He is church school superintendent and is a member of the Trinity Builders Sunday school class. He is also a certified lay speaker in the church.

He is past president of the Albia Community School board and has been a member for 10 years.

He is a member of the Monroe County Farm Bureau and Monroe County fair association. Other activities include County Compensation Board, County Health Board, township field assessor and member of the Iowa State University president's advisory committee.

The Kaldenbergs have three children: Karen (Mrs. Keith Henderson) is a farm wife and beautician at Plano; Dennis is a graduate student and teaching assistant at ISU; and Tom, also an ISU graduate, farms with his father.

Malcolm McGregor
Chickasaw County

Malcolm McGregor farms 3,200 acres in partnership with his brother, Ron. They feed 1,200 cattle a year and maintain a herd of 400 beef cows.

About half the land is in row crops, the other half in pasture and hay. "That's where the beef cows fit in," he says.

They started with 25 cows in 1958 and had a herd of about 400 by 1970. "I knew we had to produce a high-quality calf," he says. "This is one of the reasons we use artificial insemination to take advantage of proven sires and make selected matings.

"I enjoy doing things to improve the community," he says. He is presently chairman

McGregor

of the administrative board and has served on the board of trustees of the United Methodist Church in Nashua. He has served on the Nashua Community School board for 11 years and was president for five years. He served on a committee to reorganize the school district and has been a 4-H leader for 14 years.

McGregor has served on several local and area Extension committees. He was on the board of directors and is past president of the Chickasaw County Cattlemen's Association. He is currently a state director for the Iowa Cattlemen's Association. He is also a member of the American National Cattlemen's Association and Iowa Beef Improvement Association.

He has served as township director and is now vice president of the Chickasaw County Farm Bureau. He has accepted an appointment on the beef advisory committee of the Iowa Farm Bureau. He is also a member of the Beef Improvement Corporation.

Mr. and Mrs. McGregor have six children. David, a graduate of Iowa State University, farms with his father. Mary, an ISU graduate, teaches home economics at Odebolt-Arthur. Alan, an animal science graduate from the Hawkeye School of Technology in Waterloo, is farming with his father. Evelyn is a freshman at ISU. Karen, a junior, and Scott, a freshman, both attend Nashua Community High School.

Robert Schultz
Clayton County

Robert Schultz farms 320 acres. He farrows 85 sows, feeds out the pigs and maintains a dairy herd of about 100 cows.

"Accurate dairy records are a must," he says. That's why he's been us-

Schultz

ing the Dairy Herd Improvement Association's testing program ever since he started farming 29 years ago.

High-producing cows are a tradition on his farm. His herd has consistently averaged 600 pounds or more of butterfat, and last year had a 669-pound lactation average on 43 cows.

Schultz was named Distinguished Dairyman for Clayton County in 1970 and Iowa Distinguished Dairyman in 1973. He has received the Progressive Breeder's Registry Award from the Holstein-Freisian Association of America for the last five years.

Community involvement is a big part of Schultz's life. He has been a member of the board of directors of the Luana Savings Bank, secretary of the state DHIA board and director on the board of Iowa Holstein Breeder's Association. He was recently appointed to the Iowa Dairy Industry Commission, is a member of the Clayton County Farm Bureau, Clayton County Pork Producers Association as well as the county and state Holstein Association.

He has served on the board of directors of the Luana Farmers Cooperative, was a 4-H leader for five years and has served as a director on the board of the Iowa Holstein Association.

A member of the St. John Lutheran Church in Luana, he has served as trustee, deacon and chairman of the congregation. He is currently serving on the parish education board.

Mr. and Mrs. Schultz have two children: Susan (Mrs. Robert Spaletto), of Alamo, California; and David, farming in partnership with his father.

Schweers

Arthur Schweers
Adams County

Arthur Schweers farms 1,090 acres. He handles 500 head of hogs and 150 head of cattle a year. He maintains a herd of 110 beef and 20 dairy cows.

Schweers hasn't plowed since 1969. He's a firm believer in minimum tillage.

"Soil erosion is the biggest reason for switching to minimum tillage," figures Schweers. "For example, a 32-inch woven wire fence in one of my fields was almost completely buried after 12 years by soil erosion even though the field was farmed on the contour. I replaced the fence and there has been less than one inch of soil pile up around it in the six years since I started using minimum tillage."

Schweers relies on the importance of accurate records. He carries a notebook in his pocket at all times so he won't forget important dates and figures.

In local activities, Schweers was a member of the Lenox Community School board for five years, serving as president for two years. He has been active in politics.

He has served on the board of the Farm Service Co-op, the Artificial Breeders Association and the Adams County Fair Association.

He has been a member of the Adams County Conservation Board, 4-H Youth Fair Association and Adams County Extension council.

Schweers is in the National Farmers Organization and is a past president of the Adams County NFO. He is presently on the national NFO board representing the state of Iowa. He was president of the NFO Collection and Reload Point at Stringtown. He is a director of that corporation.

As a member of St. Patrick's Catholic Church in Lenox, he serves on the parish council and the regional pastoral council. He is president of the men's club and takes his turn as lector and usher. He has also served on the diocesan board of the Council of Social Concern.

The Schweers have 11 children. Teresa (Mrs. Neil Parmenter) attended business school and is a homemaker in Des Moines. David, a graduate of Drake University, farms with his father. Rita (Mrs. James Hughes) is a graduate of Iowa State University and a homemaker in Fort Dodge. Anne (Mrs. Tom Pogge), a Creighton University graduate, is a homemaker living in Maryland. Catherine (Mrs. Bill Riley) is a homemaker living in Lenox.

Thomas graduated from Tarkio College and now farms with his father. Herman also farms with his father after two years at Northwestern College. Edward serves in the Army. Cecelia is a student at ISU. Francis, a senior, and Agnes, a junior, both attend Lenox High School.

Robert Zacharias
Harrison County

Robert Zacharias farms 760 acres. He handles 2,000 head of hogs a year in semi-confinement and feeds out 400 to 500 head of cattle in an open lot.

Conservation is important in his operation. "I've terraced every acre we own," he says proudly. He's also a firm believer in minimum tillage. He used a heavy disc with 22-inch blades on all but 50 acres of his ground last year.

"Good records are important for good management," he says. He keeps records with the Southwest Iowa Farm Business Association of which he is a member and uses its record analysis to make important decisions.

Zacharias is described as a "pusher" in his community. "I don't like to stand around and talk about it. Let's get it done," he says.

His list of activities includes member and past president of the Persia Improvement Club. He is also a member of the Persia Development Corp., and president of the board of the Council Bluffs Federal Land Bank.

He is active in and on the board of Mosquito of Harrison Watershed.

Zacharias is chairman of the finance committee and is on the board of the Bethany Lutheran Home in Council Bluffs. Fifteen churches are involved in running this 121-bed nursing home. He is also a member of the church council of St. John's Lutheran Church in Persia.

In other community activities, Zacharias is a charter member and organizer of the Southwest Iowa Business Association. He also holds membership in the Harrison County Farm Bureau, Iowa Cattlemen's Association, Iowa Pork Producers Association, two farmer co-ops, is a past member of the Extension council, 4-H leader and has served on the PTA.

Mr. and Mrs. Zacharias have three children: Randy is married and employed by Midwest Implement of Persia; Carol (Mrs. Jerry Plambeck) is a registered nurse in Council Bluffs; Alan is a student at Tri-Center Community School.

Zacharias

IOWA MASTER FARMERS
~
March 26, 1977

Six top Iowa farmers were named Master Farmers for 1977 at an awards luncheon at Adventureland Inn in Des Moines March 24. Brief descriptions of their operations and activities are listed here.

Wallaces Farmer has sponsored the Master Farmer program since 1926. The honor is aimed at calling attention to the high level of management these men demonstrate and to award them for unselfishly devoting part of their time to community leadership roles.

The 1977 selections bring the total to 275 men and one woman who have received the award since 1926.

Judges were Marlowe Feldman, president, Master Farmer Club; Everett Stoneberg, Iowa State University farm management specialist; and Monte Sesker, editor, *Wallaces Farmer*.

Gordon Enyart
Jasper County

Gordon Enyart farms 350 acres in partnership with his son, Doug. They farrow about 140 litters and market about 1,200 hogs a year. Last year, they averaged nine pigs per litter marketed. They also have a 50-head beef cow herd.

This is a close knit father-son partnership. "I feel we have to give young men an opportunity to farm," says Gordon. "The important thing is to be able to communicate and understand each other and to have the same goals."

They have a formal partnership agreement in writing that they review and update annually. Their wives are included in that review session.

Emphasis is still on hogs in this

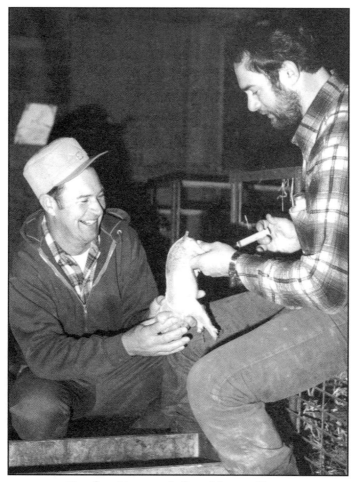

Gordon Enyart, left, with son Doug

operation. Enyart admits that his hogs haven't always been top quality. But through records, purebred breeding stock, and grade and yield selling, he believes he is getting much better feed conversion and a superior product for the consumer. Plus, he consistently gets premium dollars on grade and yield.

Their hog operation includes farrowing crates in a remodeled dairy barn, a confinement nursery and open front confinement finishing.

"I'm really concerned about soil and water conservation," says Enyart. To control erosion on their rolling land, they use strip farming, grass waterways, terraces, contouring and have gone almost entirely to a big disc and chisel plow for tillage.

Enyart served as a member of the new Monroe school board for six years. With his work on a citizens committee, a new school building was constructed.

He is a committeeman with Jasper County Farmer's Home Administration. He's a member of the Prairie City Co-op and has been a cooperator with the Agricultural Stabilization and Conservation Service for 20 years.

In local activities, Enyart is a member of the Farm Bureau, Jasper County Pork Producers, Master of the Prairie City Masonic Lodge, American Legion member and a substitute rural mail carrier for Prairie City.

As an active member of the Prairie City United Methodist Church, Enyart is immediate past chairman of the council on ministries, a church board member and has served as Sunday school superintendent and teacher.

Mr. and Mrs. Enyart have two children. Doug is married and farms with his

father. Doreen (Mrs. Mike Pearson) is a student at St. Luke's School of Nursing in Cedar Rapids.

Farris Gray
Taylor County

Farris Gray farms 680 acres. He feeds out 700 head of hogs per year in a farrow-to-finish operation. He also maintains a herd of 110 crossbred beef cows.

"One way I keep machinery costs down is by buying good, used equipment," points out Gray. "And I do my own repair work." His machinery costs per rotated acre run about $39.75 compared to $46.02 for the average of the Southwest Iowa Farm Business Association.

Gray feeds hogs in a modified 35- by 64-foot open front confinement building. It has a solid concrete floor. Hogs work the manure into a gutter along the front side of the building, which is emptied with a liquid manure spreader. "Even though the pigs keep the floor reasonably clean, I'd use slats over a pit on part of the floor if I were doing it over," he admits.

Gray is active in conservation. He recently received the district and regional Soil Conservation Award. He is a director of the 102 River Watershed Project and a member of the county and regional RC&D board, serving on the forestry committee. He served on the Taylor County Conservation Board for the past six years and was chairman two terms. He was an ASCS committeeman.

A member of the Taylor County Pork Producers Association, he was selected 1975 county and district Master Pork Producer.

Farris Gray used old axles to make a round bale carrier.

Gray is a member of the Southwest Iowa Farm Business Association.

A member of the county Democratic party, Gray has served as treasurer, member of the Taylor County election board, member of Congressman Tom Harkin's agricultural advisory committee and township trustee.

He is vice chairman of the Taylor County Farmers Union, served as a delegate to the state convention and was a member of the state rules committee.

A former 4-H leader, Gray has served on the Taylor County 4-H and youth committee. He was recently appointed to serve on the Bedford Community School board. He was awarded the Honorary Chapter Farmer award by the Bedford Future Farmers of America chapter.

A member of the Bedford United Methodist church, Gray is chairman of the board of trustees, usher and former church board chairman.

Mr. and Mrs. Gray have two children. Linda is a senior at Northwest Missouri State University majoring in music and elementary education. Nancy is a senior at Bedford Community High School.

Robert Johnson
Clinton County

Robert Johnson farms 400 acres. He and his sons feed out 1,400 head of cattle a year.

He starts calves and yearlings weighing 500 to 750 pounds in the open lot and finishes them in confinement. His 208- by 54-foot cold-confinement building was completed in Oc-

No gates for Robert Johnson. A cattle guard saves time.

tober 1975. It has a 400-head capacity.

"A good-sized feed bunk is important if you feed a lot of roughage and your pens hold 80 head of cattle," he says. "Otherwise, you'll be feeding several times a day."

Johnson used sliding doors on the ends of the building. However, he says if he were doing it over, he'd use overhead doors with automatic openers. "We open and close those doors more often than we thought we would," he admits.

"Insulation is important, too," he continues. "It's 10 degrees cooler in the barn in the summertime even when it's full of cattle. And we don't have a steam problem in the winter."

Johnson is president of the Clinton County Cattlemen's Association. He is a member of the National Livestock Feeder's Association and the American National Cattlemen's Association. A Farm Bureau member, Johnson has been captain of the township membership committee.

In local activities, Johnson is a volunteer fireman, a past 4-H leader and chairman of the Clinton-Cedar counties farm-city swap committee. He was named Clinton County's Outstanding Young Farmer in 1964.

Johnson is past chairman of the Andover Faith Lutheran Church council, past president of the Lutheran brotherhood and past chairman of the committee to obtain a new pastor.

Mr. and Mrs. Johnson have five children. Douglas is married and is vice president and farm service director of the Guaranty State Bank in Beloit, Kan. Dwight is working into a partnership with his father. Diane is employed by Dial Finance advertising department in Des Moines. Darwin is a senior and Dawn a sophomore at East Central Community High School.

Bob Joslin
Cedar County

Bob Joslin farms 850 acres. He handles about 2,800 head of hogs and feeds 750 head of cattle a year.

Joslin is a firm believer in soil conservation. He retired his moldboard plow in 1967 and has used minimum tillage ever since. Three years ago, he began construction of parallel terraces laid out for his farm by the Soil Conservation Service. He now has four miles of the project completed.

"Use of outside expertise is important in my operation," says Joslin. He utilizes the Farm Bureau record-keeping system, the Beef Improvement Corporation serves as his cattle buyer and the Interstate Producers Livestock Association sells his cattle for him.

Joslin is past president of the Mideastern Iowa Mental Health Center, which he helped organize. He is vice president and a member of the board of directors of the Iowa Farm Bureau Federation. He is secretary of the board of directors of FS Services, Inc. He is a member of the board of directors of the Cedar-Johnson Farm Service Company.

In other activities, Joslin is a member of the Cedar County Pork Producers Association, the Cedar County Cattlemen's Association, Iowa Corn Grower's Association and the Iowa Soybean Association. He was named a Master Swine Producer in 1975.

He has served on the Iowa State University Extension advisory committee and on a grain advisory committee to the U.S. secretary of agriculture.

In local activities, he is a member of the Clarence Li-

Joslin

ons Club, the American Legion and the Masonic Lodge.

As a member of the Clarence United Methodist Church, Joslin has served as chairman of the administrative board, the council on ministries and was chairman of the building committee. He presently serves on the district council of ministry and the district building committee.

Mr. and Mrs. Joslin have four children. Chris (Mrs. Dallas Ferguson) lives in Tulsa, Okla. Kathy (Mrs. Mark Young) lives in Wellington, New Zealand. Ann is a librarian in Great Falls, Mont., and Meg is in the fifth grade at Clarence-Lowden School.

Ralph Mehl
Woodbury County

Ralph Mehl farms 600 acres. He handles about 2,700 feeder pigs per year. He sold an average of eight pigs per sow in 1976.

Mehl believes providing good working conditions and incentives for hired help is important in his operation. For example, he provides 80 acres of cropland for his two hired men to farm.

He furnishes the machinery and they provide the seed, fertilizer and herbicides. The crop is theirs to sell. "It's an added incentive and fringe benefit," says Mehl.

Only one of the hired men is furnished a house. Mehl gives the other $1 per pig sold to even out the fringe benefits.

A trick Mehl believes is worthwhile is to use straw bedding twice. Bedding that's cleaned out of the farrowing house goes into the gestating sow lot. "If there are any scours bacteria in the bedding, it will help the sow develop immunity before farrowing," he reasons.

Mehl is in his 13th year as a member of the Westwood Community School board. He is Willow township Republican committee chair-

Mehl

194

man. He has also been a member of the Hornick Cooperative Elevator board.

Mehl is a member of the Woodbury County Extension board, past fair board member, county Pork Producers Association member and is on the Woodbury-Monona drainage board.

A member of the Masonic Lodge of Sloan and the Sioux City Kiwanis, Mehl also entertains foreign visitors in his home for the Sioux City mayor's committee for international visitors.

Mehl is a member of the Hornick United Methodist Church board, past Sunday school superintendent and chairman of the council on ministries.

Mr. and Mrs. Mehl have one child. Rebecca is a school teacher in Grand Island, Neb.

Weaver

Wiley Weaver
Cerro Gordo County

Wiley Weaver farms 800 acres in partnership with his son, Tom. He handles the cattle, feeding out about 1,000 head per year. Tom handles about 2,500 hogs per year in a farrow-to-finish operation.

Weaver has fed cattle all his life. Three years ago he put up a 51- by 154-foot open front confinement building. Capacity is 320 head.

"I looked over at least a dozen buildings before I found the right set-up for me," he admits. "All the farmers I visited were happy with confinement feeding, but weren't quite satisfied with the pit. Finally, I found a farmer who used precast concrete pits, and it seemed the logical way to go. It is more expensive, but I think it's the best way to do it."

Weaver figures his ration with all corn silage, haylage plus one pound of ground ear corn for every 100 pounds of body weight. "Everything my cattle eat goes through the silo," he says. His system is completely automated. "You are more dedicated to cattle feeding with an automated system" he says. "After all, you can always sell a feed wagon."

He is a member of the Cerro Gordo County Cattlemen's Association, which he helped organize. He is also a member of the Iowa Cattlemen's Association and the Cerro Gordo County Pork Producers Association and the Farm Bureau. He has been active as a 4-H leader and on the Extension council.

He is a director of the Farmer's Community Cooperative Elevator of Rockwell. As a member of the Rockwell Lions Club, he is co-chairman of the committee to manage a farm which the club rents.

Weaver is also a member of Governor Ray's EPA Advisory Committee.

As a member of the Rockwell United Methodist Church, Weaver has been chairman of the finance committee and a trustee.

Mr. and Mrs. Weaver have four children. Sandra (Mrs. Richard Hitzhusen) is an Iowa State University home economics graduate. Tom is married and farms with his father. Sharon (Mrs. Robert Cadwell) is a graduate in livestock marketing and management from Ellsworth Community College. Sheryl is a graduate of Mankato Community College.

Doug and Gordon Enyart

Five top Iowa farmers were named Master Farmers for 1978 at an awards luncheon at Adventureland Inn in Des Moines, March 23. Brief descriptions of their operations and activities are listed here.

The 1978 selections bring the total to 280 men and one woman who have received the award since 1926.

Judges were Don Johnson, president, Master Farmer Club; Wesley Shafer, vice president, Master Farmer Club; Everett Stoneberg, Iowa State University farm management specialist; and Monte Sesker, editor, *Wallaces Farmer*.

Loren Eddy
Appanoose County

Loren Eddy and his sons farm 740 acres. They farrow 24 sows four times a year in a farrow-to-finish operation. They also maintain a 115-head beef cow herd.

Even though the Eddy's hog operation is confinement, he doesn't believe in spending a lot of money on new, expensive facilities. "I'm pretty conservative. We don't have fancy facilities," he says. "We've substituted labor for extra expense in our operation."

Eddy's 52- by 28-foot farrowing house is his own design. It has 10 stalls on one side and 10 pens on the other. He feels pens work better for farrowing than stalls. "You can feed and water the sow right in the pens. Also, there is less stress on the sow," he adds. He farrows 90% of his sows in the pens and then moves them later to the stalls.

Eddy utilizes corn residue as roughage for his beef herd by stacking it. He also stacks alfalfa-orchard grass hay. "We really like our stacking machine," he says. "But, I don't think it is right for everyone."

In local activities, Eddy is an Athletic Booster Club member and past 4-H leader.

A Farm Bureau member, Eddy is a past township director. He is an ASCS township committeeman, a district soil commissioner and an SCS cooperator. He is a mem-

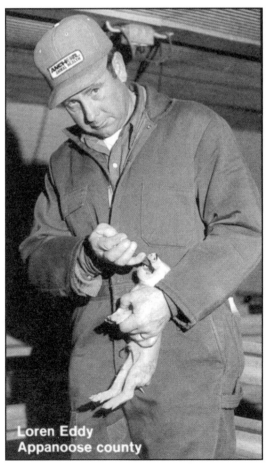

**Loren Eddy
Appanoose county**

ber of the Appanoose County Rural Water Association.

Active in the Appanoose County Pork Producers Association, Eddy has served as treasurer. He was named a Master Swine Producer in 1975. He has been vice president of the local fair board.

Other activities include director, Chariton Valley Regional Services Agency and chairman of the County Land Preservation Policy Committee.

As a supporter of the state 208 pollution control project, Eddy serves as a member of the county resource coordinating committee and the Southern Iowa Conservancy District advisory committee.

A member of the First United Methodist Church, Eddy has served as chairman of the trustees, on the parish council, as a Sunday school teacher, and as chairman of the administrative board and education commission.

Eddy and his wife, Wilma, have four children. Mike, a graduate of Indian Hills Community College, farms with his father. Randy is a sophomore at Iowa State University. Lisa is a freshman at Indian Hills Community College. Todd is a freshman at Centerville High School.

Merlyn Groot
Calhoun County

Merlyn Groot farms 600 acres. Corn and soybeans are his main crops. But pasture, hay and oats also fit in to provide feed for a herd of 45 beef cows.

With a waste-not, want-not approach,

Merlyn Groot
Calhoun county

Groot makes good use of crop residue in balanced rations to get good gains in his beef feeding operation. Convinced of the benefits of production tested bulls, he's used them since he started his herd from scratch in 1957.

A strong believer in the fertility benefits of manure, especially on high pH soils, he points out that a majority of the high yields in contests are on fields where liberal amounts of manure have been applied. A spot yield check showed 59 bushels per acre in one of his bean fields last fall.

"A good set of 'homemade' records has been a valuable tool in helping me make production, marketing and financial decisions," says Groot. He feels the key to making records useful, particularly production costs, is to keep them as real as possible with little estimation. For example, a meter on his gas tank helps keep accurate track between field and road use of fuel.

"Keeping my own records takes time," notes Groot. "But since I do the figuring instead of a computer, I really know what's going on."

Groot is active in the Calhoun County Cattlemen's Association, Iowa Corn Growers Association and National Corn Growers Association. He is a member of the dean's advisory committee at Iowa State University and the USDA-FGIS advisory committee.

He has also served on the Iowa agriculture marketing board, Manson Jaycees, Bethesda Hospital board, Olson Foundation and the Manson Industrial Development Board.

Other local activities include membership in the Farmers Co-op Elevator of Manson, the W&H Co-op Oil Company and 1973-1977 delegate to Boone Valley Co-op Processing.

As an active member of the Iowa Soybean Association, Groot has served as its president and as a director. He has served as secretary of the American Soybean Association and is currently the vice president/president elect. He has been a director since 1974.

As a Farm Bureau member, Groot serves on the field crops advisory committee.

Groot is a member of the St. Paul Lutheran Church and has been a Sunday school superintendent. He sings in the church choir as well as in a barbershop quartet.

Merlyn and his wife, Vara, have three children. Deborah is in first grade. Denise is 4 years old. Rachel was born Oct. 15, 1977.

Ward Handorf
Marshall County

Ward Handorf farms 1,200 acres in partnership with his sons, Craig and Lynn. They maintain a sow herd of 75 to 90 head and market about 2,500 head, farrowing 2¼ times per year. They also feed about 5,000 head of feeder pigs purchased from outside sources. A 50-head beef cow herd is also part of the operation.

Since he believes facilities are the limiting factor in expansion, Handorf has converted existing buildings into confinement units. An old barn has been converted to a total confinement nursery, for example.

Handorf markets hogs when they weigh

Ward Handorf
Marshall county

210 to 220 pounds. "I don't know when to sell corn, but I know when to sell pigs," he declares. He adds that he sells hogs when they are ready to go to market despite prices.

"However, a good marketing strategy is the most important aspect of a hog operation like ours," he adds. "For example, we try to phone four or five packers when we think we are ready to sell hogs. We've found as much as $2 per cwt. difference in the bids," he says.

A Farm Bureau member, Handorf has held all offices in the township and county. He has also served on the state Farm Bureau resolutions committee and state policy study committee. He was also a delegate to the American Farm Bureau resolutions committee.

Handorf was appointed by Secretary of Agriculture Earl Butz in 1973 to serve as chairman of the state ASCS committee.

In local activities, Handorf has been active in school affairs, serving as president of the Gladbrook Parent-Teachers Association, first president of Gladbrook American Field Service to promote international understanding for students, and member of the school board.

He is a township trustee and has been a member of the county Extension board, 4-H leader and township ASCS committeeman. He has also been on the board of directors for the local FS Supply Company.

A member of the Gladbrook Chapel United Methodist Church, Handorf has been Sunday school teacher and superintendent, a lay speaker, on the building committee and is currently chairman of the administrative board.

In an effort to promote better international understanding, the Handorfs have had young men from Japan, England, Sweden, South America and several African countries live in their home.

Handorf and his wife, Margaret, have four children. Craig is a graduate of Gladbrook Community College and farms with his dad. Alice (Mrs. Robert Sienknecht) attended Westmar College and is a farm homemaker. Lynn, a graduate of Iowa State University, farms with his dad. Sue (Mrs. Stanley Koster) graduated from Westmar College and is a homemaker.

Robert Rawson
Cherokee County

Robert Rawson operates 1,060 acres in partnership with his twin sons, Jack and Jerry. The farm's main enterprise is a herd of 250 crossbred cows. He also feeds out approximately 300 calves annually.

A firm believer in records and herd improvement, Rawson began with 70 Hereford cows in 1967 and steadily built numbers and quality. Only superior, performance tested sires have been used naturally. However, he now uses artificial insemination for about 25 days.

Beginning with Charolais, Rawson has infused Simmental, Gelbvieh, Brown Swiss and Red Angus into his herd. Birth weight of his calves last year averaged 87 to 101 pounds.

This breeding has produced the Champion Progeny Group of Five (live basis) in the futurity division of the

Robert Rawson
Cherokee county

1972 National Beef Improvement Association records. It was a Simmental-Hereford that gained 4.8 pounds per day and had a yearling weight of over 1,400 pounds.

Part of this success can be attributed to good culling, as well as good breeding. Heifers and cows are retained for the herd on the basis of femininity, weaning weights and calving ease.

"If a cow gives birth to a 'small' 65- to 70-pound calf, her records are reviewed to determine her previous calves gain ability," says Rawson. She is culled if those calves did poorly. Cows again come under scrutiny when calf-weaning weights are available.

Rawson is well-known for his pasture management. He's succeeded in building his pasture fertility and management so that each cow requires less than an acre of land.

A member of the Iowa Beef Improvement Association, Rawson last year received that organization's commercial cow-calf producer of the year award. He also serves on IBIA's sire evaluation committee.

Rawson has appeared on the program at Siouxland Beef Days, at a multi-state program in St. Joseph, Mo., and has spoken at the Corn Belt Cow-Calf Conference at Ottumwa.

An advocate of conservation, Rawson has served on the Cherokee County Conservation Board 10 years. His farm received the Cherokee County Soil Conservation Achievement award.

Other activities include serving on the county Extension board. Past activities include school board member and president, board member and past president of the Marcus Co-op Oil Company, as well as past board member and president of the Farmers Co-op Elevator of Pierson.

Rawson and his wife, Marsaline, have 11 children. Dorothy (Mrs. Dale Nachazel) lives in Colorado Springs, Colorado; Sylvia (Mrs. Ronald Fischer) in Hinton, Iowa; Jerry and Jack both live in Pierson, Iowa; Mary Lou (Mrs. Ronald Badtram) in Ashland, Oregon; Bonnie and Margaret in Minneapolis, Minnesota; Roberta in Muscatine, Iowa; Tyrone Artz in Wichita, Kansas; Marcia (Mrs. Frank Escue) in Cherokee, Iowa; and Tyler Artz in Rochester, Minnesota.

Louis D. Tronchetti
Greene county

Louis Tronchetti
Greene County

Louis D. Tronchetti farms 1,140 acres in a family operation with sons, Barry and Dan. They maintain a purebred SPF herd of Durocs. They farrow about 70 litters per year and have sold breeding stock in several states and three counties.

Tronchetti has been a diversified farmer since beginning in 1947 with grain farming, cattle feeding and commercial swine production. Cattle feeding was discontinued several years ago and those facilities have been converted to hog production.

Sows are farrowed in a remodeled barn on solid concrete with farrowing stalls. The barn becomes a nursery when the pigs are weaned. Hogs are finished in an open front remodeled cattle shed with a solid concrete feeding floor. Breeding and gestation is done on dirt lots with portable buildings.

Tronchetti is an innovator in the hog business in that he production tests the boars he sells. As president of the Iowa SPF Association, he encourages other SPF producers to do on-farm production testing.

In local activities, Tronchetti has served eight years as a 4-H leader, six years on the Greene County fair board and a term as president.

A longtime Farm Bureau member, he has served as a director on the county board.

For nine years, Tronchetti served on the board of directors of the local Federal Land Bank. He has also held all offices in the Greene County Beef Producers.

Other honors include being named an Iowa Master Swine Producer in 1960. The local Jaycees named him Greene County Outstanding Farmer in 1961. He won the Greene County corn yield contest in 1976.

The Tronchettis are member of the First United Methodist Church in Jefferson. Tronchetti and his wife, Neva, have two children. Barry, a graduate of Jefferson Community High School, farms with his parents. Dan, a senior at Iowa State University, is also returning to the farming operation.

IOWA MASTER FARMERS
~
March 24, 1979

Five top Iowa farmers were named Master Farmers for 1979 at an awards luncheon at Adventureland Inn in Des Moines, March 22. Brief descriptions of their operations and activities are listed here.

The 1979 selections bring the total to 284 men and two women who have received the award since 1926.

Judges were Wesley Shafer, president, Master Farmer Club; Ervin J.J. Koos, vice president, Master Farmer Club: Everett Stoneberg, Iowa State University farm management specialist; and Monte Sesker, editor, *Wallaces Farmer*.

Kuecker

Dick Kuecker
Kossuth County

Dick Kuecker owns and operates 360 acres. Plus, he custom farms an additional 160 acres. Crops, however, take a backseat to his purebred Yorkshire herd.

With the help of his family and a full-time herdsman, Kuecker farrows over 1,500 pigs annually, two-thirds of which are sold as breeding stock. In a recent production sale, Kuecker's boars and gilts were sold to breeders in 14 states, Canada, Mexico and Japan.

In five out of the past six years, Kuecker has showed either the grand or reserve champion Yorkshire boar at the National Barrow Show in Austin, Minn. Last year, they showed both the grand and reserve champion boar.

Kuecker keeps his sow herd confined in open front gestation houses and concrete pens. Breeding is done both artificially and through natural service.

Sows are farrowed in a farrowing pen arrangement which Kuecker designed himself. These pens are arranged so that sows can be let out easily for feeding and exercise. Pigs are grown out in two open front finishing facilities.

In 1976, Kuecker built a sales pavilion on his farm to handle his regular purebred sales. This modern facility contains a sale ring, office and pens where prospective customers can inspect the sale offering.

In addition to

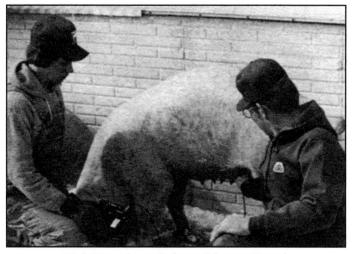

Dick Kuecker, right, with son Randy

his Kossuth County farm, Kuecker also owns farms in Ringgold County, Iowa and Adair County, Mo. Cow-calf operations are the main enterprise on these two farms. They are rented out on a crop- and livestock-share agreement.

Kuecker has been quite active in his community having served 10 years on the Algona Public School Board, three years as president. He also serves on the Federal Land Bank Board, the Iowa Swine Test Station Board and is past president of the Iowa Yorkshire Association and Iowa Pure-bred Council.

He's a Farm Bureau member, a member of the Iowa Cattlemen's Association and has been active in the Iowa Pork Producers Association. He served as president of the Kossuth County Pork Producers for six years. In 1968, he received the Iowa Master Seedstock Producers award.

Kuecker is a member of Immanuel Lutheran Church at Lone Rock where he is an elder and Sunday school teacher.

He and his wife, Beverly, have four children. Randy, 20, has returned home from Iowa State University to join the farming operation; Sheila, 18, Keith, 15, and Kimberly, 7, all attend Algona Public School.

Virginia Striegel
Keokuk County

Virginia Striegel farms 200 acres with the help of sons James, Charles, and Paul. Her main enterprise, however, is a herd of 120 sows.

The hog operation is a farrow-to-finish confinement operation. Even though she has new farrowing and nursery facilities, she did remodel some old dairy buildings into hog facilities as well. She manages a continuous farrowing operation and sells hogs grade and yield at 200 to 210 pounds every other week.

On the crop acres, Mrs. Striegel buys machinery and her sons operate it to help her get the crops in and harvested. However, she handles the livestock operation by herself.

Mrs. Striegel recently installed a new feeding system in which the feed is blown underground in air tubes from the mill to the buildings. This eliminates grinding and hauling that she used to have to do every day.

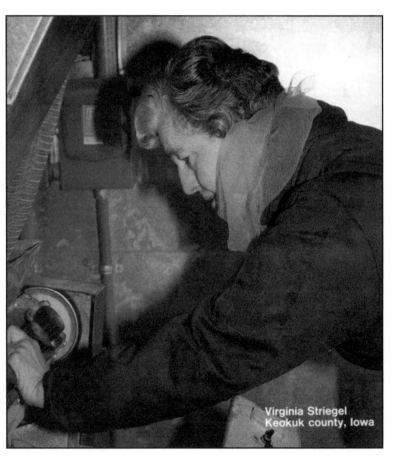
Virginia Striegel
Keokuk county, Iowa

Active in Farm Bureau, Mrs. Striegel is vice president of Keokuk County Farm Bureau. She has served on many Farm Bureau committees and has been director of the Farm Bureau Women's Chorus for about 15 years.

Mrs. Striegel is a director of the Keokuk

County Hospital board. She has been chairman of the Women's Farm Bureau board and is an assistant State Soil Conservation District Commissioner for

Rempp hitched up his disc behind the stalk shredder.

Keokuk County. In 1977, she was appointed to the State Soil Conservation Committee by Gov. Robert Ray.

A member of the Pork Producers Association, Mrs. Striegel has won a number of trophies and prizes.

A member of St. Joseph's Church in What Cheer, Mrs. Striegel has been active with the church choir and has taught religious education for about 25 years. She personally sings at nursing homes, senior citizen's dinners, etc.

Mrs. Striegel's husband died in an automobile accident 19 years ago when her youngest child was two years old. Children ranged in age from two to 14 years old. Besides taking over the farming operation, she raised a family of seven boys. Marion, a farmer, along with other employment, lives at Oskaloosa. James lives in Delta, Iowa, and is a farmer. Charles is a farmer and lives at What Cheer. Paul is also a farmer and lives at What Cheer. Floyd lives in Ojai, Calif. Phil lives in Missouri Valley. Michael is a senior at Iowa State University.

William Rempp
Poweshiek County

William Rempp farms 720 acres. He and his son, Kevin, have a farrow-to-finish hog operation. They handle about 900 head of hogs per year. They also feed out about 85 head of cattle a year.

Rempp believes the term "bigness" is overemphasized in many aspects of agriculture today. "I'm more interest-

Rempp

ed in net return in both livestock and cropping operations than to expand to the point where a large amount of each year's profits have to be used for loan payments. Further, I don't want a lot of large bills for someone else to pay if something should happen to me," he adds.

A firm believer in saving time and energy, Rempp pulls a stalk shredder in front of his disc in a single, attached unit. This unit is run both ahead of the moldboard plow and chisel plow. He says advantages include stalks are shred and cut up so well that plowing and chiseling is easier. Further, the disc behind the stalk shredder incorporates stalks before they are blown all over the field.

Active in Farm Bureau, Rempp has been past membership chairman, past vice president and is now president of Poweshiek County Farm Bureau. He is chairman of the county's national policy committee.

Rempp has been president of the Montezuma Lions Club, past president of Poweshiek County Cattlemen's Association, and has been a delegate to the state and national Cattlemen's Association conventions.

He was named outstanding young farmer in his area in 1962. He received second place in state competition sponsored by the Jaycees.

Rempp has served as a member and advisor for the Farmers Home Administration. He is also a member of the Pork Producers Organization.

A member of the Jackson Church of Christ, Rempp is past chairman of the church board, past treasurer and has served as a trustee. He is Sunday school superintendent and has been a Sunday school teacher for several years. He also serves as a deacon.

Rempp and his wife, Marjorie, have two children. Denise (Mrs. Steve Harlan) is a registered nurse and lives in Iowa City. Kevin, a graduate of Montezuma Community High School, farms with his dad.

Curtis Pflum
Des Moines County

Curtis Pflum is the first Master Farmer from Des Moines County since 1927. With the help of one full-time employee, he and his family farm 1,450 acres, primarily corn and soybeans.

They run a 40-cow beef herd to make use of some rough land, and this past year have updated their swine facilities. The farrow-to-finish hog operation is being expanded to 110 sows. He plans to farrow 20 sows a month in confinement.

Starting out in 1956 by renting 120 acres on a crop-share lease, Pflum likes the idea of being diversified. Pflum feels the diversified farmer is better able to financially survive in today's agriculture. "That's particularly true of the hog farmer," he observes. "Over the years, as a way to market cheap corn, hogs have been pretty good property."

Pflum

He spent a lot of time visiting other farmers with various kinds of confinement hog setups before deciding on which route to take.

Cropping land that borders the Mississippi River, Pflum wrestles with a wide range of soil types, often within the same field. "That can make weed control, tillage and fertilizer application kind of tricky," he notes. Spot checks showed a strong 45-bushel per acre for his beans and a 130-bushel-per-acre corn yield average last fall.

Conscious of trying to hold down crop costs, he's doubled up on some operations to save a trip over the field. "It's tough to hold down machinery costs and still be tooled up

enough to get fieldwork finished on time," he observes.

He harvests his entire acreage with one combine (six-row corn head). "We practically live in it in the fall," he says. "But since these things cost more than 80 acres did, not too many years ago, it sure helps out by being able to get by with only one. To get the most use out of machinery and still get top trade in value, you have to take darn good care of it."

A good set of records is a valuable tool in helping make financial decisions. "Records take time, but it pays to know your production costs and returns when you're trying to decide where to spend that last dollar," he says. "Especially when much of your land is rented like mine is."

Pflum recently installed a grain leg and dump pit for his storage bins. In tune with the sentiments of most farmers, he admits that he'd like to become a better marketer of what he produces.

In addition to duties on his second, three-year term as a Federal Land Bank director, Pflum is also a township trustee and chairman of his township ASCS committee. Past president of Des Moines County Pork Producers Association, he was recently elected to the Des Moines-Louisa county levee board. A member of St. Luke's United Church of Christ, Burlington, he's served on the church council.

Pflum and his wife, Joan, have four boys. Kyle is 20, Randy is 17, Rick is 13 and Marc is 5.

Don Nielsen
Clay County

Don Nielsen farms 870 acres. Crops include corn, soybeans, oats and hay. He handles about 900 head of cattle a year. A 500 head modified open front hog confinement building will be completed in 1979.

Nielsen feeds his cattle in the open yard and provides adequate concrete in each lot to keep cattle out of the mud. He also utilizes corncobs for bedding. However, about half of his corn is harvested as shelled corn.

"I couldn't get the neighbors to help shell corn any more," he quips. So, he went to high moisture shelled corn. Now, what corn is left over after his sealed storage structures and concrete stave silos are filled, he picks on the ear and shells later.

Even though Nielsen is primarily a cattleman, he is getting back into the hog business. "I used to raise hogs when I had a neighboring college student to work for me. However, he went off on his own and I didn't want to hire an extra man at that time. But, now I've decided to go into the business and maybe hire some help."

Records are important to Nielsen. He relies on the computer-feeding program offered by Felco, Land O' Lakes to figure least-cost rations. He figures his cattle have been gaining 2.5 to 2.8 pounds per day on a ration of hay, cracked corn and corn silage.

Nielsen is a member of Northwest Iowa Farm Business Association, which provides a complete analysis of his whole program at the end of the year.

"Trading for new equipment is an important part of my management program," notes

Nielsen

Nielsen. He trades his main tractors every four years. He feels this reduces down-time because his equipment is in better condition. He also says investment credit and depreciation help justify frequent trades for new equipment.

In local activities, Nielsen served six years on the Everly Community School board.

He has served as secretary and president of the Everly Co-op Elevator board and served three years on the F.H.A. Board. In other activities, Nielsen is a member and past president of the Everly Lions Club and is on the Hartley Community Hospital board. He also is a member of the Clay County Cattlemen's Board.

A member of the United Methodist Church of Everly, Nielsen is chairman of the administrative board, is a past lay leader, finance chairman and Sunday school superintendent. He is also active in United Methodist men and is a member of the chancel choir.

Nielsen and his wife, Marlene, have three children. Lori is a 1978 graduate of Everly Community School and is living at home. Brenda is a junior and Shelley is a freshman at Everly High School.

Nielsen installed an electric gate in this feed lot.

CHAPTER 6

~

1980 - 1989:
Inflation, Farm Financial Crisis

In the 1970s, farmers "learned" that borrowing relatively low interest rate money to buy land that was "certain" to be worth more tomorrow "worked." They applied the same logic to buying machinery. Many farmers bought land and machinery on variable interest rate loans.

Throughout the 1970s, Washington had tried various strategies to control inflation. None succeeded. By borrowing to buy, farmers were structuring their debt-and-asset portfolios to profit from inflation, which they expected would continue, or even accelerate.

No longer crying "wolf"

In October 1979, new Federal Reserve Board Chairman, Paul Volcker, launched a policy of sustained monetary restraint. It involved higher interest rates, larger reserve requirements and changes in Federal Reserve operating procedures to slow money-supply growth rate. After repeated failed efforts to control inflation in the 1970s, it was little surprise that most Americans, including farmers, viewed the Fed's action as another instance of Uncle Sam crying wolf.

But chairman Volcker and the Fed remained resolute. Core inflation, which surpassed 11% in 1979, fell to less than 5% in 1982.

Cure is painful

Unfortunately, wringing inflation out of the economy caused great pain for those who had borrowed heavily to buy. Interest rates shot up. Cash flow needs to service variable interest rate debt skyrocketed. But the "buy now" inflationary mentality kept pushing land values higher to a $2,147 an acre peak in 1981.

Actual inflation was coming in much lower than farmers' expectations. Still, through 1980 and 1981 most highly-leveraged farmers did not restructure their debt-and-asset portfolios in line with lower inflation; some because they expected inflation would resurge, and others because their heavy debt load made refinancing difficult.

Farmers began defaulting on loans and installment land contracts. Lenders began foreclosing. Defaults and foreclosures dumped land on the market. Land prices plummeted. Lower land values made more loans go bad. The tailspin in land values finally bottomed at $787 an acre in 1986.

Once the tailspin began, most highly-leveraged farmers could not realign their debt-and-asset portfolios with the new reality of lower inflation fast enough, if at all.

Grain export growth stalls

As the Fed fought inflation, a major world recession hit in 1981. Grain exports faltered, stocks built and prices sagged. Farmers earned less income as debt-service requirements climbed.

Some blame the export slump on President Jimmy Carter's partial embargo on grain exports to the Soviet Union after the Soviets invaded Afghanistan in 1980. Others contend that the "high" target prices in the 1981 Farm Bill created a price umbrella under which foreign competitors could expand production and gain market share. The worldwide recession reduced the rate of demand increase for food.

For many farmers, the early 1980s were, indeed, bleak.

Iowa State University economists looked at earnings of the high, medium and low profit groups of Iowa Farm Business Association farms. The Iowa data revealed just how concentrated the debt was in the early stages of what became known as the "farm debt crisis." The Iowa numbers showed that 10% of farm operators had debt-to-asset ratios above 70%, held 9% of the assets and were responsible for 25% of the debt. A total of 28% of the farmers had debt-to-asset ratios over 40% (which was viewed as the danger line), held 30% of the assets and were responsible for 65% of the debt. That was worrisome for the lenders involved as well as for the farm debtors.

Focus on conservation

Conservation interests had a greater influence on the 1985 Farm Bill. Conservation compliance became a requirement for getting farm program payments.

The 1985 bill also launched the Conservation Reserve Program. In the following 20 years, CRP's goals shifted and expanded. But in 1985, policymakers saw three goals for CRP:

* Take land out of production to trim surplus stocks and hopefully lift prices.

* Idle environmentally-fragile land to capture conservation benefits for society.

* Inject cash into rural communities for farmers to pay bills and debts thereby helping to sustain rural communities.

By 1989, Iowa land values had bounced $352 off their low to $1,139 an acre. Mike Duffy, an Iowa State University economist, contends the 1985 Farm Bill drove the rebound. "The 1985 bill brought a big step up in government farm program payments," he explains. "I believe farmers rapidly capitalized those payments into land values."

1980 Iowa Farm Facts

FARMS & INCOME

Number of Iowa farms	119,000
Crop production value	$4.2 billion
Livestock production value	$5.5 billion
Iowa net farm income	$469 million

LIVESTOCK

	Inventory	Average price
Cattle and calves	7.1 million head	$65.36/cwt (beef)
Hogs and pigs	16.1 million head	$38.87/cwt
	Production	Inventory
Chickens (Layers)	1.8 billion eggs	7.6 million birds
Milk	4.0 billion lbs.	

CROPS

	Harvested acres	Yield	Production	Avg price
All Hay	2.2 million	3.54 tons/acre	8 million tons	$48.5/ton
Corn	13.3 million	110 bu./acre	1.5 billion bu.	$2.97/bu.
Soybeans	8.3 million	38.5 bu./acre	318 million bu.	$7.44/bu.
Oats	1 million	62 bu./acre	62 million bu.	$1.71/bu.
Wheat	92,000	38 bu./acre	3.5 million bu.	$3.85/bu.

IOWA MASTER FARMERS
~
March 22, 1980

Six top Iowa farmers have been named Master Farmers for 1980.

Wallaces Farmer has sponsored the Master Farmer program since 1926. The honor is aimed at calling attention to the high level of management these men demonstrate and to award them for unselfishly devoting part of their time to community leadership roles.

The 1980 selections bring the total to 290 men and two women who have received the award since 1926.

Francis M. Toale
Buchanan County

Francis Toale returned home from the Navy in 1945 to join his parents' crop, dairy and hog operation.

Thirty-four years later, he and his son Don are farming the same land now expanded to 640 acres. The cows are gone but not the hogs.

Toale annually farrow-to-finishes 1,400 hogs. The hog operation utilizes a mix of remodeled and new buildings.

Sows are farrowed in an old barn converted to a farrowing house in 1966. Approximately 45 sows are farrowed four times annually. The farrowing unit has 18 stalls and 12 pens. Sows and pigs are moved from stalls, to 6- by 10-foot pens as stalls are needed for other sows.

Pigs are weaned at three weeks of age and moved to a 23- by 44-foot, 300 -pig environmentally controlled nursery purchased in 1978.

Toale finishes his hogs out in a 36- by 100-foot totally enclosed, partially slatted unit built in 1975.

Manure from the hog operation is knifed into the crop ground, a practice Toale says reduces odor and saves plant nutrients.

The 600 acres of cropland on the Toale farm are fairly evenly split between corn and soybeans. All soybean and some corn ground is chisel plowed.

Since 1956, Toale has tiled all his land, working closely with the ASCS to lay out his tile lines. He is currently an ASCS committeeman.

Active in his community, he's been a county Farm Bureau committeeman and served on the farm market and steering committee. He was a 4-H club leader for 10 years.

A charter member of the Buchanan County Pork Producers Association, Toale has held various offices in that group. He and his wife, Clara, have been active in pork producer promotional activities. Last year, they traveled

Toale

to San Diego, Calif., on a Fine Meats promotion with other producers to help promote pork. In 1966, Toale was named a state Master Pork Producer.

A member of St. John's Catholic Church in Independence, Toale ushers and has served on his church's advisory board, finance committee, parish school board and been an officer on the parish council.

Toale is currently a township trustee and election worker. Also, he is president of the Buchanan County Co-op Association board of directors and is a director of the Northeast Iowa Experiment farm near Nashua.

Francis and Clara have six children. Rosemary (Mrs. Ron Engelhardt) is living in Elkader, Iowa. Richard lives in Cedar Rapids, and Roger resides in Los Angeles, Calif. Thomas is a third-year seminarian at St. Paul, Minn. Sue is a student at St. Catherine's in St. Paul and Donald has returned home to join the family-farming operation.

David L. Williams
Page County

David Williams and son Bruce are full partners in a 590-acre swine and beef operation. They farrow 120 to 130 sows twice a year and handle 100 beef cows in a cross-breeding program.

Disease prevention in both the swine and beef herds is important to Williams. He started an SPF foundation swine herd 16 years ago and has stayed free of external parasites since, even though it is not an SPF herd at this time.

His swine herd is state accredited brucellosis and pseudorabies free. He maintains a testing program to sell gilts.

The Williams handle corn and soybeans in a rotation system in 30-inch rows. Williams does not own a large horsepower tractor but figures it is more economical to rent one.

Moldboard plowing hasn't been used on the Williams farm for at least five years. They use a heavy disc and chisel plow as well as let the cows graze the stalks. They like to chisel the bean ground in the fall.

A Page County district soil commissioner, Williams believes too many farmers are cropping rough ground that shouldn't be in production. He says the alfalfa and brome grass pastures would be a better utilization of this type of ground.

Active in various organizations, Williams has been a director for the Tallcorn Cooperative since 1963 and served one term as president. He is a member of the board of directors of Farmland Industries, Inc.

Williams

Williams is a member of various livestock producers organizations, and the Page County Farm Bureau. He has served as a leader on the county 4-H youth committee, and the county Extension council. He was instrumental in the formation of a non-profit organization to build and operate a nursing home in Villisca. He served as co-chairman of a community fund drive to raise money to buy and furnish a local youth center. He is also a director of Valfco, a locally owned aluminum foundry.

Active in church leadership roles, Williams is a Sunday school teacher and has served on various boards of the United Methodist Church.

Williams and his wife, Corrine, have five children. Stuart, a forestry graduate of Northern Arizona University, is now with ACORN in Denver, Colo. Bruce, an Iowa State University graduate, farms with his father. Brian is a senior at the University of Arizona in Tucson. Sarah is a senior in high school and Steve is in eighth grade.

George A. Helmers
Osceola County

"Farming is my life. I really enjoy it. You get a lot of satisfaction at the end of the year if you have a good harvest, and fields have been kept weed-free."

Those are the thoughts of George Helmers, only the second from Osceola County to be named Master Farmer.

Helmers farms 800 acres, primarily corn and soybeans, in northwest Iowa. Twelve-row equipment (planter, cultivator) is used to increase labor productivity as Helmers does most of the farming himself. Part-time help is hired during the spring and fall.

In addition to raising crops, Helmers also finishes 1,000 feeder pigs a year. Hogs are fed a corn, soybean meal, oat ration.

Helmers is a firm believer in keeping operating costs low. Existing buildings have been modified to handle the hog operation. Hogs are finished on cement lots.

Helmers was named a State Master Pork Producer in 1961. He also raises 120 head of cattle a year. Yearling heifers are fed on a high roughage program. Steer calves are grazed on nontillable acres, brought into the finishing yard in December and sold in the spring.

Active in many organizations, Helmers has served on the Sibley school board since 1966 and has been board president three years.

He has also served as an officer and director in the Farmers Co-op Elevator (Sibley), Osceola County Cattle Feeders and Pork Producers Associations.

Helmers is also a member of state Extension advisory council, Ameri-can Legion, Farm Bureau, Sibley Rotary Club (past president), township ASCS committee, township trustee since 1949 and Northwest Iowa Experimental Farm development committee.

Active in the Sibley United Methodist Church, Helmers has been a trustee, finance committee member, high school youth counselor and Sunday school teacher. He also sings in the choir and is currently chairman of World Hunger Committee.

He and his wife, Dolores, have three children, all of whom are graduates of Iowa State University. Scott is a medical doctor practicing in Sibley. Cynthia (Mrs. Brian Kemp) operates a sewing shop in Sibley. She was Miss Iowa in 1971. Rick is currently studying medicine at the University of Iowa.

James E. Sage
Black Hawk County

James Sage handles 590 acres in a corn, oats, hay and pasture rotation system. He also feeds out 180 head of cattle a year, and produces 1,000 head of hogs a year, farrowing 110 to 115 sows in a pasture farrowing setup.

Sage says he is very much sold on rotation for the type of land they farm. Some of the fields are in a four and some in a six-year rotation system. Sage credits the pasture rotation system as one of the reasons he's still in the cattle business. "The cattle are able to utilize the pasture and hay and provide fertilizer." Sage is concerned about the intensive use of nonrenewable resources such as N, P and K.

"These resources won't last forever,"

Helmers

he says, "I'd like to leave something for my children and their children."

As a confirmation of this fact, Sage Farm received the "Four Ton Club" membership in 1977 for recognition of staying within Iowa's allowable soil loss table.

In his cattle feeding operation, Sage buys 500- to 600-pound calves from the western part of North Dakota. He likes to feed heifers and feels their rate of gain is comparable to steers, and he doesn't feed them as long as steers. His cattle are fed on pasture and in open lot, and he has switched to upright sealed storage and silage bags for storing grain and haylage.

Sage

Sage's main enterprise is his 110- to 115-sow summer pasture farrowing operation. He has three other farrowings of 12 sows each, two in the fall and one in February. He also farrows 12 gilts in April to test new boars before he includes them in the overall breeding program.

Sage was named an Iowa Master Pork Producer in 1965.

A firm believer in soil and wildlife conservation, Sage has set aside approximately nine acres for wildlife habitat. He has planted trees and he built a pond in 1973.

A member of the Black Hawk County Pork Producers, Sage was secretary in 1964. He is a member of the Black Hawk County Livestock Feeders Association and was secretary-treasurer. Sage is treasurer of the Black Hawk County Farm Bureau, and is a member of the Northeast Iowa Experimental Farm, and served as a director for four years. Sage has been 4-H leader for five years, and has served on various county Extension committees. He was a member of the Black Hawk County Soil Conservation Board and was chairman for three years.

Sage has served as president of the Waterloo Community School board and is a member of the Masonic Equity Lodge No. 131. He is also a member of the Waterloo Chamber of Commerce and served on the Black Hawk County Selective Service Board for eight years.

In church activities, Sage is a member and has served as deacon, trustee, and elder in the First Presbyterian Church in Waterloo and has taught Sunday school there.

Sage and his wife, Ann, have four children. Tim is a sophomore in farm operations at Iowa State University. Amy is a senior at the Capitol Page School in Washington, D.C. and is a page in the House of Representatives. Craig is a sophomore at East High in Waterloo and Pat is in kindergarten at Krieg School in Waterloo.

Larry and John Wall
Johnson County

Brothers Larry and John Wall operate 653 acres in a 50-50 partnership in addition to feeding approximately 200 head of cattle annually. The partnership has placed emphasis on their swine enterprise.

Beginning with a pasture farrowing operation 20 years ago with 60 sows, the partnership now farrows about 130 sows twice annually in total confinement.

The brothers were considered innovators

14 years ago when they were among the first in their area to build a slatted floor nursery. The farrow-to-finish operation today is totally confined.

John says the move to confinement was made to better utilize available labor and to tie up less ground for cropping. He adds that confinement also provided more consistent production, removing many uncertainties such as weather.

Firm believers in saving the soil, the Wall brothers have practiced conservation tillage the past 10 years. The chisel plow is the primary tillage tool replacing the moldboard plow.

The 23-year-old partnership is "strictly a family operation although two families are involved," says John. All expenses and returns are split down the middle. Labor devoted to specific enterprises is more or less divided by the two brothers. Larry and John's wives, Margaret and Mary Ellen, are in charge of keeping the records for both crops and livestock.

Each of the Wall brothers has been active in both state and local activities. They were named Master Pork Producers in 1963 and have received other additional recognition for hog management.

In addition, Larry has served as member and president of the West Branch School board and director of the Farmland boar test station at Lisbon. He also has been secretary of the Johnson County Cattlemen's Associa-tion, as well as that county's Extension council and fair board, serving as president for both groups. Larry also is a director of the First National Bank of Iowa City.

Larry and his wife, Margaret, have five children. They are: Patricia (Mrs. Dennis Corcoran) Lake Orion, Mich; Lawrence, Jr., Tipton, Iowa; Jane, now obtaining her MS at the University of Washington in Seattle; JoEllen (Mrs. Roy Browning, Jr.) Riverside, Iowa; and Barbara (Mrs. Steven Smith) McFarland, Wis.

John Wall has served as director and president of the Johnson County Pork Producers Association and is a director on the Iowa Pork Producers Association state board. He's currently serving as secretary of that board. John has also served on the legislative and membership committees of his county Farm Bureau and is on the pork advisory committee for the Iowa Farm Bureau Federation. He's a member of the Johnson County Agriculture Association, American Legion and the Knights of Columbus. John also has taken an active role as a 4-H club leader and livestock judging coach.

Larry Wall (left) and John Wall (right)

John and his wife, Mary Ellen, have two children. Tom is a sophomore at Iowa State University. Mary is a junior at West Branch High School.

Both Larry and John are active members of St. Bridget's Catholic Church at Nolan Settlement.

1981
IOWA MASTER FARMERS
~
March 28, 1981

Wallaces Farmer has sponsored the Master Farmer program since 1926. The honor is aimed at calling attention to the high level of management these men demonstrate and to award them for unselfishly devoting part of their time to community leadership.

Alan Stevens
Worth County

"It's vital to stay on top of things when farming. If you don't keep expanding or improving in some area, your enterprise starts deteriorating."

Alan Stevens has used these words to build a strong operating foundation for his farm. He's constantly looking for ways to improve his farming operation, while keeping costs down.

In 1970, the Worth County farmer converted a dairy barn into a hog finishing facility.

Stevens recently built a 500-head finishing unit he hopes will increase feed efficiency.

He produces 2,500 hogs a year in a farrow-to-finish operation.

Stevens farms about 400 acres, primarily raising corn and soybeans. All 400 acres are tiled. Stevens also helped organize an area watershed – the Deer Creek Watershed – and

Alan Stevens

Stevens

serves on the watershed committee.

Active in many community organizations and activities, Stevens has served on the Northwood-Kensett School advisory committee. He's also a member of the Worth County Farm Bureau, where he has held several offices, including president. Stevens was the first president of the Worth County Swine Producers and was named Master Swine Producer in 1964.

Stevens is also involved in working with young people as a 4-H project leader, through Extension council and various 4-H committees.

He and his family belong to the First Lutheran Church in Northwood. Stevens is past president of the church's congregation and council.

When not busy with community affairs, Stevens likes to collect and restore antique tractors. He and his two sons, son-in-law and father currently have 20 John Deere tractors.

He and his wife, Mavis, have four children. Michael, in addition to helping his father, farms 360 acres. Susan (Mrs. Stephen Pederson) lives near Saint Ansgar. Jill is attending a cosmetology school in Mason City. Tom is a fifth grader at Northwood-Kensett Grade School.

James Jorgensen, Jr.
Franklin County

The wind can blow hard over the flat, open fields in northern Iowa, taking with it valuable topsoil. Like other Iowa farmers, James Jorgensen, Jr. knows the importance of soil conservation. Saving that rich topsoil is vital, especially when you're farming land that has been in your family for three generations.

"I don't know any farmer who isn't willing to cut the number of trips across the field or to do as much with conservation as possible," says Jorgensen. "Switching from conventional practices to conservation tillage is primarily a matter of gaining confidence in doing something new."

Jorgensen operates about 1,800 acres, growing corn and soybeans. Corn is planted in 30-inch rows and beans are grown in 20-inch rows. Seed production is a big part of Jorgensen's operation. About 400 acres of corn are raised as seed corn. Seed beans are produced on all his soybean acreage.

During harvest, grain is easily handled with Jorgensen's nearly 160,000-bushel on-farm storage. Included with the storage is a 90-foot grain leg.

Jorgensen also raises about 3,000 head of hogs a year in partnership with his father. The

Jorgensen

215

farrow-to-finish operation uses existing buildings which have been converted for hog production. Hogs are sold grade and yield.

Two full-time employees help Jorgensen with the various aspects of his farming enterprise.

When not farming, Jorgensen enjoys keeping busy with two of his favorite hobbies – collecting unusual antiques and restoring antique tractors.

Jorgensen's many activities and community work include serving on the Franklin General Hospital board (chairman for two years), the Iowa Falls Farmers Co-op Elevator board, and the Farmland Foods (Kansas City, Mo.) board.

Other organizations he has served include Franklin County Extension council, North Iowa Area Development Program and ASCS. In addition, Jorgensen is a member of Trinity Lutheran Church in Hampton.

Jorgensen and his wife, Helen, have five children. Karen (Mrs. Roger Spath) is a teacher in Detroit, Mich. Jeanine is a senior at Morningside College, majoring in music. Peggy (Mrs. John Badger) lives near Hampton, Iowa. Barbara is a junior in Hampton High School. James is attending Hampton Junior High School.

Mogler

Howard P. Mogler
Lyon County

Ten years ago, Howard Mogler had "all his eggs in one basket." He fed 1,800 cattle, had no hogs and farmed 433 acres. His oldest of four sons was 12 years old.

But a lot can happen after 10 years, and Mogler's operation is almost totally different from what it was then. Today, he feeds 2,000 to 3,000 head of cattle, farms nearly 800 acres, and farrow-to-finishes approximately 4,500 hogs annually. His son Rodney, 23, the oldest of seven, manages the hog facility.

Mogler began farming with his father 25 years ago upon return from military service. He bought his father's share in 1961 and in 1976, began a family corporation for the cattle, swine and crop enterprises.

Approximately 200 of 600 acres of corn is chopped for silage, with the rest harvested for high moisture grain. All tillable acres are terraced. Mogler has practiced conservation tillage since 1957.

The cattle operation includes both yearlings and calves. Feeding facilities include open lots with fenceline bunks, scales for both livestock and ration formulation and a 640-head confinement shed.

Mogler's hog operation includes a 210-sow herd with a yearly 19.6 pigs weaned per sow average. Hogs go into the finishing unit at 50 pounds and are marketed at 218 pounds.

Confinement units were designed by Mogler. The finishing unit features a scraper system with aboveground liquid manure storage.

Mogler is currently on the Northwest Iowa Technical College board of directors. He's served six years on the Lyon County Cattle Feeders Association board, two years as county president and as a state vice president. He helped organize the Lyon County Cattle

Seberg

By 1969, with wife Louise keeping the books, he was raising 400 hogs in a farrow-to-finish operation and feeding out 75 cattle annually. That year his son, Duayne, joined the operation and they expanded cropland from 300 to 650 acres.

The Sebergs embarked on a major hog expansion in 1976. The farmers sized up the land market and decided raising more hogs would provide a better cash return on investment and better overall cash flow than buying more land.

The Sebergs built a 30-stall farrowing house and nursery in 1976. They also put up an eight-pen, 120-head capacity open front gestation house. They still use a 20-sow portable farrowing house. Their goal is to farrow 50 sows every six weeks. In December of 1979, they put the first pigs in a new 750-head capacity finishing house.

Last year, the Sebergs sold 1,850 market hogs. They finished 750 in a mixture of older buildings that were remodeled for hogs. They also sold 700 feeder pigs.

The Sebergs background about 300 head of calves a year. They generally buy 200 head in the fall at 450 pounds and sell them in the

Feeders. He is presently vice chairman of the National Cattlemen's Association grading and inspection committee and chairman of the joint grading subcommittee.

Mogler has served on several Extension service programs, planning committees, and two, three-year terms on the Merrill Pioneer Hospital board. He's a Lyon County State Bank director.

He is also an active member of the Apostolic Christian Church.

Howard and his wife, Lillian, have seven children. Rodney, 23, manages the hog corporation. Kent, 22, is a senior at Iowa State University. Brian, 19, is the assistant manager of the cattle and crop operations while twin sister, Beth, 19, is in her second year at Kirkwood Community College. Dwight, 15, Perry, 11, and Wendy, 10, attend West Lyon Community School.

Glen M. Seberg
Henry County

Glen Seberg returned home form the Navy in 1946 to join his parent's crop, hog and cattle operation.

Seberg

spring at about 750 pounds. They usually buy another 100 for summer feeding.

Glen Seberg has held every major office in the Olds American Legion and is a firm believer in veteran's programs.

Seberg was a member of the steering committee when the Wayland, Crawfordsville, Olds school district was formed in 1966. He's been a director for both the Olds Farmers Elevator and Henry County Cattlemen's Association.

The Sebergs attend Finley United Methodist Church. He's been lay leader, finance chairman and served on several church committees.

The Sebergs also have a daughter, Joyce. She is married to Ronald Deck and lives in Red Oak, Iowa.

John "Ted" Huser
Sac County

Change would be the best word to describe the history of John "Ted" Huser's farm. Huser had a high-producing Brown Swiss and Holstein dairy herd. But then he decided to disperse the herd in 1973 to expand his hog operation.

With the help of his son Paul, Huser has remodeled many of the dairy facilities to form the base of his farrow-to-finish operation. His goal is to farrow 24 sows every seven weeks. Currently he has a weaned average of eight pigs per litter.

Huser feels good records are a key to profitable production. He joined the swine enterprise record-keeping system two years ago and belongs to the Northwest Iowa Farm Business Association.

Huser

A strong advocate of conservation, Huser recently switched to conservation tillage on most of his land. Only 10% of the 500 acres he operates in partnership with his son Paul is moldboard plowed. A chisel plow and disc are used to ready the ground for corn and soybeans. Soil tests are conducted every three years to maintain the soil's fertility.

Other conservation practices include construction of a drainage ditch, 3,500 feet of "narrow-based" terraces and tiling. He also maintains a five-acre wildlife habitat and an extensive windbreak system.

Active in many organizations, Huser is a strong promoter of farm commodities.

He is a past chairman of the Iowa Soybean Promotion Board. He is also a member of the Sac County Farm Bureau.

Other activities include being a member of the Iowa State University Dean of Agriculture's advisory board, 4-H leader, Masonic Lodge and Cedar Township trustee.

A member of the Sac City Presbyterian Church, Huser has served as Sunday school teacher. He is also a church elder and trustee.

He and his wife, Rachel, have four children. All graduated or plan to attend ISU. David is a bank loan officer. Paul is farming with his farmer. Tim is a senior at ISU. Becky is a senior at Sac City High School and plans to attend ISU this fall.

1982
IOWA MASTER FARMERS
~
March 27, 1982

Wallaces Farmer is proud to name six Iowa producers Master Farmers for 1982. The Master Farmer program, sponsored by *Wallaces Farmer*, was begun in 1926 as a means of recognizing individuals demonstrating a high level of management and to award them for unselfishly devoting time to community leadership roles.

With the 1982 selections, a total of 301 men and women have been recognized over the past 56 years.

Judges were Earl Zumbach, president, Master Farmer Club; Roland Jensen, vice president, Master Farmer Club; Everett Stoneberg, Iowa State University farm management specialist; and Monte Sesker, editor, *Wallaces Farmer.*

Allen J. Korslund
Humboldt County

Since graduating from Iowa State University and returning to farm near Eagle Grove in 1951, Allen Korslund has produced a lot of crops and livestock. His wife, Charlene, has been right there helping him. "But the most important crop we ever raised," says Allen, "are those four boys."

Those sons admit that a few years ago – when getting up at 6 a.m. to pitch hog manure before school – sound business judgment, character and responsibility weren't on their minds. But that's what Korslund was teaching them.

"Our parents not only told us, they showed us that honesty, truthfulness and fair play are important to a happy life," says one son. "Also, no matter how busy dad is, he's always willing to sit down and discuss problems."

John, an Iowa State University veterinary medicine graduate, has farmed with his father since 1979. David is a correspondent banking officer for a Chicago bank. Doug is an electronics engineer for a livestock equipment firm. Jim is an ISU senior in agricultural engineering.

Korslund was an early pioneer in using herbicides and narrow row (30- and 15-inch) soybeans. His consistently high bean yields have won county contests several times. The Korslunds use minimum tillage on bean stubble, keep accurate field records and yield check varieties each fall.

They have one full-time employee, Kurt Friesth. The 260-sow herd is farrowed in a two-year-old facility that has four farrowing rooms (11 stalls each), a breeding area and nursery. Other innovations include efficient use of remodeled buildings for hogs, an on-farm feed processing center, and use of artificial insemination with frozen semen to maintain a completely closed herd.

The Korslunds produced 450 hogs in 1981, averaging 8.1 pigs weaned per litter. About half of the production is sold as feeder pigs. Finished hogs are sold grade and yield, averaging $1.50 to $2 premium per hundredweight.

Al has served on the Eagle Grove School board for 12 years, six as president. A 4-H leader and member of the county Extension council, he also serves on the Iowa Central Community College advisory board. He was named a Master Pork Producer in 1969.

Korslund is an active member of Eagle Grove Evangelical Lutheran Church.

Korslund started his four children on 4-H projects, which eventually paid for their college education.

Korslund

Philip R. Stillman
Palo Alto County

In 1954, Phil Stillman started farming by renting land on a crop-share basis. He borrowed $5,000 from the bank, bought a tractor and three sows, and borrowed machinery from his brother and brother-in-law in exchange for labor.

Today, he and wife, Ann, raise 215 acres of corn, 215 acres of soybeans and 20 acres of oats. With the help of a part-time employee, they also feed out about 200 head of cattle per year and have 25 sows in a farrow-to-finish hog operation.

But farm life isn't all work for the Stillmans. They are active in community affairs, their church and politics. Phil and Ann have four children. Marsha is a senior in high school, Maria is a junior and Michelle is a freshman. Son Mark attends grade school.

Stillman was a 4-H leader for 10 years, president of his county 4-H federation and recipient of a 4-H Alumni Award in 1979.

Stillman is active in Farm Bureau, including three years as county president and delegate to state and national conventions. He is on the board of directors of the local FS Co-op and is director of Top of Iowa Marketing Association.

Other recognition includes being named Palo Alto County's outstanding farmer in 1976. He has also served on Gov. Ray's Health Planning Council. Stillman is an active member of St. Thomas Catholic

Stillman

Church in Emmetsburg.

Stillman raises corn and beans in 30-inch rows. He doesn't think raising beans in narrower rows would be worth the effort on his farm. He's already getting above-average yields and says it's hard to justify the equipment expense of going to narrow rows.

Studying his fields, weed problems and soil types has helped him do a top job of fertilizing and weed control. Relying on a regular soil-testing program, he feels it's very important to match corn hybrids to plant population and soil fertility levels. Keeping equipment in good shape, he trades fairly often to take advantage of its value.

What advice would he give to a young farmer starting out today? "Work hard to get the job done the right way. And learn all you can about grain and livestock marketing. Keep good records so you know production costs to help you recognize a good price when you see one. The biggest mistake most of us make is waiting for top price and then missing it," he says.

Jim and Ned O. Mohr
Scott County

Brothers Jim and Ned Mohr operate 960 acres in partnership, in addition to farrow-to-finishing 110 sows and operating a 100-head cow-calf herd.

The partnership originally began with three brothers in 1950. One brother, Erwin, died in 1957 and the partnership between Jim and Ned has continued to now. The operation was incorporated this past July.

Responsibilities are split. Jim takes management responsibilities for the 900 tillable acres. Ned manages the livestock, involving 1,400 to 1,600 pasture-farrowed hogs annually, a 300-head capacity finishing building, the cow-calf herd and feeding of approximately 150 steers.

With strong beliefs that land must be preserved for the next generation, the Mohrs pay special attention to crop rotations, waterways and contour farming. They also minimum till corn and soybeans.

Both brothers are active in local and state organizations.

Ned and Jim Mohr

Jim is currently a director of Agri-Industries, past president of the Eldridge Cooperative, and a Sheridan Township trustee. Jim has also been active in Farm Bureau, serving as Scott County president, as a voting delegate and on several committees.

He attends Faith Lutheran Church of Eldridge.

Jim and his wife, Charlotte, have four children: Patricia (Mrs. Robert Hendrickson), Wheaton, Iowa; Margo (Mrs. David Underwood), Mason City, Iowa; Paul, West Branch; and Jerome.

Ned is a member and past president of the North Scott School board and director of the Central Scott Telephone Company. He was also a charter member of his county pork group and has served on its board. He has also served on the board of the Iowa Pork Producers Association. Ned is a Hickory Grove Township trustee, has worked on various Farm Bureau committees and holds memberships in several other organizations.

He is an active member of St. Johns Methodist Church in Davenport.

Ned and his wife, Norida, have three children: Mary Beth and Robert, Eldridge, Iowa; and William, at the University of Wisconsin, Milwaukee.

Donald L. Doolittle
Webster County

Don Doolittle operates about 1,100 acres, ranging in quality from 600 acres of flat Nicolette-Webster soil to 300 acres of rough timber along the Des Moines River valley.

To take advantage of his diverse farmland, Doolittle maintains a 200- to 250-head cow herd. Sires consist of Charolais, Red Angus and Simmental obtained from IBIA test stations, at the Iowa Winter Beef Expo, and from individual breeders. Most of his cows are purchased and include a Charolais cross. He recently has been artificially inseminating some cows with Chianina semen.

As you'd expect, some calves are large – up to 115 pounds at birth. Calving difficulty has not been a serious problem.

Calving begins in February and runs to mid-April. Calves are fed out along with an additional 200 to 400 calves purchased. His herd has been culled down in response to profitability, but he hopes to increase cow numbers again and stop buying feeders. He's found profits best for calves he raises himself.

Cropland includes approximately 400 acres for corn and 350 for soybeans. About half the corn is fed to cattle, including 100 acres used for corn silage.

Winter feeding includes cornstalks run through a stacker. During winter, the stacks are fed to cows in feedlots and are used as bedding for calving cows in the spring.

Doolittle has served as member and president of the Webster City School board, vice president of the United Co-op and president of the Hamilton County Beef Producers Association.

He was active in stopping construction of a dam planned for Brushy Creek and also helped a Vietnamese family establish a home in Webster City.

He is an active member of the Trinity Lutheran Church, Webster City.

Doolittle and his wife, Shirley, have four children: Kristin

Doolittle

(Mrs. Emmett Cooney), Dayton, Iowa; Polly, Houston, Texas; Dan, farming in partnership with his dad; and Patricia, a recent graduate of animal science at Iowa State University, now taking on cow-herd management responsibilities.

Alvin J. Gilbert
Chickasaw County

"Learning from our mistakes and looking ahead are the keys to our farming growth," say Alvin and Pat Gilbert.

Gilbert

"Today's challenge is disciplined marketing," she adds. "When you get a reasonable profit, sell. Don't hold out for the high."

Pat and Alvin (his friends call him Alvie) were married in 1950. "I started working as a hired man," he says. "Then my father-in-law helped me rent a farm. Two years later, we went on our own.

"When my father retired, I bought his farm," says Gilbert. "For the next seven years, I farmed and worked at Rath Packing in Waterloo to supplement cash flow."

Gilbert now owns 1,220 acres. He rents another 160 acres. With the help of two full-time hired men, he raises 700 acres of corn, about 300 acres of beans, and 40 acres of oats and hay.

What does he do with the other 320 acres? "We rent it out to a young farmer," explains Gilbert. "We had a tough time getting started. So one of our goals is to help young, ambitious men who otherwise couldn't make it get a toehold in farming. Another goal is conserving the land."

The Gilberts now farrow and finish 3,200 hogs per year. Their long suit is using older but adequate facilities to hold down fixed costs.

Gilbert is currently on the New Hampton-St. Joseph Catholic Church council. He's served five years on the New Hampton First National Bank farm board.

Gilbert was named Chickasaw County Master Pork Producer in 1970. He is a past vice president of the Chickasaw County Swine Producer's Association. He was on the Chickasaw County Beef Producers board of directors.

To help others shoot for top yields, he was a director of the 100 Bushel Corn Club. He's also served on the ASCS county committee.

Alvie and Pat have four children: Mary Lou (Mrs. Tom Still), Madison, Wis.; Jeanette (Mrs. Mike Kolthoff), Bloomington, Minn.; Paula, a student at St. Catherine College, St. Paul, Minn.; and Steven, a fourth grader at St. Joseph Community School, New Hampton.

IOWA MASTER FARMERS

~ March 26, 1983

Six outstanding Iowa farmers are being named Master Farmers for 1983 by *Wallaces Farmer*. Brief descriptions of their operations and activities are listed here.

Bob Christensen
Mills County

Christensen

"I don't keep a record book anymore! That's because I have this new tool called the computer," declares Bob Christensen.

"I had the bug to buy a computer for a long time," notes this southwest Iowa cattleman. "But it wasn't until I went to night school in Omaha and learned more about the computer that I overcame my fear of the thing," he explains.

Now Christensen does all his record keeping on his Apple II computer. He also uses it for letter writing and mailing labels for the Iowa Simmental Association, of which he is executive secretary-treasurer.

Analyzing PIK for the Christensen operation was also done on the computer.

Bob, his wife, Naomi, and son, Doug, formed a three-way partnership five years ago. They operate 1,700 acres of corn, soybeans, pasture, hay, cattle and hogs.

"Giving Doug a chance to buy in was a sacrifice on our part. But it's worked out well and Doug is building up equity," points out

Christensen

Naomi. "It's hard to turn your back and let him do things differently from the way you like," adds Bob. "But you have to accept the fact that your son is grown up."

The Christensens run a herd of 90 purebred Simmental cows. They sell club calves and usually have a spring production sale. "When we sell club calves, we try to sell the top of the line so the kids have an animal they can take home, do well with, and make some money," explains Christensen.

Besides the cattle, the Christensens have a farrow-to-finish hog operation. They farrow 40 sows every two months. "We cut that back to 20 sows in the winter, due to a lack of adequate nursery space," notes Bob.

Christensen has been a member of the Mills County Farm Bureau for 28 years, served as a township director and has also served on the county FmHA committee.

He received the Seedstock Producer of the Year award from the Iowa Beef Breeds Council in 1981, was named Farm Manager of the Year in 1968 by the ISU Ag Business Club, and was named a Mills County Master Pork Producer in 1980.

In other activities, Christensen has served on the school board, county Extension council, ASCS committee, on the Mills County Fair board and beef sale manager for 20 years, been involved in 4-H activities, and as a township committeeman for the Republican party.

The Christensens are members of the Strakan United Methodist Church, where Bob has served as a trustee, lay leader, choir member, on the Council of Ministries and as literature secretary.

Bob and Naomi also have a daughter, Donna, who works in Newton.

Howard Lyon

Howard and Joe Lyon
Tama County

Howard and Joe Lyon operate about 1,200 acres, with roughly 900 tillable, near Toledo, Iowa. They own about 700 acres in various partnerships with family members.

The Lyons have a 90-cow beef herd. But their main livestock enterprise is a 150-cow dairy herd. It is a partnership known as Lyon Jerseys.

One of Howard's sons, Stuart, and one of Joe's sons, Eric, own 24 % of a dairy partnership. Another of Howard's sons, Jim, works for the operation. Jim isn't married, but the Howard Lyon farm still has to support four families.

The Lyons

Howard is an Iowa State University mechanical engineering graduate. He has major responsibility for the cropping operation, machinery care and maintenance, and in keeping the farm records.

Joe is an ISU dairy science graduate. He has responsibility for managing the dairy herd.

The Lyons house their dairy herd in a modern freestall barn. They milk in a double-four herringbone parlor with a low-line pipeline milker. The milking parlor is an old remodeled dairy barn. They recently built an open-front shed for housing herd replacements. They keep calves outside in hutches.

The cropping program includes a

Joe Lyon

rotation of corn, soybeans and hay on most all of the tillable acres. The Lyons use minimum tillage, strip-cropping and terracing.

What's the long suit of the operation? "I guess the ability to maintain a family partnership for more than 30 years," says Joe.

The Lyons are both strong supporters of Extension and higher education. They helped initiate and establish the Iowa Dairy Expo in Waterloo. Each year, the expo provides dairymen with up-to-date information on all segments of the industry.

Howard and his wife, Margaret, have 13 children. All have attended college or are currently in school, and all but one plan to obtain college degrees.

Joe and his wife, Norma, have nine children. They are all college graduates or in college now.

R.C. Mathis
Polk County

In 1927 while earning a degree from Drake University, Ralph Mathis was attracted to Henry Wallace's corn-breeding work at Johnston, Iowa. Ralph continued his own corn breeding experiments while teaching high school math and science in Clinton, Iowa, in the 1930s.

In 1937, Ralph returned to central Iowa to farm with his father near Elkhart. He also established Iowa State Hybrid Corn Company, now in its 48th year under the personal management of Ralph and his wife, Dorothy.

In 1972, the 800-acre family farming operation was separated into three divisions among the five Mathis children, with Ralph and Dorothy still actively involved.

A progressive thinker, Ralph helped pioneer the use of many modern farming methods, including chemical fertilizers and weed control, irrigation, narrow-row soybeans, improved drainage and conservation tillage. In 1982, he planted all his corn and soybeans no-till and was quite successful.

Ralph and Dorothy no longer have livestock, but have passed their livestock production savvy on to their sons.

Ralph helped found the Iowa Tractor Pullers Association. His innovative spirit developed inner-coolers for engines long before tractors came from the factory with them. A few years ago, Ralph installed a wind generator to make electricity to power the farmstead.

This successful project is but one example of Ralph's deep concern for assuring a reliable supply of reasonably priced energy for rural areas. He has served on the Marshall County REC board since 1947. In recent years, Ralph has worked tirelessly in promoting on-farm ethanol production.

An elder of Elkhart Christian Church, he teaches a Sunday school class. Ralph helped establish the Elkhart Christian Church Education Fund, a nonprofit trust that lends money to young people for college. Presently, it is assisting eight students.

This page: R.C. Mathis

Many other organizations and groups have benefited from Ralph's longtime active support and generosity, including the Iowa Crop Improvement Association, ISU Extension service, Associated Hybrid Producers, local 4-H clubs, vocational agriculture, FFA, school board, Polk County Fair board, Democratic party and Farm Bureau. He is chairman of the Polk County

land use preservation committee, an active member of Iowans for Tax Relief, and attends many local and state government budget meetings, speaking out for tax relief.

Several years ago, Ralph worked through the Iowa Kidney Foundation to provide posters in all drivers license stations in Iowa. These call attention to the availability of organ donor cards, which you can sign when your driver's license is renewed.

Ralph and Dorothy have five children: Mrs. Kenneth (Penny) Howard, Cambridge; Alan (Chip) Mathis, Elkhart; Jim Mathis, Elkhart; Mrs. David (Pam) Fitzgerald, Iowa City; and Mrs. Mark (Di) Jamison, Elkhart.

There are 11 grandchildren and one great-grandchild.

Myers Rossiter
Henry County

Myers Rossiter graduated in 1950 from Iowa State University with a degree in agricultural engineering. He served two years in the Air Force.

In 1953, he started farming by renting 160 acres from his parents.

Through careful management and a progressive hog operation, Myers has grown to 800-owned acres, and a farrow-to-finish operation producing about 4,500 hogs annually.

Sows and gilts are bred in open lots and farrowed in completely slatted crates. The rest of the hogs are kept in total confinement.

The farrowing unit was built in 1966. A grower was added in

1975 and additional farrowing and nursery units in 1979. These units are tied together so pigs can be transferred from farrowing, to nursery, to grower without setting foot outside.

Pigs are weaned at three weeks of age into a flat deck nursery with woven wire flooring. The nursery has 4- by 6-foot pens, holding up to 16 pigs each. The grower-nursery was built with concrete slat flooring over a pit. But Myers has found nursery pigs do better on the wire deck flooring he installed above the concrete slats. Hogs are finished in a Hog Hut finishing unit, built in 1973, which Rossiter remodeled by placing a roof over the finishing floor.

Feed is ground through an electric mixer. A pneumatic unit delivers feed to bulk bins. Rations are built on-farm with soybean meal and a vitamin-mineral pre-mix.

This page: Myers Rossiter

Rossiter raises 200 acres of soybeans and 600 acres of corn annually. Corn and beans are planted in 30-inch rows. Minimum tillage is used on most of the cropland. A great deal of terracing, tiling and land reclamation has been done through the years.

Myers has two full-time employees.

A believer in cooperatives, Myers is a director of Growmark, Inc., a regional supply and grain cooperative. He is also a director on the local FS Cooperative.

He is a director of the southeast Iowa PCA, acting as chairman for two years; has been a member of the county Extension council; on the county 4-H swine committee; served as president of his local Lion's club; served on the boards of both his county Farm Bureau and pork producers organizations; and in 1974, was named a state Master Pork Producer.

Rossiter is active in the Winfield Methodist Church, where he's taught Sunday school for 10 years, been chairman of the church board and trustees, and now serves as finance committee chairman.

A flying enthusiast, Myers maintains a plane and small airstrip on his farmstead and is a district director of the state's Flying Farmers organization.

The plane has made traveling to visit their children easier. Myers and wife, Marlene, have two daughters: Mrs. Bradley (Julee) Nichols, Des Moines, and Mrs. Irwin (Vicki) Kirsner, Sunrise, Fla. The Kirsners have a son, Michael.

Loren Schuett
Cherokee County

If you have questions about no-till, Loren Schuett is the kind of farmer you want to talk to. For 16 years, he's been no-till planting corn and soybeans on rolling land north of Holstein, Iowa.

Operating 400 acres, Loren and his wife, Ramona, grow corn, soybeans and oats. Their farrow-to-finish hog operation cranks out 1,700 to 1,800 head a year. They also have a 25-head beef cow herd. Their northwest Iowa farm is diversified to make the most of its soil resources, while also protecting these resources for the future.

With no-till, contouring and terraces, the Schuetts have virtually stopped soil erosion. "But the biggest advantages of no-till for us have been time and labor savings," notes Loren. Operating with a minimum of hired labor, they employ one person in the summer. Ramona and the three daughters have helped with hog chores and at harvest.

The Schuetts have been able to hold the line on machinery costs with no-till. Also, they've controlled fertilizer costs by using liquid manure from the hog confinement operation to full advantage. A student of crop production, Loren produces above-average yields. He built a sprayer specifically designed for no-till and is constantly studying his weed control program.

High-moisture corn is used in the hog operation. Their hog management program emphasizes a higher-than-average number of pigs weaned per litter.

Loren takes time to share ideas with other farmers. He speaks at local farmer meetings and

at larger conferences, promoting soil conservation and efficient hog production methods. He is currently serving as a commissioner for the Cherokee soil conservation district and has helped organize a no-till club in the county. The Schuetts have installed 21,715 feet of terraces on their rolling land.

Active in the United Methodist Church at Holstein, Loren has served on various boards and committees. He's also served on the county Extension council, local school advisory committee, Iowa State University advisory committee, is involved in Farm Bureau, a past president of the county pork producers group, and has also served as a director of the Northwest Iowa Farm Business Association.

Loren and Ramona continue to support 4-H. Ramona has been a 4-H club leader for 11 years.

The Schuetts have three daughters: Mrs. Keith (Lori) Long, Arden Hill, Minn.; Linda, a junior at Southwestern State University, Marshall, Minn.; and Julie, a freshman at South Dakota State University.

This page: Loren Schuett

1984 IOWA MASTER FARMERS
~
March 24, 1984

Wallaces Farmer is proud to name seven Iowa producers Master Farmers for 1984. The Master Farmer program, sponsored by *Wallaces Farmer*, was started in 1926 as a means of recognizing individuals demonstrating a high level of management and to award them for unselfishly devoting time to community leadership roles.

Including 1984, 314 men and two women have been recognized over the past 58 years.

Judges were: Robert Zacharias, president, Master Farmer Club; Virginia Striegel, vice president, Master Farmer Club; Everett Stoneberg, ag economist and farm management specialist; and Monte Sesker, editor, *Wallaces Farmer*.

Kenneth Cook
Hardin County

Kenneth Cook started farming in partnership with his father, Maurice, 27 years ago. Last year, Kenneth bought another farm, so he is now operating 720 acres. About 450 acres are planted to corn, 180 to soybeans, and the rest are in oats or hog pasture.

Cook's primary interest is in hogs, but he did feed cattle until last year when his father died. "We fed cattle because that was Dad's love."

Cook farrows most

Cook

of his hogs out on pasture in A-huts. Last year, they sold 3,600 hogs on the farm. The only hogs that are not farrowed on pasture are about 1,000 winter pigs raised in an older building on the farm.

Cook figures he turned out 450 litters last year. His gilts averaged about 7.5 to 7.6 pigs per litter farrowing on pasture, while the sows averaged 8.5 to 9 pigs per litter. In addition to trying to keep up-to-date in his farming operation, Cook has devoted much of his time to the community.

He served on the local school board for eight years and was president. He has also been on the board of his co-op, a local insurance board and is serving on the county FmHA committee.

In other activities, he is a member of the Ruritan Club, a local service organization; and has also served as a 4-H leader.

Perhaps Cook's greatest contribution has been to the Quakerdale Children's Home, where he has served on the board for more than 23 years.

Active in the Honey Creek-New Providence Friend's Church, Cook has been on the church building committee, chairman of the ministry and council, a Sunday school teacher and past youth sponsor.

228

Kenneth and his wife, Evelyn, have four daughters: Mrs. Dan (Diane) Nelson, New Providence; Andrea, Tipton; Patricia, Ames; and Sheryl, a student at Taylor University in Upland, Ind.

Wilfred and Richard Groves
Hamilton County

Wilfred "Bill" and Richard "Dick" Groves operate a partnership called Groves Brothers. Bill's sons Wilfred and George are also partners in the operation. Together they operate some 1,300 acres. They grow around 550 acres of corn and 600 acres of beans each year. The Groves' operation markets 5,000 to 6,000 hogs per year, and has a beef herd of 40 Hereford-Angus cows. Calves are weaned in December, backgrounded and sold in the spring.

Hogs have always been part of the operation. Farrowing is done in a 62-stall facility remodeled from a corncrib. The building houses a 550-pig nursery. Two 200-head capacity "hot nurseries" handle newly weaned pigs up to 20 pounds. A 720-head grower unit holds pigs from 40 to 100 pounds. Finishing facilities include a 400-head open-front, a 400-head remodeled barn, a 150-head remodeled barn, plus some outside poll sheds.

Both Bill and Dick have been active in local government and school affairs. They have also been active in the Hamilton County Pork Producers, and were champion county Master Corn and Soybean Growers in 1970. Both are members of the Hamilton County beef and pork pro-

Richard, left, and Wilfred Groves

ducers associations.

Bill and Dick are active in many other organizations including Farm Bureau, Lion's Club, Rotary Club, Elk's Club, American Legion, county fair board, 4-H, and the Farmers Home Administration county committee.

Both families are members of the United Congregational Church in Webster City. Both Bill and Dick have served on various activities in the church.

Bill and his wife, Jeanette, have three children: Wilfred A.J. Groves, III, farming; George, farming; and Mrs. Delbert (Margaret) Shepherd, Iowa Falls.

Dick and his wife, Donna, have two children: Mrs. William (Lee) O'Brien, Towanda, Pennsylvania; and Mrs. Jerry (Mary) Foster, Denver, Colorado.

Albert 'Bud' Knake
Jackson County

Bud Knake grew up in Bellevue on the Mississippi River, not on a farm. When he tired of blacksmithing and repair work, his farm-raised wife, Lillian, encouraged him to try farming.

The Knakes started on a crop and livestock share lease 31 years ago. Five years later, they bought their first land. Over the years, they've expanded and now own 940 acres and rent an additional 1,360 acres. The Knakes have used this real estate base to help sons Mike and Pat get a start in farming.

Knake was among the first in his neighborhood to strip-crop, build convention-

Knake

al and tiled terraces, and to try both minimum tillage and no-tillage. Efforts toward preservation of the soil are why Bud Knake has been able to achieve consistently good yields on relatively poor Jackson County soils. Knake has been recognized in both the landlord/tenant division and the owner/operator division of the Iowa Soil Conservation awards program.

Knake's diversified livestock operation includes a 350-cow beef breeding herd, and 60-cow dairy herd.

The Knakes feed out 500 to 800 head of feeder cattle and finish about 1,200 feeder pigs per year. Knake gets the feeder pigs from a sow corporation in which he is a shareholder.

In community activities, Knake has served as president of the Bellevue Community School board, and served as a chairman and director of the Eastern Iowa Production Credit Association. He is also chairman of the board of the Bellevue Rural Fire Department and the Jackson County board of adjustment. Bud was an officer and board member of the Jackson County Farm Bureau and has also served on the Farm Service Co-op and Land O' Lakes boards.

Knake is active in St. John's Lutheran Church in Bellevue and coaches two girls softball teams.

Albert and his wife, Lillian, have four children: Mrs. Jim (Donna) Mueller, Bellevue; Michael, farming; Patrick, farming; and Penny, Dubuque.

Harlan Murley
Buchanan County

Harlan Murley is a team leader. The team is a close-knit family operation that involves Harlan; his wife, Karen; son Larry, assistant production manager; Dave Pech, production manager; and occasionally Dave's wife, Bev.

Karen handles all financial records, most marketing duties, and helps in the field. Dave Pech coordinates crop and livestock production. Son Larry works on both crops and livestock.

Murley

The Murleys raise about 1,120 acres of corn, 560 acres of soybeans and around 30 acres of oats. They grow seed oats and beans. About two-thirds of their crops are grown on rented land.

The operation farrow-to-finishes about 2,400 hogs per year. Confinement units are used for farrowing, nursery and gestation. All hogs are finished in pen-front buildings. Boars come from test stations or from the Pig Improvement Company. Sow indexing is used to cull approximately 40% of the sow herd annually. Murley says use of veterinary consultation has helped improve health of the swineherd.

Harlan was an early adopter of 30-inch corn rows and minimum tillage. Expertise gained in these areas led him to roles as chairman of the Buchanan County Soil Conservation District, serving as a Buchanan County Soil Conservation District commissioner and on the exhibits committee for the Eastern Iowa Tillage Show.

In other activities, Murley is a member of

the Iowa Soybean Association, the Iowa Corn Growers Association, the Iowa Pork Producers Association, Iowa Farm Bureau, and has served as president of the Buchanan County Pork Producers Association. In 1979, he was named Master Pork Producer.

Oosterhuis

As a member of the Grace United Methodist Church in Lamont, Harlan has served as Sunday school superintendent, lay leader and board chairman.

Harlan and Karen have three children: Larry, farming; Kent, a student at Iowa State University; and Sheryl, studying at Kirkwood Community College in Cedar Rapids.

Marlin Oosterhuis
O'Brien County

In 1954, Marlin Oosterhuis started farming by renting 80 acres and using his father's equipment. In 1962 after serving in the army, he returned to O'Brien County and rented more land. Eventually, when Marlin's father retired, Marlin and wife, Arlyce, expanded the farming operation. Located near Hospers in northwest Iowa, they own 300 acres and rent an additional 740 acres, growing mostly corn and beans.

A substitute school teacher, Arlyce maintains an active interest in the financial management of the operation. They've been toying with the idea of buying a microcomputer to help with that chore. At present, son Marty charts the corn and bean markets for the operation.

Motivated by a longtime concern for soil conservation, Marlin was one of the first farmers to make ridge-till farming work on a large scale in O'Brien County. Although he's been ridge planting for nine years now, he keeps modifying and improving his conservation tillage system and his equipment to do a better job each year.

Marlin is chairman of the Northwest Iowa Ridge Runners, a group of farmers who meet to swap ideas about no-till and conservation tillage. He's a past president and past director

Oosterhuis

231

of the local Federal Land Bank Association in Sheldon, and he is currently on the board of the American State Bank in Hospers.

Other activities have included the ag advisory panel for Land O' Lakes, the local Farmers Co-op elevator board and Congressman Berkley Bedell's advisory committee. He's also served four years on the O'Brien County Extension council. Marlin was an O'Brien County Soil Conservation District commissioner for six years, and in 1983 was one of nine Iowa farmers to receive the state outstanding soil commissioner award.

Marlin is an active member of St. Paul's Lutheran Church in Sheldon, where he sings in the choir. He also writes articles and gives talks at the church concerning soil stewardship.

In addition to the farming operation, the Oosterhuis family keeps busy doing other things together, too. Marlin and Arlyce have four children: Martin, 17; Kristin, 16; Jim, 14; and Margaret, 12. They take time for 4-H, school and church activities.

Petersen

Roland Petersen
Clinton County

Efficiency is the name of the game for Roland Petersen. By paying close attention to inputs that encourage a high rate of gain, Petersen and his family have built a successful operation that revolves around cattle and hogs.

In 1960, he rented a 150-acre farm on a 50-50 crop-share lease. Roland used his father's equipment and borrowed operating money from his father-in-law. At that time, Petersen fed about 50 cattle per year and finished pigs from 12 sows twice a year.

The business has grown from that modest beginning. Now Roland, his wife, Bette, and son Mark work closely together to market about 600 cattle and 2,500 hogs annually. Together they farm about 1,200 acres and own roughly 800 acres.

Roland is active in many farm and community organizations. He has participated in local FFA activities, school activities, Clinton County Cattlemen's Association, Farm Bureau, county Extension council and Lion's Club.

He is also active in the Clinton County Pork Producers and was named an Iowa Master Pork Producer in 1976.

Roland is currently serving on the board of directors for the Miles Savings Bank, Clinton County Farmers Home Administration, and the C & J Service Company. In addition, he has qualified for both the Clinton and Jackson county 100-Bushel Corn Clubs.

The Petersens are members of the Faith Lutheran Church in Andover, where Roland has served as a council member, on the advisory board and on the stewardship committee.

Roland and his wife, Bette, have three children: Mark, farming; Marsha, Clinton; and Michelle, Clinton.

1985

IOWA MASTER FARMERS

~

March 23, 1985

Wallaces Farmer is proud to name five Iowa producers Master Farmers for 1985. The Master Farmer program, sponsored by *Wallaces Farmer*, was started in 1926. The honor is intended to call attention to the high level of management these people demonstrate and to award them for unselfishly devoting part of their time to community leadership roles.

The 1985 selections bring the total to 319 men and two women who have been recognized over the past 59 years.

Judges were: Virginia Striegel, president, Master Farmer Club; John "Ted" Huser, vice president, Master Farmer Club; Robert Jolly, Extension economist, Iowa State University; and Monte Sesker, editor, *Wallaces Farmer*.

Anderson

Richard Anderson
Cedar County

"Well bought is half sold" is the heart of Dick Anderson's cattle feeding strategy. "We try to buy the type of cattle packers want," he explains. "That way, if the market turns sour, we can still get the best price possible."

However, cattle feeding is only one aspect of the Anderson operation. Dick, his wife, Ma-

rie, and son Barry also raise about 655 acres of corn, 300 acres of soybeans and 95 acres of hay. Always searching for more profitable ways to market crops and livestock, Anderson has found a local dehydrating plant to be a good market for alfalfa.

After high school graduation in 1941, Anderson worked as a farmhand for his father. In 1945, he rented 80 acres from his father. Two years later, he bought that 80 acres. He inherited no land, but has continued to buy land and now owns 1,050 acres with his son Barry.

Anderson has been active on the Iowa Soybean Promotion Board. Through those activities, the Anderson family was asked to entertain the ambassador from the People's Republic of China and a Filipino agricultural trade team at their farm.

In 1958, Anderson was selected as an Outstanding Young Farmer. He's a member of both the Cedar County and National Cattlemen's Associations, as well as being a member of the Farm Bureau. Anderson spent 15 years as a 4-H Club leader.

In other community activities, Anderson is trustee of the Herbert Hoover Presidential Library Association in West Branch, chairman and trustee of Cookson Memorial Home, and director of Springdale Mutual Insurance Company. The Anderson family is active in the First Methodist Church in West Branch.

Besides Barry, Dick and Marie have three other children: Richard, Jr., a realtor in West Branch; Dean, a florist in Tipton; and Julie, a student at the University of Iowa.

Bjustrom

Charles Bjustrom
Kossuth County

Family partnerships have been a way of life for Charles "Chuck" Bjustrom. He has been involved in three since he started farming. Nearly 30 years ago, Chuck and his father raised cattle and hogs in partnership.

The second partnership involved his two brothers, Francis and Harold. The arrangement benefited all of them, but when it was dissolved in 1975 it had served its usefulness. Their individual families were growing and each wanted to begin their own farming careers.

Bjustrom's current partnership involves his immediate family. His son David, 23, is a full partner. Full-time help is also provided by his sons-in- law, Brian Goodman and Roland Hamerlinck.

David is responsible for the farrowing and breeding houses. Brian manages the nursery and growing facilities. The feed grinding and finishing house is the responsibility of Roland. He also takes care of the open-front housing when Chuck is gone.

The Bjustrom family operates 1,350 acres near Whittemore in northern Iowa. They own 660 acres and rent another 750 acres. All but 100 acres are tillable. They grow 950 acres of corn and 300 acres of soybeans.

Chuck was named Iowa Master Pork Producer in 1975 and Iowa Pork All American the next year. He's also a top-notch promoter of pork. In 1980, Chuck was a member of the four-man U.S. Pork Export Team to Japan, which was sponsored by the U.S. Meat Export Federation. He currently serves on the federation's executive board.

On both the county and state levels, Chuck has served as president and vice president for the Pork Producers. For three years he was a district director. He just recently started his second three-year term on the National Pork Producers Council executive board. For two years, he served on the USDA pseudorabies virus ad hoc committee.

Bjustrom is a top-notch pork producer and promoter.

234

He's also active in the Iowa Farm Bureau, Iowa Corn Growers Association and Iowa Soybean Growers Association.

The Bjustroms are members of St. Michael's Catholic Church in Whittemore where he serves as a lay minister.

Chuck and his wife, Marilyn, have five children: Mrs. Brian (Diane) Goodman, Whittemore; David, farming; Nancy, Ankeny; Jeff, a freshman at University of Northern Iowa, Cedar Falls; and Gail, a freshman at Algona High School.

George Hoffman, Jr.
Ida County

Married in 1941, George Hoffman, Jr.,

event attracted over 5,000 people from a five-state area. Another no-till field day was held on the farm in 1982.

The Hoffmans have always used crop rotation, grass waterways and contour farming. They also have always raised a lot of livestock, and proper management of manure has been used to boost yields while holding the line on fertilizer costs. The 480-acre farm (315 tillable) has an oat-hay-corn-bean-corn-oat rotation.

The 130 grazing acres help support a 70-cow herd and 60 head of sheep. They also have a sow herd.

George has been active in REC, Pork Producers, Cattlemen's Association, Sheep Producers, ASCS and others. He was a 4-H leader

Hoffman

and wife Ruth farmed rented land for several years until they bought their first farm in 1943 with his folks. Then in 1961, they decided to buy the Hoffman home farm where they live and farm today.

The Iowa State University Extension service and USDA Soil Conservation Service have had many field demonstrations on the Hoffman farm. Back in the days when no-till was first getting started, George and Ruth hosted a minimum tillage field day in 1968. One of the first "no-till" days ever held in Iowa, the

for 30 years and served as beef superintendent at the Ida County fair from 1939 to 1984. He's been a director of the Federal Land Bank from 1982 to the present.

George helped organize the local Retarded Children's Association in 1956 and served as president for several years. A lifelong member of Ida Grove United Methodist Church, George has served on various church committees.

George and Ruth have four children. George III has a PhD in economics from the University of Minnesota. After working for

USDA in Washington, D.C. for 11 years, he and his family now live in St. Paul, where he works for Pillsbury. A daughter, Linda Witten, lives with her husband, Art, and family on a farm near her parents. Daughter Anita lives at home. Son Danny farms with his family.

Elmer Paper
Scott County

In March 1953, Elmer Paper was discharged from the Armed Forces. Within a few days, he had rented a 105-acre farm. He bought

Paper

nine bred gilts and with two dairy cows from 4-H days he started his career. By Jan. 1954, the milking herd was up to 12 cows. Then that spring Elmer and wife Loretta moved to a larger, 165-acre farm. They began DHIA production testing of their herd that year, moved to the DHIR program just two years later and have been testing continuously since then. The Holstein herd was all registered in 1959 and has been recognized as one of the high-placing herds in state fair competition several times.

The hog operation was discontinued several years ago to concentrate on dairy. The herd has evolved from their own breeding program with most herd replacements home-grown. The herd was increased to a peak of 56 cows in 1982. "We've cut back to about 44 cows since then," says Elmer. "I know there is just too much production for the demand, and we need to reduce the supply." He feels strongly about that, and has voluntarily taken cows out of the barn.

Elmer is serving on the executive committee of the National Milk Produc-

Paper

ers Federation and is on a task force to formulate legislation for a national milk program. The Paper operation is a family affair. In 1981, the business was incorporated and two sons, Loren and Nyle, became partners. Together they farm 450 acres. The rolling land lends itself to a crop rotation of corn, soybeans, oats and hay.

Among Paper's honors are Iowa Distinguished Dairyman, Iowa Holstein Hall of Fame, State 4-H Alumni Award and Keeling Dairy Leadership Award.

He's been a director of the Swiss Valley Farm Cooperative since 1963 and president since 1971. Paper has worked closely with local 4-H and Extension committees. He has served in all offices of DHIA, on the Quad City Dairy Council and as president of the Iowa Holstein Breeders. He has judged many Holstein shows and has hosted many foreign visitors, farm tour groups, and been on countless other committees and projects.

The Papers have three other children: Randall and wife, Lisa, live in Pleasant Valley; Russel and wife, Charlene, Stockton; and Pamela (Mrs. William) Kucera, Davenport.

Dale Sexton
Calhoun County

Sharing machinery is one way Dale Sexton, Calhoun County, has spread costs of high-priced equipment. Since 1969, when he and brother Verle decided to switch to 30-inch rows, they have shared their planting and harvesting equipment.

"We just couldn't see the need for each of us to own a planter and combine even though we each had our own land," says Dale. "Together, we farmed more than 1,300 acres, so we needed dependable, high-capacity equipment."

The answer to that? Dale bought the combine and Verle the planter. Today, they have an eight-row combine and a 16-row planter. Dale's son Keith joined the operation in 1979 and is in the process of buying into the business. He agrees with the philosophy and plans to continue the arrangement.

Dale and Keith are cash grain farmers growing about 800 acres of corn and soybeans. That means Verle has to plant more for Dale and Keith than they harvest for him.

Since the original cost of the equipment isn't equal, the brothers worked it out so the expenditures more or less balance. They charge each other for planting and harvesting, using machinery depreciation and actual operating costs as guidelines. At year end, they sit down together, go over the costs, and "settle the bill."

Dale has been active in many community and state activities including the Soybean Association, Rural Co-operative board, Federal Land Bank, township trustee, 4-H leader for 10 years and county fair board. He is a Farm Bureau member and is a lay director for the St. Francis Catholic Church.

Dale has had a lot of help from wife Mary. Besides son Keith, they have four other children all living in Iowa. They are (Mrs. Doug) Marcia Frerichs, Steamboat Rock; (Mrs. Robert) Marlene Buckley, Des Moines; Monica, Jefferson; and (Mrs. Tim) Carol Stevens, Ft. Dodge.

Sexton

1986
IOWA MASTER FARMERS
~
March 22, 1986

Wallaces Farmer is proud to name four Iowa producers Master Farmers for 1986. The 1986 selections bring the total to 323 men and two women who have been recognized over the past 60 years.

Judges were: John "Ted" Huser, president, Master Farmer Club; Marshall King, vice president, Master Farmer Club; Robert Jolly, Extension economist, Iowa State University; and Monte Sesker, editor, *Wallaces Farmer*.

Walter Goeken
Clay County

Walter Goeken studied engineering while in college and that training seems to have paid off in his farming operation. For example, Goeken designed and built his own 1,800-head hog finishing facility.

Goeken also has designed and manufactured his own concrete slats for his hog operation as well as concrete feed bunks when he was feeding cattle.

Goeken used to have a farrow-to-finish operation but switched to buying feeder pigs in 1980. The building is 220 feet long and 60 feet wide. It features 20 feet of slats in the middle over a 2-foot pit with a scraper system. "Scrapers take the manure to the north end of the building where it is dumped into a deep pit and then pumped up into a slurry store

Goeken

system," says Goeken. Storage capacity of the slurry store system is about six months, which means manure is hauled each spring and fall.

Goeken uses high moisture corn in his feeding program and has 50,000-bushel storage capacity in a 30- by 80-foot silo that was constructed on the south end of the new finishing facility.

The hog operation is shared with son Richard who has his own farm as well. Richard owns one-third of the hogs. Goeken himself annually markets around 2,800 head of hogs.

Goeken's farming operation consists of nearly 800 acres in a corn-soybean rotation. He tries to chisel plow corn stubble in the fall, weather permitting. He uses a V-ripper with a "beaver tail" to cover the trash. His goal is to till 10 to 12 inches deep.

Goeken does not till soybean stubble until spring when it's time to plant corn. Then he uses either a field cultivator or a disc for the first pass. Herbicides and anhydrous ammonia are applied with the field cultivator.

Activities and organizations Goeken has been involved with include: board of directors for Land O' Lakes, Clay County school board, Everly Community School board, Iowa Cattlemen's Association, Iowa Pork Producers Association, Everly Lions Club and the Clay County Farm Bureau.

Goeken and his wife, Clara, are members of the Hope Lutheran Church where he has served as president of the board, Sunday school superintendent and president of the building committee.

The Goekens have five sons, three of whom are farming in the Everly community. They are Thomas, Richard and John. David is a computer specialist in the NASA program in Houston, Texas and Robert works at the State Bank of Everly.

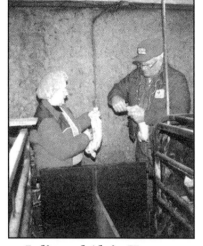
Lelia and Alvin Hansen

Alvin Hansen
Cerro Gordo County

For the last 30 years, Alvin Hansen and his family have purchased month-old Holstein heifer calves from Wisconsin and raised them to springing heifers.

This operation was quite profitable for the Hansens until recent dairy herd reduction programs changed all that. Therefore, about two years ago Alvin converted some of the dairy facilities to hogs. They haven't got completely out of the dairy calf business however, as they plan to buy 185-pound heifer calves this fall and raise them for replacement heifers.

Hansen's hog production system is a farrow-to-finish operation using a combination of confinement and pasture. Except for a nursery and finishing house, all farrowing and finishing buildings are older, remodeled buildings, using raised crate and a well-designed ventilation system. His sow herd currently consists of 93 head.

The Hansens currently operate 480 acres of corn, soybeans, oats and alfalfa. Corn is planted in 30-inch rows on soybean stubble that has had no fall tillage. He uses a field cultivator for seedbed preparation in the spring. Herbicides are broadcast with the planter.

Hansen uses a disc chisel on corn stubble in the fall, weather permitting. A moldboard plow is used on the heavier soils, which is about half of the tilled acres. On bean ground, pre-plant incorporated herbicides are applied with a disc in the spring and then the ground is hit with the field cultivator just ahead of the planter. He also bands a herbicide over the row with the planter.

Hansen also owns his own tractor-driven tiling machine and tries to do some tiling on the farm each year. "I have installed some tile myself every year for 10 years up until last year," he notes.

Hansen has been active in many local, county and state organizations including the Owen township school board, the Cerro Gordo Pork Producers Association, Iowa Farm Bureau, the Extension council, Lions Club, and served nine years on the Production Credit Board, five years as chairman and many others.

Hansen and his wife, Lelia, are members of the First Covenant Church in Mason City. He has served as Sunday school teacher and has been deacon and church chairman.

Alvin and Lelia have six children: Mrs. Paul (Vikki) Ostendorf, Mason City; Rosemary Bruellman, Ames; Dixie Williams, Des Moines; James, farming; Kurt, Eden Prairie, Minn.; and Dawn, a student at Iowa State University. They have three grandchildren.

Loyd Martin
Linn County

Wheat, sale of livestock equipment, light manufacturing, custom farming and tourists are part of the alternative agriculture on the 450-acre Loyd Martin family farm operation near Marion. Wheat fits in their soil conservation program. Making and installing grain legs has helped some neighbors and kept them employed in winter months.

Offering farm vacations has not only helped educate folks about agriculture, but has been a rewarding, learning experience for the Martins, leaving them "rich" in friendships.

Along with son David, Loyd manages a purebred sow herd of 107, producing 214 litters with an average of eight pigs weaned. Hamps, Durocs and Yorks make up the purebred program.

Sows are farrowed in a remodeled machine shed where they are fed and watered in individual pens. Sows and litters are pastured in late summer and weanlings held there until it gets too cold. The old dairy barn was converted to hold "extra" farrowing stalls.

Hogs are finished in open front sheds. Several pens are continually monitored in on-farm testing for rate of gain. Hogs are also placed in state test stations periodically throughout the year. Loyd's swine management ability is well-known, being recognized in 1980 as an Iowa Master Seedstock Producer.

Concern about conservation prompted the Martins to abandon the moldboard plow some seven years ago. They now follow a conservation tillage program. Loyd replaced some soybean acreage nine years ago with wheat to protect the soil. That production has increased from 30 acres to about 80 acres. Rate of return now looks better than soybeans and with hybrid wheat they hope to get near that 100-bushel per acre yield level.

It's truly a family operation. The Martins share the work and some machinery with a son, Stephen, who farms nearby and a son-in-law, Tim Clemens, who is married to daughter Kathy. Together they farm nearly 2,000 acres. Each family owns its own big tractor and specialty implements. However, a four-wheel-drive tractor, planter, combine, and tillage equipment are owned

Martin

under a partnership agreement.

Loyd has taught Sunday school for many years at Prairie Chapel United Methodist Church and he and Lois are youth counselors for UMYF. Loyd was 4-H leader for 10 years.

Other family members include a third son, Daryl, of Oskaloosa, director of Youth for Christ in Mahaska County, and a daughter, Marcia (Mrs. Jeffry Jordon), Marion, who lives on a farm and helps with farming responsibilities.

Howard Mueller
Bremer County

Specializing in corn production, Howard Mueller and his wife, Fran, also work hard at promoting their product. The Muellers bought "one of the poorest farms in Bremer County" in 1957, located across from Howard's father's home farm. They turned it into a productive farm by tiling, contouring, using reduced tillage and by picking up rocks for many years. Cattle were raised until 1968, hogs until 1976.

Armed with an ag degree from ISU, Howard started farming with his father and brother. Today, Howard and Fran provide all of the management and most of the labor for their 1,200-acre operation.

"We prefer not to raise soybeans, so almost all of our cropland is devoted to corn," he adds. "Our soils are somewhat fragile, and we get very good yields with corn and also control erosion. Sure, soybeans are a cheaper crop to produce. It costs more to grow continuous corn with the fertilizer, insecticide and tillage required. But we've grown continuous corn on some fields since 1957, with no more than the normal problems."

The Muellers chisel plow cornstalks in the fall, apply anhydrous ammonia in the spring, field cultivate and plant. They don't disc. Dry P and K are applied in strips, knifed-in with the chisel plow, which has a 3-ton fertilizer hopper mounted on top of it. Howard feels that it gives the corn plants an added boost to put the P and K 10 inches deep, which is where the roots are instead of spreading fertilizer on top.

Howard is a past chairman of the Iowa Corn Promotion Board, still serves as a director there, and is a past director of the Iowa Corn Growers Association. He recently completed a term as chairman of the U.S. Feed Grains Council. He's a past chairman of the National Federal Land Bank Association advisory committee, past chairman of the Cedar Falls Land Bank Association, and a past member of the ISU State

Mueller

Extension Advisory Council. He also served on the Waverly-Shell Rock School board.

A choir member at St. Paul's Lutheran Church in Waverly for 27 years, Howard has served on the church council and is a member of a national committee for Church in Society of the American Lutheran Church. In 1985, Fran and Howard jointly received the Community Service Award from the Waverly Chamber of Commerce.

Sons Mark and Steve are no longer directly involved with the farm. Mark, an ISU graduate, works for Mike Brayton Seeds of Ames. Steve is continuing in graduate studies at ISU.

Wallaces Farmer is proud to name four Iowa producers Master Farmers for 1987. The 1987 selections bring the total to 327 men and two women who have been recognized since the program was initiated 61 years ago.

Judges were Marshall King, president, Master Farmer Club; Buddy Jorgenson, vice president, Master Farmer Club; William Edwards, Extension farm management specialist, Iowa State University; and Monte Sesker, editor, *Wallaces Farmer*.

Donald Burt
Marshall County

"I am very cost conscious. Everything I do is strictly least-cost as long as it will work."

That's how Donald Burt of near Marshalltown, in Marshall County, sums up his management philosophy. "We can't keep doing things like we did when corn was $3 a bushel," he continues. "In the 1970s, we substituted capital for labor, now it's the opposite. "In the past, we could afford to be sloppy managers, but not any more," adds Burt. "In our operation, we do as much repair work, carpentry, etc., that we can to save on labor costs."

Until 10 years ago Don and his wife, Kathryn, had been farming in partnership with his parents, Richard and Bertha. Everything was 50/50 including land purchases. Then they decided to divide up the farms – Don and Kathryn taking the land suitable for livestock and his parents taking the cropland.

They also set up a family corporation. As Burt's sons got older and wanted to farm, the corporation bought more land.

"Our goal has been for this to be an ongoing family operation," declares Burt. "The farm has been in the family for more than 100 years. We intend for our sons to carry it on."

Even though Burt doesn't like government farm programs, he admits he did participate in 1986 for the first time ever.

Donald and Kathryn Burt

"The feed grain program is now better suited to livestock producers because you can seal corn and redeem it with PIK certificates and then feed it," he notes.

In 1987, Burt will plant about 570 acres of corn and 500 acres of beans. His normal practice is to chop stalks and disc in the fall. "I justify chopping stalks because it leaves the trash on top of the ground and also guards against plugging up equipment in a wet spring."

On soybean ground going to corn he simply uses a field cultivator. Herbicides are banded with the planter – another move that "cuts our costs in half," he notes.

Burt is a firm believer in diversification so livestock is also a big part of the operation. He feeds 500 to 600 head of cattle a year and finishes 300 plus litters of pigs per year. Burt's main interest is cattle. Son Allen is in charge of the hog operation.

Clifford Chesick, who has worked for the operation since 1960, helps keep things running smoothly. Burt buys and hauls all the livestock himself. "If you hire someone to buy them, haul them, and sell them, you are just giving that money away," he declares.

Copenhaver

Burt also spends a lot of time on marketing and uses a computer market news service. "It's available at an affordable price and it gives me a lot of information every day."

Burt has been active in many local and county organizations including the Green Mountain School board, Iowa Valley Community College board, Marshall County Cattlemen, Marshall County Farm Bureau, Marshall County Pork Producers, Iowa River Farm Service board and the local Farm Credit Services board.

Donald and his wife, Kathryn, are members of the Gladbrook Chapel United Methodist Church where he has served as Sunday school superintendent, trustee, youth counselor and chairman of the building committee.

The Burts have four children: Carol (Mrs. Glen Mann), Marshalltown; Barbara, Las Vegas, Nev.; Allen, who farms in the family operation; and Darrel, a student at Iowa State University.

Paul Copenhaver
Buchanan County

A desire to farm pulled Paul Copenhaver away from his job with Standard Oil of California in 1964 and brought him back near the farm on which he was raised.

Some 23 years and a national farm crisis later, the Buchanan County farmer and his wife, Gayle, say they don't regret the move in the least. Their farrow-to-finish hog operation produces an average 2,900 head a year. And their crops grow on 572 acres.

But Copenhaver's return to the farm didn't stifle his nonfarm interests. He was elected to the Iowa House of Representatives in 1982 to finish a term for the late Kenneth Miller. At the end of the term, he ran for the seat again and was elected to a full term. He didn't run in the following election because he wanted to spend more time with Gayle and their three children – Steve, 19, Ann, 16, and Sarah, 13.

His farm was demanding more time as well. A mix of totally enclosed and open-front hog facilities are used on the Copenhaver farm located near Independence. The operation boasts a 3.61 feed efficiency including sows. The sows and gilts farrow continuously, producing 380 litters a year. Hogs are marketed grade and yield every two weeks, weighing about 235 pounds.

As long as sows are paying their way, Copenhaver keeps them. Another practice that has worked well for him is feeding gestating sows only once every two days. "They're very satisfied and it evens up the boss sow/timid sow problem," he says.

Hog manure plays a big role in Copenhaver's fertilizer program. He knows his finishing hog manure has a 40-30-30 analysis, the nursery manure has a 30-20-20 analysis, and the sow manure has a 16-15-10 analysis. He uses those figures along with soil test data to determine where he'll put the manure and how much fertilizer he'll need to buy.

Keeping soil loss on the ground he farms below tolerance levels also reduces potential runoff. Copenhaver chisel plows cornstalks across the slope or following the contour. Bean ground is only tilled before planting.

Storage facilities on Copenhaver's farm operation hold 52,000 bushels. He built a prestressed concrete structure over the grain pit on the home farm. It keeps the pit clean and protects machinery in the off-season. The structure is strong enough to hold a feed processing plant or another 3,000 to 4,000 bushels of storage.

Copenhaver serves on the Northeast Iowa Farm Business Association board of directors. He's a member of the state salary compensation board, which makes recommendations to the governor on salaries for elected officials. He is an elder at the First Presbyterian Church in Independence. He has served as a soil district commissioner and on the school board.

While his son, Steve, is interested in working in agriculture when he graduates from Iowa State University in a couple years, Copenhaver says he's not going to pressure him either way.

Wayne Northey
Dickinson County

Cattle beat out hogs on the Wayne and Margaret Northey farm when they decided a few years back that they needed to specialize in one or the other.

Their son, Bill, had gone to Iowa State University. Left with a labor shortage, they sold the hogs. They had just added a cattle confinement building to their Dickinson County farm near Spirit Lake and figured they were better equipped to feed cattle.

Between 600 and 900 head of feeder cattle are in their lots year-round. Wayne buys 650-pound cattle from ranchers in nearby states as well as some from southern Iowa. Cattle are fed outside until they reach 800 pounds, and then they're put into a confinement building, which holds as many as 400 head. Northey likes to feed the cattle to around 1,150 to 1,250 pounds.

Increasing rate of gain is one of Northey's primary goals. To do that he's feeding 89% concentrate rations to cattle toward the end of their feeding period.

Northey bought an IBM personal computer two years ago. By using the computer to help answer "what if" questions he was able to see the potential benefit of higher rates of gain and what it would take to reach his goal.

Not all of the farm's records are on the computer yet. In fact, Margaret still keeps most of them with a sharp pencil as she has ever since the couple first started farming in 1958. But gradually they hope to put all the farm's records on the computer. Their daughter, Nancy, and her husband, Doug Pringnitz, who now farm with them, are making more use of the computer.

Besides feeding cattle, Northey farms 1,029 acres and custom farms another 175 acres in a 50/50 operation with Nancy and Doug. They raise corn and soybeans and some hay.

Although about half of the corn is grown for the livestock, it doesn't always end up in the feed-bunk. "Returns from feeding grain to livestock do not always compare with the returns from selling it," explains Northey.

Thanks to cattle manure, fertilizer rates were cut without sacrificing yields. "We cut back mostly on P and K. We found high enough levels – especially where we had spread livestock manure," adds Northey. But possible runoff is still a big concern.

Another concern of Northey's is education. He's true to his alma mater, Iowa State University. He's president of the Northwest Iowa Cyclone Club and a member of the Order of the Knoll, an organization that promotes private funding for ISU.

Northey is also treasurer of the newly-formed Spirit Lake Community School Foundation, which will fund activities at the local high school not funded by tax dollars. Northey also serves as chairman of the Emmetsberg Federal Land Bank board of directors and the Iowa Cattlemen's Association tax and finance committee. He's also active in Farm Bureau and the United Methodist Church of Spirit Lake.

Northey began farming in a partnership with his parents, Sid and Maude Northey. Now both his son and daughter are farming with him. His son, Bill, and daughter-in-law Cindy, have two children, two-year-old Jessica and six-month-old Emily.

Marvin Schlitzer
Dubuque County

Marvin and Barb Schlitzer rarely lose a calf on their dairy farm located just outside Dubuque. In their hands, a calf coming from one of the North Ridge Dairy Farm's registered Holsteins has a 98% chance of survival.

They attribute the high survival rate to good basic management like proper ventilation, vaccination and close watching. Marvin says it might also have something to do with the fact that Barbara is the one who takes care of them until they're three months old.

All replacements are home-grown. Some bull calves are sold as veal calves and a few are held back and sold for breeding purposes. But, of course, their main goal is producing milk efficiently and they do it well. On

Schlitzer

245

92 cows the rolling herd average is 17,922 pounds milk and 655 pounds fat.

To keep production per cow high, Schlitzer selects sires for production and type. Schlitzer says he uses only semen from bulls with a minimum of 1,000 pounds milk and +1 point in type on the sire summaries.

Marvin and Barbara Schlitzer

Although the herd has been on Dairy Herd Improvement Association testing since 1960, Barb still takes care of the general farm records. She keeps track of things like breeding dates, calf birthdays, individual cow histories and an animal's location on the farm.

Schlitzer uses a stanchion barn with a pipeline system. The cow overflow is housed in a recently built freestall barn. Producing cows feed from one of four silos year-round, even when pasture is available.

Keeping those silos full with high-quality forage takes a good deal of work. Schlitzer and his son, Mark, farm 80 acres of corn, 150 acres of hay and 40 acres of barley. They maintain a rigid soil testing and fertilization program on the farm while shooting for 6 tons of alfalfa and 130 bushels of corn per acre. Barley is used as a nurse crop for the alfalfa seedings and works well in the cows' rations, says Schlitzer. He uses a long meadow rotation with alfalfa

stands staying productive for five to six years. Fields stay in alfalfa until production drops. "I hate to plow down a good stand of alfalfa," notes Schlitzer.

Milk from the dairy is marketed through Swiss Valley Farms, of which Schlitzer is vice president. He's been on the board of the cooperative for 13 years. Work with the cooperative has been an education. "I got more out of it personally than I thought I was giving. There's no doubt about it, you can't help but learn." Schlitzer makes a couple trips a year to Washington, D.C., representing Swiss Valley Farms.

Schlitzer serves as a delegate for the Iowa Dairy Products Association and is a National Milk Producers Association director. He's also a member of the Grandview United Methodist Church.

The Schlitzers have one grandchild, 13-month-old Beth, the daughter of Mark and his wife, Twila. The Schlitzers have two daughters. Susan Plum lives in Arizona. Laurie was recently married and lives in Davenport with her husband, Gordon Bieri. Another member of the family, although he's not related, is Tom Hense, the Schlitzers' herdsman of 11 years.

1988

IOWA MASTER FARMERS
~ June 21, 1988

Edgar Keith
Kossuth County

Edgar and Joyce Keith's farming operation, north of Algona in northern Iowa, signifies the strengths of a "family farm." Ed is the third Keith generation to farm this land. Ed and Joyce are now bringing their daughter, Lorelei, and her husband, Al Koenecke, into the operation – the fourth family generation on this farm.

Ed and Joyce have stayed with a diversified livestock and crop operation, which Ed credits with helping this farm weather the financial storm that hit all of agriculture in recent years.

In 1988, the farming operation consists of about 500 acres of corn, 500 acres of soybeans, 200 acres of set-aside, and 200 acres of pasture and hay. The Keiths own 478 acres, and the rest is rented and custom-farmed. The farrow-to-finish hog enterprise is based on 100 sows and the sheep enterprise is centered on a 200-head ewe flock, with the lambs fed out

Edgar and Joyce Keith

on the farm.

"Ed, in his 33 years as a farmer, has always had an interest in improved cropping practices," says his father, Wayne Keith. Now 79 years old and retired, Wayne farmed 50-50 with son Ed for 15 years. About 10 years ago, Ed switched to planting beans in a 15-inch row width on all his bean acreage after yield testing 30-inch vs. 15-inch row widths several years.

"Our results from the first four years of comparing 30-inch rows against 15-inch rows convinced me to go 100% to 15-inch rows," explains Ed. "On the average, the narrow rows have yielded 3 to 6 bushels an acre better than 30-inch rows."

Ed refers to Carl Simmons as "my right-hand man." Ed, son-in-law Al Koenecke, and full-time employee Simmons provide the labor for this farm.

Simmons, who has worked for other farmers in Iowa and other states has been employed by Ed Keith off and on for a total of 15 years. "It's a pleasure to work for someone who's progressive, efficient, and organized in his business, who values my judgment and shows me that he appreciates me," says Simmons. "Ed treats people with respect. He's more like a friend than an employer."

Ed and Joyce keep their own records at home, using a Plan-A-Farm computer record-keeping system. "Keeping good records takes time and effort," says Joyce. "Our CPA definitely appreciates it, and these records allow us to keep close tabs on what's going on. That way, we make better management and marketing decisions."

Not all land in northern Iowa is flat. Wayne Keith foresaw the need to control soil erosion on his slopes and hill ground, so he started building terraces nearly 30 years ago. His son, Ed, continues to carry on that conservation ethic.

Several years ago the Keith family was honored by the Kossuth County Soil Conservation District and received a state Regional Soil Conservation Award recognizing the 28,000 feet of tile outlet terraces that have been built on the Keith farm. The Keiths also use hay in rotation and improved pasture management on the steep land, maintain grass waterways, and have developed 21 acres of wildlife habitat and a farmstead windbreak. They completed their SCS-approved soil conservation plan for the entire farm this spring.

As parents, Ed and Joyce have actively supported the activities of their five children over the years. Ed and Joyce have six grandchildren. Daughter Lorelei and husband Al Koenecke live on the home farm and are responsible for managing the hog operation. Daughter Christine and her husband, Larry Groen, reside nearby at Burt. Daughter Lynne and her husband, Terry Hoover, live near Algona. Daughter Merriam Keith lives in Algona, and son Brian Keith is in the U.S. Marine Corps.

Actively involved in the First Presbyterian Church of Algona for many years, Ed has also given his time and talent to several other farm and community service organizations. A soft-spoken man, he doesn't hesitate to mention that he served for 10 years on the Burt Community School board. "Being a school board member was quite an education for me, and I'm proud of what we accomplished for the children of this community," he says. Ed also served as one of the charter board members who helped start the Kossuth County Pork Producers and was its first secretary.

Bill Petersen
Scott County

William (Bill) Petersen began milking cows with his father in Scott County long before he got out of school.

In 1949, his father was killed in a traffic accident. At the youthful age of 22, Bill faced some big decisions. He chose to continue the operation, which had been in the family since 1876. A year later he married Marian Schroeder.

In 1958, Bill and Marian purchased the 160-acre home place from his mother. In 1970, they bought 60 acres more. They've rented another 150 acres since 1965.

The 370-acre operation has about 95 acres of hay or oats, 105 acres in corn, and about 115 acres of soybeans. The Petersens have moved steadily into conservation. Only sod ground gets moldboard plowed. The liquid manure injector rig is the only fall tillage tool used.

Petersen plants corn in 38-inch rows. Then he moves the outside rows and markers in on the four-row planter. He plants beans in rows averaging 32 inches without the expense of a separate planter or bother of changing tractor wheel spacings. He also drills some beans.

Spring tillage is generally limited to discing to incorporate herbicides. Already heavily involved in conservation tillage, Petersen is slowly but steadily moving toward no-till.

Dry weather helped the Petersens finish up harvesting first crop hay in top quality by late May. Some went in the silo. Some was baled. "Despite the hot, dry weather, the second crop began greening up pretty well," says Marian. "But it won't keep growing and yield well if we don't get more rain soon."

Oak-Krest Holsteins, the Petersen dairy herd, has grown from 20 cows in 1950. Today the milking herd runs 80 to 90 registered Holsteins with, again, that many replacements.

Production averages 16,000 to 17,600 pounds of milk and 600 to 670 pounds of fat per cow. One cow recently completed a 1,040-pounds fat record on a 305-day lactation.

The herd is housed in a slatted floor barn with 76 freestalls and a feedbunk down the middle. The herd is split into high and low producers. Each group is fed accordingly from two stave silos attached to the barn.

Rations consist of haylage, corn silage, dry hay, and a ground corn and oat concentrate. Cows are milked twice a day in a double-four herringbone parlor.

Soil conservation has been an important consideration in the Petersen operation for many years. Grass waterways were tiled in the late 1950s and early 1960s. Two erosion control dams were built on the home farm in 1964. Rental acres were tiled in 1967. Extensive terracing began in 1983. To date, 7,506 feet of tile have been laid and 9,800 feet of terraces constructed. More are planned.

Labor demand is high on a dairy operation. The Petersens' eldest son, Bill Jr., has been dairy herdsman since graduating from Iowa State University in 1975. Bill Sr. and Marian still do most of the crop work. One full-time employee, Todd Schmidt, helps with both the dairy and crops.

Bill and Marian Petersen

Bill Jr. and wife, Rita, have been investing in the Oak-Krest operation. They now own the herd 50-50 with Bill Sr. and Marian.

In years past, Bill Sr. did some custom work for younger son David. David and his wife, Amy, own and operate Majestic Manor Dairy in Muscatine County.

Innovation is a key to growth and efficiency in the Petersen operation. In 1950, Bill was the first Scott County dairyman on the owner-sampler testing program. He began using artificial insemination in the 1950s. He mastered the technique himself in 1971. In 1968, he constructed one of the first automated grain-handling systems in the area.

"Bill's most progressive stride is the confinement dairy facility constructed in 1971," says daughter-in-law Amy Petersen. "It was one of the first of its kind in the Midwest. It boasts labor efficiency that's hard to beat today." Petersen has been active in many local and county organizations including the Scott/Muscatine Farm Service Board, Swiss Valley Farms, Scott County DHIA and dairy promotion committee, Scott County Farm Bureau, Holstein-Friesian Association of America, and Scott County Corn and Soybean Growers Association.

Bill and Marian are sponsors in the 4-H UP program. They are members of St. Paul Lutheran Church where Marian is a van driver and Bill serves on the stewardship committee.

In addition to the two sons involved in farming, the Petersens have a daughter, Mrs. Dean Ehrecke, who lives in Davenport.

Dwight Puttmann
Woodbury County

Dwight Puttmann has a simple philosophy about money and the human mind. "Pay as you go, sleep good at night."

He admits that reluctance to go into debt for anything other than land may have "held us back some" in 30 years of farming. "But moving ahead gradually also kept us out of trouble," he adds quickly.

The "us" is Dwight and wife, Sally. The operation is a true partnership. They share the decisions and the work. "We talk about everything from hog production to crop production to painting the living room," she says. "We've been lucky to make some right choices. There's been a lot of satisfaction in doing it together."

The "luck" has been helped along with a lot of plain hard work and common sense.

It began in 1957 when the young couple moved back to his family's 160 acres near Kingsley

Dwight and Sally Puttman

in Woodbury County. An Iowa State University graduate, Dwight had been teaching agriculture for only a year when his father decided to retire and sell him the farm. They have expanded through the years as capital allowed, owning 620 acres of the 710 operated.

The Puttmanns chose to diversify the operation from the beginning and that's helped keep things profitable. An extensive hog enterprise is the backbone. Over the years, that's grown to where 1,500 to 2,000 hogs are now marketed annually. Until 1974, most of what they fed they farrowed. With facilities and labor tight, Dwight and a friend decided to put together a feeder pig cooperative. They found 10 shareholders and built the facility near Correctionville. A full-time manager oversees the 550-sow herd. The board meets monthly and another independent area farmer serves as a liaison between the co-op manager and the board. "If there's a problem, they talk it out before the independent approaches the acting president," explains Puttmann. "Though we've never had much of a problem, that interaction helps smooth out the wrinkles.

"Feeder pig co-ops aren't for everyone," he cautions. "The key is to find shareholders who are compatible. We don't agree on everything, but we talk things out."

At home, the Puttmanns have made use of converted buildings to feed hogs. An open front cattle shed with sloping concrete apron holds seven pens of various weights. When they hit the last pen at about 225 pounds, they go to Sioux City. About two loads a week are marketed. Another old cow barn has been refurbished to handle fresh pigs from the co-op.

With only the two of them providing the labor, there is a need for efficiency. So Dwight devised and installed his own overhead auger system to deliver feed to the pens. Pressure switches in the feeders signal the need and a fresh supply automatically comes from the grinding center, an old corncrib. A neighbor custom feeds another 300 to 400 head of hogs annually for the Puttmanns. "It's been a good agreement. We're short of space and this was one way to help us both," he says. "He's paid by the head, plus a hog for every 100 marketed."

Being handy and patient enough to "do-it-themselves" has been a factor in holding debt-load low. Some examples: They built much of their new home in 1970, he put together an automatic corn drying system, refurbished the old and built new farm buildings, made a low-boy trailer, and a tricycle trailer to tow as a chemical tank.

Since the Puttmanns' daughters, Kay Michaelson of LeMars, Iowa, and Sandy Salmon, Mt. Juliet, Tenn., are married and their husbands had no interest in farming, they have looked elsewhere for help. A year ago, they interviewed seven Iowa State University juniors and selected one to work with them for the summer. The plan was, if they liked each other he would join them upon graduation and eventually become a partner in the operation. "We wanted someone who wanted to farm that wouldn't otherwise have the chance to," says Sally. "We're happy Joe Hlas of Toledo will come with us this spring."

Besides hogs they maintain a 30-cow beef herd to use the grazing and hay land available. The crops are pretty much rotated between corn and soybeans. They minimum-till and are strong believers in soil conservation. Two miles of new terraces were installed this year, not to conform with farm program provisions, but just because they felt they were needed.

The active couple still finds time to participate in many community activities. Sally was one of the first women in the state to be elected a county Farm Bureau president. "It was a great experience and I hope I contributed to an organization I believe strongly in," she says. She is also a member of the state soil conservation committee.

Dwight has held many offices, including Farm Bureau, the county compensation board, FmHA board, Kingsley-Pierson School board, Lutheran church deacon, township clerk and has served on countless committees.

Do they look upon farming as a way of life or a business? "If you treat it as a business, you'll have a great way of life," they agree.

Carl Willhoit
Wapello County

New challenges are the spice of Carl Willhoit's life. He thrives on finding innovative solutions to the problems he encounters in farming 1,270 acres near Batavia with his wife, Eloise, and sons, Terry and Mark. Mark and his wife, Becky, have two sons, Andrew and Eric.

Their efficient cattle and grain operation has benefited from each new technology the Willhoits have applied. Soil conservation terraces drape across every field on the farm. The Willhoits adopted minimum tillage and maintain a 180 to 200-bushel corn per acre yield average. They cut costs with split fertilizer applications and have reduced herbicide rates by a third.

Pasture and hayfield renovation and re-seeding have increased production of rolling ground to supply their Angus and crossbred cow herd. They have also experimented with no-till planted into sod and alternative crops on set-aside acres.

Two years ago they started a certified seed business that is growing steadily. "We started the seed business because we wanted more income. We wanted to be more diversified," says Willhoit.

Some of the soybean varieties planted on 216 acres are Pella 86, Harper 87, Zane, Chamberlain, Sherman and Hobbit 87. This year, 20 acres of wheat will be harvested for the seed business.

Last winter the men installed a cleaning mill to clean and bag seed. Carl modified the spotless mill and supporting framework to fit the new building addition it is housed in.

The bagging system runs like clockwork. He adapted the conveyor belt to stop after a bag is filled. He also modified an old shop vacuum to pull up individual seed labels automatically.

"A man offered to set this up for us for $2,500. We figured we could do it for less. We spent about one-tenth that amount," smiles Willhoit.

The 180-head cow herd was started more than 50 years ago when Carl's father gave him and his brother Max two Angus heifers for 4-H projects. A purebred Angus herd of 40 cows provides the nucleus for crossbreeding with Gelbvieh, Simmental and Tarentaise.

"We keep the purebred cows to retain Angus characteristics. After seven or eight generations of crossbreeding, I think some of that hybrid vigor runs out and you need to return to the purebreds," explains Willhoit.

A majority of their cows are artificially inseminated. To improve the Angus herd they use top sires and excellent replacement females.

Carl and Eloise Willhoit

They purchased a daughter of the Angus bull, Pathfinder, and have been well-pleased with the results. "The cow herd is producing some good offspring. We keep about 35 of our very best heifers. We feel we can raise good replacement heifers more easily than we can go out and find them."

Usually 200 feeder cattle are finished each year. A new mixer mill, airtight silo, and scale formulate more concise feed rations. A rule of thumb is applied to all heifers and steers fed out on the 90-day finishing schedule.

"For each 100 pounds of body weight, we start a calf with a half pound of corn. A 600-pound calf is fed 3 pounds of corn. If we feed a steer out to 1,200 to 1,300 pounds we increase corn to 13 to 14 pounds per day."

While quick to adopt new technologies, the Willhoits strive to produce livestock as simply and naturally as possible. No medications are mixed in their rations and they don't use implants, although they follow a complete vaccination program. "If our cattle came from a sale barn it might be important to do those things, but our calves are weaned off their mothers and we don't have to go through that situation."

Their philosophy comes from a strong Christian belief. In addition to his many community responsibilities, for several summers Carl has led a prayer meeting for rain at the Wapello County fairgrounds in Eldon. "Our prayers were answered. Our faith in God has helped us seek new goals and find solutions. We've been truly blessed here with our life and our family."

IOWA MASTER FARMERS
~ June 13, 1989

Arnold Grau
Buena Vista County

"Hogs provide the cash flow and cattle help pay for the big ticket items...although not always."

That pretty well sums up Arnold (Arnie) Grau's philosophy on farming. He is a firm believer in diversification. He also believes you have to have a firm grip on expenses if you are going to stay in farming these days.

"We have several projects on hold just because we don't want to overextend ourselves," points out Grau, who farmed in partnership with his father, Ivan, until his death in 1983.

From the time they started farming together in 1964 until 1980 the Graus did all the work themselves with part-time and seasonal help. From fall 1980 until fall 1985 the Graus employed full-time help. However, since then the work has been done by Arnie, his wife, Karen, son Gordon, and daughter, Julie, with occasional part-time help.

"When the hard economic times hit we felt we had to cut back somewhere. So we decided not to write checks to a hired man. It meant longer hours for the family but it was a decision that had to be made," he points out.

Arnie admits that as a result, some things don't always get done when they should, but that's just the way things have to be. Even so, Arnie has kept his priorities in line. For example, Gordon graduated from Newell-Providence High School last month. He was a member of the track team this spring. "I decided I would always be able to plant corn. But I would never again have a chance to see my son participate in high school track so we took time off for that," notes Arnie.

In 1989 the Graus have about 435 acres of corn, 215 acres of soybeans, 25 acres of oats and 50 acres of alfalfa. Normal yields are about 160 bushels per acre for corn, 55 bushels per acre for soybeans and 100 bushels per acre for oats. Weather has been hard on yields the

Arnold and Karen Grau

last few years. "In 1988 we were in a dry pocket. Corn averaged only 106 bushels per acre, beans 34 bushels per acre and oats, 40 bushels per acre," notes Karen. "In 1986 we had some drowned out spots due to excess rain or rain that came too fast," she laments.

The Graus farrow-to-finish about 1,700 head of hogs a year.

Hogs are finished in a total confinement and sows have access to dirt lots for breeding.

Arnie buys 400 to 500 head of feeder cattle each year to feed out in dirt lots. Feed is stored in three, 20- by 80-foot Harvestores. One is used for haylage, one for haylage from government ground, and one for high moisture shelled corn. All three are conveniently located next to a feed distribution center. Feed is hauled to the lots using feed wagons. An older Minneapolis Moline tractor powered by propane fuel is used to pull the wagons. "That old tractor is really handy," says Arnie. "I always did like the propane fuel. It burns cleaner and that means longer engine life."

Grau's hobby, however, is a herd of Saler cows. "It started out as a hobby in 1985," explains Arnie. "I read about the Saler cattle being fertile mothers, having fewer calving problems, and good carcass qualities." He currently has 18 cows calving and eight heifers to breed as replacements.

Looking at ridge-till, Arnie switched from a chisel plow to a V-ripper in 1987. "I felt I just needed to till a little deeper," he explains. Now, he is looking at making another major switch in tillage-planting operations. "I really like what I see with ridge-till in my area, but I still have a few questions to answer. Plus, I have to be ready financially to make the necessary equipment changes."

The Graus have been very supportive of their children's activities as well as the local community. Arnie served on the school board for nine years, served as president of the Buena Vista County Pork Producers Association six years, and has been on numerous other boards. He also coached Peewee baseball for

six years.

A member of the Nain Lutheran Church in Newell, Arnie has taught Sunday school and served on the church council.

Son, Gordon, will be a freshman at Iowa State University this fall majoring in agribusiness. Daughter, Julie, will be a senior in family and consumer sciences at ISU.

Ralph Howe
Marshall County

With 15 borrowed sows on an aging farmstead, a young central Iowan traded a pair of scissors for a scoop shovel. It was 1948 and the licensed Master Barber had no thought of being named a Master Farmer in 1989.

Ralph and Rita Howe of Clemons farrowed 105 pigs out of those bred sows and then returned them to her father, Arthur Dunn. The gilts from those litters were the beginning of today's 2,000-head, farrow-to-finish, pork operation. In 41 years the Howes have never purchased a replacement gilt. But they do buy feeder pigs. Some 2,000 head, on another nearby farmstead, fill out their annual production of around 4,000 hogs.

The numbers aren't the only things that have changed over the years. Hogs on pasture to slatted floors and automated feeding, the farmstead has gone through a complete renovation. Much of it was recycled, like the lumber from the original house.

It was used to construct what Ralph calls a "porktel." Built in 1967, the unit he designed was the first controlled confinement building in Marshall County. Half of the 154- by 24-foot building houses 30 farrowing crates over slatted floors. The other half is for growing pigs on full slats.

"They told me we could expect to get about seven years out of the equipment in these units," he says. "We've replaced the crates and several gates, but the rest has lasted 20 years with continuous farrowing."

When a sow comes out, the unit is washed down and another goes in. The 100 bred sows average 10 pigs per litter. Thirty bred gilts are brought into the herd four times a year and average 7.5 pigs.

"We work hard to keep things up and to manage both the facilities and the hogs. That little extra attention has paid big dividends in building life and herd performance," he says.

"Of course, experience helps. We can look at a litter and about tell if it's going to break with scours. We did have a bout with pseudorabies and tested out in three years. New gilts are vaccinated and tested."

The herd has been constantly improved through a crossbreeding program. Two of the four purebred boars are replaced every year. They are bought in September and kept isolated until November. The boars are turned in with the breeding herd routinely every two days. That has helped keep conception rate high.

Rita and Ralph Howe

Boars are selected through test station records, many from Iowa State University. Howe wants a strong boned boar with a full ham and good loin. "You can select for too much leanness," he warns. "We look for a good balance of marbling."

Pigs are started on creep feed at two weeks and weaned at four weeks. They are moved into the growing side at 40 pounds and then to an open front finishing house at 100 to 120 pounds. Its sloping cement floor and gutter are connected to the 100,000-gallon liquid manure storage tank.

At the heart of the setup is the granary. The 45-foot high, 20-foot x 20-foot structure is built of 2 x 4s laid flat. "It's an idea I got at the 1968 Farm Progress Show," he says. "We built it ourselves and it has been a low maintenance unit for us."

The center houses an automatic mix-mill. A network of 4-inch overhead augers supplies bulk tanks for the porktel and finishing unit, while a feed wagon is used for gestation and breeding lots.

Hogs are marketed at about 230 pounds, once or twice a month. He subscribes to a computer marketing service to keep up-to-date on marketing quotes. His bank also provides marketing services for grain and livestock. The Howes' hogs may be the best known porkers ever. Most of you have seen them — at least two of them. They have been pictured on posters, buttons, billboards, you name it, as the familiar "Hogs Are Beautiful" photo. Taken in 1968 for a cover and story in *Farm Quarterly* magazine the two pigs with snouts almost touching won the hearts of millions around the world. "A copy was even presented to President Nixon by H.R. Gross," recalls Howe.

"If I'd just had a royalty," he sighs, jokingly.

Right-hand man son Roger, 26, is working into the operation. Besides operating his own 250 acres, he shares a percentage of the farrow-to-finish operation and has an equal share in the feeder pigs. "I couldn't get along without him. He supplies a lot of the muscle," smiles dad. They share some machinery, too. Roger provides a tractor and sprayer and splits some expense on other implements. "It's a way to ease him in at a price he can afford."

All of the 400 acres of corn is fed, and the 80 acres or so of soybeans are sold. He relies on soil tests to fertilize.

"We test every 20 acres on the flat fields and every 5 acres on the rolling land, then spot fertilize according to specific needs," he explains. Corn hybrids are checked over a three-year period in on-farm test plots. During last year's drought the hybrids ranged from 7 bushels per acre to 35 bushels per acre. Needless to say, they planted more of the tolerant corn this spring.

In the house, partner Rita is on the phone and on the radio almost constantly some days. The radios keep her in touch for parts and messages. Ralph is immediate past chairman of the National Livestock and Meat Board. Among many activities, he's served as president of Marshall County Pork Producers; treasurer, vice-president and president of the Iowa Pork Producers; named a Master Pork Producer in 1968; represented Iowa on the U.S. Animal Health Association and Brucellosis committees; hosted countless foreign groups at the farm; worked in the "Iowa Fine Meats" campaign; served on the school board; is a member of the Sacred Heart Church in Saint Anthony; and as township clerk.

The family also includes Connie who is a member of the Sisters of Mercy, Cedar Rapids, Iowa; Rick, Lenexa, Kansas; Carmen (Mrs. Mike Bolton), Red Oak, Iowa; Russell, Boston, Massachusetts; and Tamma, Ames, Iowa.

Don Newby
Polk County

In front of all three football-field-sized hog houses on the Don Newby farm are neatly planted rows of flowers blooming in the summer sun. Thousands of flowers are planted each year by the Newbys for themselves and their guests.

Several hundred visitors from all over the world tour their 1,200-acre crop and livestock operation every summer. Visitors from foreign lands may have only one opportunity to visit an Iowa farm and often it is the fertile Don Newby farm. "I think American agriculture needs good public relations," says Don Newby, smiling. "Whether you're hosting foreign visitors or people from Des Moines or Chicago, it's good to let others know about our business."

Newby's willingness to share his knowledge and learn from others has made him a respected and innovative leader in the agricultural community and an appropriate choice for a 1989 Master Farmer.

The Newby family has farmed in Polk County for four generations. After farming with his father for two years near Runnells, Don bought his first 120-acre farm at Stuart. He taught school and sold insurance during the daytime and farmed evenings. Don's wife, Irene, also worked as a substitute teacher and started raising their family of three. Their son, Dave, is farm manager. Julie lives in Burnsville, Minn., and works in farm management. Lisa is a registered nurse in Des Moines.

In 1965 when Don and Irene moved to their farm northeast of Bondurant, the site contained an old peat bog and was filled with marshes. Don organized a drainage district with other farmers in the neighborhood and installed a mile-long tile line that drained the swamps.

Now his farm has a three-year average of

160-bushels per acre corn and 57 bushels per acre soybeans. He won the 1987 county soybean contest with a 63.75-bushels per acre yield and the 1988 county corn contest with 173 bushels per acre. He has also won past district honors.

Newby's innovations extend from the hog enterprise to his cropping practices. Don was one of the first to use modified open-front buildings for the 7,000 to 9,000 feeder-to-finish hogs sold annually.

High moisture corn is fed to the hogs by an entirely automated feeding system. Pigs have average daily gains of 1.5 pounds per day with a top of 1.76 pounds per day, and a 3.5-pound average feed efficiency.

Manure is collected in a slurry storage tank and is used to meet the potassium (K) and phosphorus (P) fertilizer needs of their cropland. "It supplies all the P and K for our crops and most of the nitrogen. We even have to watch the levels now so that we don't apply too much."

With the help of Dave, and seasonal help this summer from Doug Williams and Kurt Lohner, Don manages their farms by delegating the work and leaving certain areas of responsibility to others.

"We do everything we can do well, such as most of our own repair work. Yet if there is a specialized job others do better we leave it to them. For instance, the nutritionist advises us on our rations and the local cooperative crop specialist estimates our rates of herbicides and insecticides. I research new concepts carefully and if it's not economically feasible, we don't try it," says Don.

Newby uses a minimum tillage system that leaves crop residue on the surface. "I'm a real sloppy farmer," laughs Don.

They plant corn in 30-inch rows for a harvest population of 25,000 plants. Soybeans are drilled in 10-inch rows. "We feel we get an extra bushel per acre from the drilled beans and, of course, you can't cultivate. There are no skip rows. To control weeds we can drive right over the small beans with a 60-foot sprayer. Another advantage of drilled beans is that we can combine whichever direction the beans are leaning," explains Don.

Newby keeps soybean herbicide and insecticide costs to about $12 per acre, although he applies the

Don and Irene Newby

chemicals only as needed. "For eight to 10 years, I've used 1 quart of Treflan, ½ rate Basagran with 1 gallon of 28% liquid nitrogen. We don't cultivate or walk the beans and we've had few weed problems. I try not to use anything that will hurt the following year's crop," says Newby.

Don and Irene offer much of their time to many community activities. Irene went back to school a few years ago to get a degree in psychology. In addition to keeping all the farm records and hosting visitors, Irene does private counseling and volunteers as their church counselor.

Both Newbys give countless hours to Grace Community Church in Pleasant Hill. Don is chairman of the church trustees. He helped build the church and is ready with his skid steer loader and backhoe to help build a new home this summer for their minister.

Don was named an outstanding young farmer by the Jaycees and the Kiwanis, and was honored as a Master Pork Producer. He has served on the Farmers Co-op Elevator board and state Farm Bureau advisory committees. He was president of the Polk County Pork Producers and Bondurant Lions Club, and chairman of the Guthrie County Extension council.

Don loves old cars and has restored several to mint condition. He received the President's Cup for the finest antique car shown in the United States in 1984 for his 1946 Mercury Sportsman. He also finds time to golf and fish.

The Newbys truly enjoy people. They have given generously to their community, donating a new rescue unit and funds for Bondurant's first library. Some years they have hosted 2,000 or more foreign visitors for the USDA, Farm Bureau, Iowa Department of Agriculture and Land Stewardship, farm commodity groups, and private industries,

"We make time for others because we really feel we owe something back. We just like to do things with people," says Irene.

"It takes a lot of time," says Don. "All the sprucing up, the flowers, and the hours it takes to tour with visitors, but it's important to promote agriculture and good will.

"People are all the same. We all have different customs and lifestyles but we are all interested in basics like each other's work and families," says Don.

It's impressive to consider how many people from foreign lands who come to Iowa see only one farm – the Newbys'. Their positive influence is far-reaching, extending beyond borders and politics. Their commitment is commendable and *Wallaces Farmer* hopes they continue to be ambassadors of Iowa agriculture for a long time.

Oscar Steele
Washington County

The farm isn't large, in fact, according to the 1987 Census of Agriculture, it's under Iowa's 313-acre average operation.

"But they have sure done a lot on 260 acres."

"His major fault may be the priority he places on community work, in promoting soil conservation and generally working for a better agriculture. For that he may have sacrificed some personal gains in his farm operations. He's always willing to serve."

"A thinker, that outsiders may consider conservative, is truly an individual with foresight who recognizes where his family fits in agriculture. They have thrived in times of adversity."

"4-H and Extension owe much to this couple's leadership and hard work."

The words from neighbors, friends, bankers, church, and ag leaders support Oscar and Wynne Steele of Riverside, Iowa, as 1989 Master Farmers. Hogs, a beef cow herd, corn, and soybeans have provided diversity, while the family provides all the labor in their Washington County operation.

"Do a good job with livestock, keep your overhead as low as possible, and do things yourself has been our formula," says Oscar.

They started in 1962 when Oscar purchased 200 acres in partnership with his brother. Prior to that he graduated from ISU and taught vo-ag for seven years. In 1964, he had the opportunity to join his father, Elmer, and brother in partnership on 520 acres.

That continued until 1976 when the partnership was divided. Elmer is still involved and at the age of 85 helps with repairs and general farm maintenance.

Oscar has always advocated soil and water conservation. "It's our responsibility to not only maintain it, but improve it for the future," he asserts. Their rolling land is farmed on the contour, crops are rotated, grass waterways maintained, a pond was built, and dry dams installed. He still wasn't satisfied.

"With poor livestock markets and a low corn base we had to find a way to expand crop acres without sacrificing soil," he explains.

"To keep the farm within or below the established 5-ton per acre soil loss limits we had to leave more crop residue on the surface. The only way to do that on some steep fields was not to disturb the soil."

About 10 years ago, Oscar jumped into no-till "with both feet," he says. There were problems that first year killing the sod, problems incorporating the fertilizer, problems making the planter penetrate, problems with ground squirrels. Yes, ground squirrels. "They stole the seed which was barely covered in hard-packed soil,"

Oscar and Wynne Steele

says Oscar. "But we learned enough on that experimental 15 acres to plant all of our corn no-till the next year. Our goal is to leave at least 65% of the residue on the surface."

Land with a 4% slope or less is rotated from corn to soybeans. On slopes of 8% or more, continuous corn is planted or a corn/hay/pasture rotation is combined with strip-cropping. Everything is pastured during fall and winter.

In early April, as soon as it is dry enough to avoid compaction, corn ground is sprayed with Extrazine at two-thirds the recommended rate and ½-pint of 2,4-D. Next operation is to plant when the soil temperature reaches 55 degrees. The rest of the herbicide is sprayed over the top and that's it until harvest.

Steele hasn't cultivated since starting no-tilling. "That doesn't necessarily mean we shouldn't have," he admits. "The weed pressure hasn't been great, but at times there have been more than we want. I'll still trade a few weeds to conserve the soil. Moisture saved is more than a trade-off."

This year he knifed in anhydrous because it was cheaper; previously a 28% nitrogen solution was put on with the planter. Fertilizer application and consistent seed placement have been the major concern on continuous no-till.

"We wanted to get our phosphorus and potassium below the seed with minimum soil disturbance," he says. "The Kinze six-row, double frame planter was the answer. We were able to add a 4-inch by 4-inch bar and hang Yetter 20-inch ripple fertilizer coulters in front with a knife working independently behind on the same shank.

"It works slick. We can deep-band the full load of fertilizer in one pass, when the liquid nitrogen price allows. The coulters are removable and can be attached to a tool bar for side-dressing nitrogen," he says.

Steele still isn't satisfied with erosion created by the slot the coulter cuts. "I think University engineers, a creative farmer, or some company ought to push harder for a new application method. In theory, the punch-wheel ISU is playing with looks like it has possibilities."

The Steeles maintain a 40-head crossbred stock cow herd. He was one of the first to introduce artificial insemination into the herd. No bull has been used since. Either Oscar or one of his sons, Darrell or Dan, handle the chore. It's started about June 18 and finished in about 60 days. The first time through 75% to 80% of the cows are settled. The calf crop averages about 95% to 97%.

Wynne follows the records closely and selects three sires every year. "Milking ability, size and frame, calving ease, and weaning weight are all important factors," she says. "But we think it's how carefully you match the individual characteristics of sire and cow that makes the difference."

What she does seems to work. Their children have won their share of county fair honors with animals from their herd, including a grand champion steer, reserve grand champion, three grand champion carcass winners including the last two consecutive years, and many class and division winners.

The herd grazes on 30 acres of permanent pasture and another 30 acres of rotated pasture. The alfalfa/clover/timothy and brome pastures are fertilized with 40 to 50 pounds of nitrogen in the spring. Two cuttings of hay are usually taken off the new seeding before it is grazed.

The calves are all fed out, unless feed is short. They are weaned at 205 days with no creep feed at an adjusted weight of 500 to 550 pounds. "In the feedlot we'd like to say we average around 3 pounds, but more honestly it's probably closer to 2.6 to 2.7 pounds," admits Oscar.

Their hog operation is a 40-sow farrow-to-finish system, marketing about 600 head annually. The confinement farrowing building is a remodeled barn with raised crates and flush pens. The open front finishing unit has slats with an automatic curtain that raises and lowers according to temperature.

In spare time, Oscar has helped build two homes and built or remodeled every farm building.

The Steeles emphasized the role of their four children in the success of their operation; each of them generously contributed their skills, both in on-farm and off-farm work. "Their achievements have been important to the operation and to themselves," points out Oscar.

Ironically, another Master Farmer from the class of 1951, Herb Campbell of Washington, Iowa, plus his son, Bruce, are important to Darrell (also an ISU grad), his wife Carmen, and their daughters Amy and Jenna. Young Steele's farming operation began as a partnership with Bruce; he now has his own farrow-to-finish hog operation and rents most of his farm from Herb. "I'm not the only one they have helped get started. There are others. They are an exceptional family," noted Darrell.

Like his father helped him, Oscar is helping Darrell. They share equipment and work together.

Daughter, Diane, a U of Iowa alum, is a nurse/administrator in a surgery center in Denver, Colorado; younger daughter, Donna, chose UNI and now is a middle school teacher in Huron, S.D.; and son, Dan is an ISU student and is interested in a future in agriculture.

Oscar has been active in many community, county and state activities. He is a board member of the SE Iowa Research Farm, an ASCS Twp. committee member; soil district commissioner and chairman; has given countless talks on no-till and soil conservation; on Farm Bureau Board; served as president of the Washington County Beef Producers; 4-H committee and chairman; worked with the county fair for 22 years; served on school evaluation committee; church committees; etc.

CHAPTER 7
~
1990 – 1999:
Biotechnology & Globalization

As the calendar flipped to the 1990s, developments off the farm were bringing rapid change to the farm. Biotechnology not only brought profit opportunities, but also spawned controversy.

Genetically-engineered herbicide-tolerant Roundup Ready soybeans debuted in 1996. By 2000, genetically-engineered seed beans captured 59% of Iowa's soybean acreage. That adoption rate far outpaced the adoption of hybrid seed corn. Hybrid seed corn arrived in 1928, but by 1933 had only gained 10% market penetration.

Cost savings drew farmers to herbicide resistant biotechnology. They viewed Roundup as more environmentally friendly than other chemical weed control choices.

Some consumer groups feared genetically modified organisms might turn into Frankenstein food. It is true that the commercializing firms devoted few resources to consumer acceptance of genetically modified foods.

Opening trade doors

The North American Free Trade Agreement worked to promote trade among Canada, Mexico and the United States. On a global front, the World Trade Organization sought to trim tariff barriers and improve market access around the world.

Disputes over who subsidizes whom, how much, and where, plus sanitary and phytosanitary provisions, were stumbling blocks that continue to this day. Still, U.S. pork exports reached a new record every year of the decade.

Cleaner water and air

Production agriculture increasingly specialized. Many farms no longer grew both crops and livestock. Livestock producers focused on one species or even one stage of production.

Urban residents moved to the country seeking the rural lifestyle. Environmental concerns over water quality, air quality, and who can control who produces what and where, became hot button issues. Crop farmers, livestock farmers and rural residents all staked out different positions. Finding mutually-satisfactory solutions was challenging.

Tradeoffs of integration

Iowa's hog inventory grew from 13.8 million head on 35,000 farms in 1990 to 15.4 million hogs on 14,500 farms in 1999. Over the same stretch, North Carolina almost quadrupled its hog industry from 2.8 million hogs on 10,000 farms to 9.5 million hogs on 4,000 farms. North Carolina hogs were concentrating in the hands of fewer, but much larger integrated operations. That trend gained traction in Iowa.

Many independent hog producers became contract producers for larger operations. Structural changes within Iowa's livestock sector widened the rift among rural Iowans over environmental issues.

Some observers viewed the growing prevalence of production and marketing contracts between producers and packers as pork producers sacrificing their independence. Others viewed such agreements as sound business decisions and links in supply chains to meet growing consumer interest in being able to find out where and how their food was produced.

Late 1998 tested the strength of those bonds.

The hog price wreck

The hog cycle has persisted "forever." Strong prices trigger expansion. More hogs coming to market depress prices. Weak prices bring liquidation. Fewer hogs lift prices, and the cycle repeats.

The 1998 downturn was unmatched in severity. December 1998 cash hogs skidded to $14.70, the lowest monthly average since November of 1964's $14.30 per cwt. The January 1999 figures showed an even lower price, with live hogs selling as low as 8 cents per pound in some markets. At the time, industry observers identified too many hogs and not enough slaughter capacity as the cause. That reinforces the need for working relationships with supply-chain partners upstream and downstream from the farm.

Those dirt-cheap hog prices have both far-reaching and long-lasting impacts. The subsequent shakeout continued the consolidation of pork production in the hands of fewer but larger players. Second, long memories of dismal 1998 returns encouraged producers to restrain production growth rate. The slow production growth rate brought one of the longest strings of pork profits on record.

Remember the flood year?

One year, 1993, stands out for Iowa farmers. "You can't have much of a crop failure when you have drowned out spots in the spring," goes an old saying. Farmers learned otherwise. A wet spring that continued into a wet summer resulted in an Iowa average corn yield of 80 bushels, 37 bushels below the second lowest yield of the decade.

Corn yields generally kept trending higher. Prices ran in the $2.20 to $2.50 area for most of the decade. In 1998 and 1999, big corn crops depressed prices. But the 1995 Farm Bill's loan deficiency payments largely made up the difference, supporting income but at a large cost to the U.S. Treasury.

1990 Iowa Farm Facts

FARMS & INCOME

Number of Iowa farms	104,000
Crop production value	$4.7 billion
Livestock production value	$6.1 billion
Iowa net farm income	$2.6 billion

LIVESTOCK

	Inventory	Average price
Cattle and calves	4.4 million head	$75.86/cwt (beef)
Hogs and pigs	13.8 million head	$54.85/cwt
	Production	Inventory
Chickens (Layers)	2.2 billion eggs	8.3 million birds
Milk	4.2 billion lbs.	

CROPS

	Harvested acres	Yield	Production	Avg price
All Hay	2 million	3.55 tons/acre	7.1 million tons	$63.5/ton
Corn	12.4 million	126 bu./acre	1.6 million bu.	$2.21/bu.
Soybeans	7.9 million	41.5 bu./acre	328 million bu.	$5.63/bu.
Oats	600,000	68 bu./acre	40.8 million bu.	$1.14/bu.
Wheat	75,000	45 bu./acre	3.4 million bu.	$2.74/bu.

Stanley Bay
Monroe County

At an age when the desire to pursue hobbies or carefree travel draws many people into retirement, Stanley Bay accepted a new challenge.

He had the task of serving on the first Monroe County zoning board and found himself in the middle of the fracas that often surrounds new zoning plans. By contributing his careful evaluations and considerable foresight, Bay helped to forge an equitable county zoning plan.

Annette Scieszinski, Monroe County attorney, has worked extensively with Bay. She says, "Throughout a grueling schedule of meetings and work sessions, Bay exhibited a calm, reasoned approach to defining the goals for our county. He probed the ways zoning could achieve those goals, and educated the public about the purposes of zoning. His diligence in favor of land stewardship resulted in an ordinance that shows a true concern for responsible land use."

Bay's respect for the land is obvious on his 1,500-acre farm located eight miles northeast of Albia, Iowa. Fields are uniformly terraced and tiled. Crop rotations, conservation tillage, and minimal use of chemicals have been standard practices for many years.

Crop rotations are two years of corn, one year of soybeans, one year of oats, and three to five years of hay. Tillage is by chisel plow and discing, and occasionally moldboard plowing for sod. The primary source of fertilization is manure, with corn sidedressed as needed.

Steve Teno is a young farmer who lives nearby and helps Bay with the field work and livestock.

"I share crop with Steve and last year in the yield contest, we were fifth in corn and did well in soybeans, too," admits Bay, modestly. Corn yields average 125 bushels per acre for corn, soybeans 50+ bushels per acre, and oats 110 bushels per acre.

Stanley Bay

About 2,000 hogs are marketed each year from a hog confinement unit built in 1980. Bought at 60 pounds, pigs average a 1½-pounds average daily gain and are sold in four to four and one-half months at 240 to 260 pounds.

"Dad genuinely enjoys raising livestock. He likes to raise what he feeds and feed what he raises," says his daughter, Catherine.

"There's a lot of work to livestock but a good income is possible. It's paid off for us," explains Bay, as he stands inside a 60- by 160-foot metal building half full of small alfalfa bales. Another 128- by 60-foot machinery building holds equipment that is kept in top working order.

Bay formulates his own rations using a protein supplement of soybean meal and tankage. He feeds a 16% to 17% protein level for growing pigs and 14% to 15% for finishing hogs. Breakeven is about $44. Pigs are purchased from one reliable source. "We pay a premium for them, but we know the pigs are healthy. It greatly reduces disease problems."

At age 71, Bay still maintains a 100-head cow herd, although numbers were reduced from 240 cows as a result of drought and pasture renovations. He maintains a small herd of purebred Herefords and has a commercial herd of Hereford and Angus crossbreds.

After winter backgrounding, calves not kept for replacements are sold green-tagged at 650 pounds to 700 pounds. Bay often bales 50-pound round bales, which are left in the field for winter-feeding. "The feeding is done and the manure is hauled," smiles Bay.

Raising livestock fits Bay's strong conservation ethic. "The cows require a good pasture and hay field rotation. It helps keep our land from eroding into the Mississippi Delta."

Bay's well-respected qualities of hard work, good management skills and attention to detail are sought by local organizations.

In addition to long hours on the zoning board, Bay has contributed his time on the board of trustees for William Penn College in Oskaloosa, the Eddyville school board, Farm Bureau county board, and Monroe County compensation board. He was also a 4-H leader and advisor, church deacon and elder, and traveled extensively with agricultural delegations.

Bay and his wife, Emily, raised five daughters. Emily died in 1983. Bay shares farming decisions with his daughters, who have inherited their parents' strong work ethic. All attended college and are community-minded like their father.

Catherine and Marilyn live on the family farm and work at People's State Bank in Albia. Frances worked for the state of Arizona before being stricken with multiple sclerosis. Ruthanne works in retailing in West Des Moines, and Susan is a nurse in Omaha.

Edward Engstrom
Hancock County

If you're a young person thinking about whether to start farming, Ed and Bess Engstrom are the kind of people to talk to. Ed began farming in 1939. He and Bess have 45 years of valuable experience.

Making a living on 254 acres near Kanawha, Iowa, the Engstroms' greatest satisfaction is in the family they raised. "Family always came first," says Bess, a former schoolteacher. More acres could have been added over the years, but this northern Iowa couple chose instead to invest in their family – such as college educations for the children.

Ed Engstrom has been active in Farm Bureau, the Iowa Soybean Association, local elevator board, etc. However, he's most proud of his service on behalf of Iowa's loan program for beginning farmers. Since 1980, he's served on the Iowa Agricultural Development Authority. This board approves or rejects loan applications from people who apply to participate.

Through this state-operated program, $66 million in loans have been issued to help new farmers get started since it began 10 years ago.

The legislature started the program because of concern about beginning farmers not being able to obtain affordable financing.

"This program has helped 810 families start farming during the past 10 years. Even so, today the average age of farmers in Iowa is 54 years old. This worries me," says Engstrom. "Iowa has a lot of older farmers. Who will take their place? I'd rather see a family farm survive and young people stay on the land rather than see an enlargement of a corporation. The survival of small towns and future of rural Iowa will depend a lot on how this issue is resolved."

Is it harder to start farming today than 50 years ago? "Absolutely," says Engstrom. "I graduated from Iowa State University and came home to farm with my father in 1939. A farm nearby was for sale and we bought it. We raised seed corn. Hybrid corn was just getting a good start. We obtained inbreds from ISU, grew the seed, and sold it to farmers. We'd sort it, dry it and sell it on the ear."

While a person didn't need as much money to farm in 1939 compared to 1990, it wasn't easy to get started back then either. "Times were still tough following the Depression," says Engstrom. "Raising seed corn gave us extra income. Also, this farm was next to my dad's place, which made it handier for us to get started."

The Engstroms paid $108 an acre in 1939.

Today, a lot of land in Iowa cash rents for more than that. "Farming in 1990 requires so much capital," he notes. "If you use all your capital to buy land, what will you use for operating money? Seed, fertilizer, chemicals and machinery are expensive."

The Iowa Ag Development Authority sells bonds to banks or other lenders who then provide loans to beginning farmers. Interest earned on the bond is exempt from federal taxes. Since the bank can buy the bond and earn tax-free interest, the bank can make the loan to the farmer at an interest rate below conventional rates.

Ed and Bess Engstrom

Congress has discussed possibly doing away with the tax break. Another concern is that the "aggie bond" program is operating on a year-to-year basis. Congress is due again to vote on whether to renew it on Sept. 30, 1990. Engstrom hopes this law will be changed to give the program a sure future.

To cope with extra expenses as the Engstrom family was growing up, Bess went back to work as a schoolteacher. Today's beginning farmers also usually need off-farm employment. Or, help from a relative. "Even with a beginning loan, many young farmers must still work off the farm to provide adequate cash flow," says Engstrom.

"Beginners aren't able to buy all the land they need to make the operation cash flow. They aren't able to purchase even a very big percentage of land. You hope you can get other investors in, or rent additional land. Between land and machinery costs, it's hard to buy it all. Livestock facilities and good breeding stock are costly, too," he says.

"Farming requires top management today," notes Engstrom. ISU's Northern Iowa Research farm borders the Engstrom farm. "We've been able to use the latest information." he says. "ISU's research and Extension systems have helped us greatly."

The Engstroms have three children and five grandchildren. Son John Engstrom lives in Des Moines. The two daughters are Mary Beth Smith of Champlin, Minn., and Sara Ann Abbas of Worthing, S.D. Active members of their church, Bess is an organist and Ed has taught Sunday school. Ed and Bess enjoy traveling. Last fall, they were in Russia and Germany a few weeks before the Berlin Wall started coming down.

Edward Keast
Pottawattamie County

With a loan from his father-in-law in 1959, Edward and Dora Keast started farming on 230 acres near Henderson, Iowa. Today it is a family farm corporation which operates nearly 1,000 acres of cropland, produces 3,500 hogs annually, has a 40-head stock-cow herd and feeds 250 calves a year.

Together the Keasts have cycled the original farm through nearly a complete renovation. Now there is more help and changes continue. Son Russell has joined the corporation. With a degree from Iowa State University in agricultural mechanization, he brings a lot of expertise and ideas to the operation.

Russell's innovative ideas and energy come naturally. Providing much of their own labor and planning, the Keasts have built a modern pork plant. Except for sows on dry lot, it is a total confinement farrow-to-finish operation.

"We're on a 38-day clock around here," notes Edward. "We farrow 50 sows every 38 days which adds up to nine or 10 cycles a year." Litter average is 8.9 pigs and feed efficiency per pound of pork produced is consistently under 4 pounds for the entire herd, including sows.

A major part of their program is production of breeding stock for Farmers Hybrid. They buy nearly half of the production gilts every year from the 600-head finishing house. Since finishing capacity is limited, about 60% of the farrowings leave as feeder pigs.

"There's a disadvantage, because our lines are kept to two strains, some hybrid vigor is lost and our average litter size may be cut by a pig," admits Edward.

Pigs are weaned from 21 to 38 days and moved into the nursery-grower. In 1987, the Keasts bought two used buildings, including a 20-sow farrowing house, and a 400-head nursery-grower. One was moved from Illinois, the other from Avoca, Iowa. Russell and Edward handled most of the site preparation work themselves.

"With all the other work, it made for some long days and short nights," recalls Edward. "But even with installing new furnaces, replacing some slats, and other refurbishing, the buildings were installed at a fraction of what new would have cost."

Under each sow in the farrowing house the Keasts placed a half-inch thick, 2- by 4-foot pad of recycled plastic. It's a cheap, durable way to get the sows off the slats.

To add nursery capacity the answer was to build a second tier of pens on top of the bottom rows. Three upper pens straddle the partition walls of the six floor pens on each side of the building. Capacity is 10 pigs per pen on top, 12 pigs below.

The 120- by 30-foot finishing house has 12 pens. An overhead feeder drops rations several times a day. It's regulated to provide feed more often when the pigs are most active, up to once every hour.

"All we want to see are crumbs and a little feed in the corner," says Edward. "They keep the floor slick, there's little waste."

After some questions about efficiencies of feeding systems they installed a self-feeder in one pen.

The systems were compared for more than one year. Edward noticed there was more feed wasted, more manure buildup, and pigs just didn't gain as well with the self-feeder.

"I've had the same shovel for 10 years. What does that tell you?" he smiles. They market about 150 head every 38 days. About one-half are sold to Farmers Hybrid as replacement gilts to farmers in the Midwest, the rest to market grade and yield.

The pre-mix ration is customized to fit their program. Cultures are also taken from the herd to build a serum for disease prevention. Those are Russell's ideas, Edward is quick to point out. He has also rebuilt a computerized mix-mill to modernize their feeding center in a renovated barn. "The feed for various lots are all in the system. If we punch in the wrong rations, it tells us," says Russell.

The huge overhead bins for the mill are filled from nearby grain storage facilities and an overhead auger system carries it to the hogs.

Dora handles much of the bookkeeping. "When I want to know something, I ask her," says Edward. They have been members of the southwest Iowa Farm Business Association for 20 years and it has helped them in many ways. Edward says a few years ago, they were worried the machinery inventory was too high. After examining the association's comparison sheets they found their inventory ranked in the lower one-third of all farms in their category.

The Keasts were among the first to adopt no-till farming. "In 1980, we borrowed a Buffalo no-till planter to use on 10 acres. In 1981, we planted the whole farm that way, including soybeans and have ever since."

Penetration in cornstalks was the major hurdle with beans, but they figured any stand loss was made up for in less erosion.

Their new Case-IH planter isn't even equipped with a coulter in front. "It seems to slice through heavy trash with little problem," says Russell.

Corn is only cultivated if needed. Soybeans are usually cultivated once. Yields have improved with no-till. The last four years the whole farm has averaged more than 150 bushels per acre. One check strip last year weighed in at 192 bushels per acre.

Dora and Ed Keast

Keast has been active in many organizations and local projects. Among those, he has served as a cubmaster, chairman of community development for Macedonia, soil conservation commissioner, and is a school board member, including two years as president. He is active on the Farm Business Association board, helped on a committee in Farm Bureau and has held most offices of the Macedonia United Methodist Church.

The Keasts' daughter, Jill, is a head nurse in surgical intermediate cardiac care at St. Luke's

Hospital in Kansas City. Their son, Bret, a recent ISU graduate, is with Iowa Northland Regional Council of Governments as director of community and transit planning. Russ and his wife, Diane, live about a mile from the farm.

Wayne Scott
Adams County

"When I leave the farm I intend it to be a better place for the next family."

Wayne Scott says that. He has had a lot of help from wife, Donna, fulfilling that commitment.

After 10 years of renting land, the present 267-acre farm was purchased in 1960 with a Federal Land Bank loan. That was repaid within five years and since then the Scotts haven't had to borrow for any reason. "We've tried to keep overhead costs low and substitute hard work for capital," says Wayne. "It helps get you through those rough years."

Their steady ticket through those times has been hogs. They have a farrow-to-finish operation marketing 2,000 head annually. For many years it was Donna who shared the chores, working with the hogs. "The truth is he was afraid of what I might run over on a tractor," she quips.

As the operation grew and more help was needed, the Scotts found the answer by setting up an operating corporation. "The corporation owns the hogs and markets what crops we don't feed, while the land is held privately," he explains. Gary Bruning, the other member of the corporation, joined it about 17 years ago. His contributions were recognized recently when he was named a Master Pork Producer, the same honor bestowed on Wayne in 1968.

The hog facilities are a combination of open lot and confinement buildings. Wayne designed and built most of them himself.

"We took things a step at a time and expanded as time and money allowed," he says.

The sow herd is kept in open lots. They routinely farrow 25 sows per month. Pigs are farrowed in confinement on rubber-coated wire flooring. They are weaned at four to five weeks. An old barn has been converted into a nursery and overrun for farrowing sows.

A pair of sows and their litters occupy a single stall. At four weeks the sows are removed and the pigs left to grow. Extensive records are maintained on the sow's performance to aid in culling. Donna does a lot of that bookwork. A card is filed on each sow with breeding and farrowing data. In 1989, the herd averaged 8.84 weaned pigs per litter or 16.5 pigs per sow annually.

At about 50 pounds, the pigs go into one of three finishing units. It's an all-in, all-out procedure. "That's a big factor in controlling disease," says Wayne. "And we never buy feeder pigs. Everything that is finished here starts here."

The confinement houses have partial cement slats with a gutter in front. Average daily gain for the Yorkshire, Duroc, Hampshire Crossbred herd is 1.75 pounds. Scott markets at about 230 pounds on strictly a grade and yield basis. "We've put a lot of emphasis on producing quality pork," he says. "We have to offer the consumer a lean, tasty product." It has also paid off in the market place. He figures his hogs average as much as $3 per hundredweight more than the general market is paying.

The wall of their family room attests to their accomplishments. There are trophies from countless hog shows in both the live and carcass classes. In 1989 they won first place in the Midwest Market Barrow Show in Fremont, Neb.

Scott has used artificial insemination in his herd since 1978 to help upgrade their genetics. Fresh semen is shipped overnight from Swine Genetics in Cambridge, Iowa, and Kirk Swanson, Red Oak, Iowa. It's held in a portable "Coolatron" at 66 degrees.

Scott says the ability to keep it a constant temperature, while still having the flexibility to transport it from place to place has been a big reason for the high conception rate.

A new six-stall barn has recently been added to house the boars. He keeps 16 boars annually and uses them about two years. All replacement gilts are selected from the herd.

The feeding program includes a premix program. Pigs are started on a 16% ration at three weeks. A 15% Lincomix ration is used from five to eight weeks, then followed with a 14% ration for growing with CTC 50 added–the only medication used. Scott feeds all the 230 acres of corn he grows. Most of that is augered through his own mix-mill where the finishing rations are formulated.

Scott has been a member of the Southwest Iowa Farm Business Association for 30 years. He credits those records with helping him become a better manager. "It has been an invaluable tool in recognizing our strengths and weaknesses," he says.

Donna and Wayne Scott

"We've used them countless times to adjust programs. You see at a glance what it's costing you to produce a hundred pounds of pork or a bushel of grain. And the annual comparative analysis, which shows where you rank with similar operations, can be an eye-opener."

Daryl Kruse, the southwest association's consultant, says records show that with a feed efficiency for the entire herd, including sows running consistently under 4 pounds per pound of pork marketed, Scott ranks with the best.

A "Resourceful Farming Demonstration," sponsored by the National Heritage Foundation, has been conducted on their farm the past three years. It has shown definite advantages for no-till corn. Compared with fall chiseled soil followed with a one-pass field cultivator operation before planting, no-tilling into bean stubble yielded 12 bushels per acre more last year. The 191 bushels per acre was good enough to win the district's Iowa Crop Improvement Association's no-till yield contest.

The Scotts' son, Russell, is first vice president of the Davenport Bank and Trust, Bettendorf, Iowa. Daughter, Kathy, is the school nurse in Corning, Iowa, and daughter, Carla, is a personnel assistant for a Red Oak, Iowa, firm. They have eight grandchildren.

Wayne has served on many local and county committees and organizations. He helped organize the Montgomery County Pork Producers, served as president, district director and on the state legislature board. He also was a Federal Land Bank director, director of the Longbranch Watershed, director of the Nodaway Valley National Bank and director of the FmHA board.

IOWA MASTER FARMERS

~
June 11, 1991

Gerald Cornelius
Jackson County

Family, church, business and community service are the priorities of Gerald Cornelius – in that order. Despite a hectic schedule, he always takes time for a family member.

"Dad gets more done before 7 a.m. than most people accomplish in a whole day," says daughter Julie Jacobi. She is an ag sales representative for Monsanto and lives in Bloomington, Ill. with her husband, Jay.

Julie's thoughts are strongly supported by her brother, Charles, and her sister, Nancy. Charles and his wife, Chris, and Nancy and her husband, Lester, all farm with Gerald and Wanda in their seed stock businesses, Cornelius Seed Co., and Cornelius Land and Cattle Co., which owns crossbred and purebred polled Hereford and Salers.

In fact, everyone who knows Gerald (Jerry) Cornelius is amazed with his ability to manage his time, people and resources.

"He is constantly talking to employees, dealers, customers, suppliers, community people, family or whomever is on the radio system or the phone. He decides, dispatches, or delegates responsibilities in a calm and confident manner, even when about 100 youngsters are helping with detasseling," says Don Casteel, a long-time family friend.

Quiet and soft-spoken, Gerald claims he's just trying to keep up with the frantic pace of family business and community activities. Since his children have become involved in the operation, the seed business has increased 50% in the past three years.

"We're just trying to stay ahead. We keep building more dryers, and we put up another warehouse last year. Now we're talking about getting another harvester. We keep one running constantly and if you have a breakdown, you're in trouble. A second one will keep our dryers in rotation," notes Cornelius.

"If my vote is worth anything, I vote for another one," laughs Wanda. A 1982 Master Farm Homemaker, Wanda is an equal partner in the agri-businesses. Wanda, Nancy, and Chris work in the office and keep books for the seed company and farm operation.

Their 1873 Century Farm has

Gerald and Wanda Cornelius

grown to more than 2,500 acres of tillable and grazing land, a 260-head cow herd and about 250 hogs which are sold annually.

"The seed corn company is our primary enterprise. The seed corn, seed oats and livestock complement each other well. We use corn refuse from the seed plant for feeding. When things slow down a bit in winter we can do the seed processing and bagging. We gear our operation to the resources we have," explains Cornelius.

He has always been a good land steward, planting on the contour, strip-cropping, and rotating row crops with alfalfa and oats. Terraces were built on the steeper slopes, and very few changes are needed in their operation to be in conservation compliance.

Cornelius' foresight also makes him a valued member of the community. He has been a school board member, Farm Bureau county president, and officer or board member in numerous other community organizations. Currently, he is helping to organize the East Central Iowa Andrew Demonstration Farm Corporation. He was also recently elected a director of the Maquoketa State Bank.

Cornelius also finds time to be part-time church organist, a task he accepted right after he graduated from Iowa State University with an animal science degree in 1956.

His tireless work ethic, community service, and strong faith are the qualities his family and friends admire most. "My father and partner in farming has been, by his example, truly a master farmer," says Chuck Cornelius.

Morris Greenley
Buchanan County

When Morris (Mick) Greenley speaks, people listen. The big man with the quiet voice often asks a crucial question others have missed at a crop meeting. Or he suggests solutions for seemingly impossible situations. He is a well-considered man, in his thoughts and perceptions, and in the respect paid by others for his many civic contributions.

Morris and Janet Greenley farm a cash grain operation with their son, Joel, southwest of Independence, Iowa. Their 1,250 acres of fairly level cropland consists of the deep, black Kenyan, Floyd and Clyde soils of Buchanan County. Yields average 150 bushels per acre for corn and 50 bushels per acre for soybeans.

The men split the crop work and Janet handles the bookkeeping. Oldest son Robert has developed computer programs to maintain field records and projections. The Greenleys have two daughters, Debra, a teacher at Randall, Iowa, and Pam, a recent business graduate of the University of Iowa.

Greenley has always worked smart. For more than 25 years he has used a chisel plow. When neighbors became interested in saving soil and energy by reducing tillage, Greenley offered pointers on what had worked for him.

About 12 years ago, he built a 23-row, 15-inch soybean air planter and cultivator that works well on rolling ground. He's made many refinements to assure proper seed depth and distribution. Today he is experimenting with broadcasting soybeans.

"Last year we changed from the air planter to broadcasting a solid stand of soybeans on 60 acres of sloping fields. We shot for a population of 210,000 plants per acre. We incorporated the seed with light field cultivation and had good seed emergence. Yields were good, too. We harvested about 53 bushels per acre," smiles Greenley. He's already searching for ways to improve solid stand soybeans. "I've experimented with blowing seed in behind shovels on the air planter. If you put an air tube every 6 inches on a field cultivator, it should give a 100% pattern of coverage for broadcast soybeans. It would also control seed depth, so it should be better than simply broadcasting beans like sowed oats," reasons Greenley.

Another innovation is the 90-foot sprayer that has replaced herbicide applications behind the planter. Greenley changed the nozzle angle for more complete spray coverage. The high capacity unit has helped reduce crop chemical rates.

"I calibrate my own rate reductions by field testing one year, then using the successful rates over more acres the next year. We've cut back about 20% on insecticide rates and will cut another 15% this year on insecticides. We've also reduced by one-half some postemergence soybean herbicide rates," says Greenley.

He works closely with Iowa State University on new cropping concepts, conservation measures and farm profitability. As past president of the Northeast Iowa Agricultural Experimental Association, Greenley was instrumental in developing much of the research work conducted by ISU at the 260-acre research farm near Nashua.

He has also served on the State Extension Advisory Committee.

A member of many community and state organizations, Greenley also served as a board member of the American Soybean Association for 10 years during development of the soybean checkoff.

Morris and Janet Greenley

One of his greatest attributes as a farmer and community leader is his ability to spot a sound idea and put it to good use. He readily adapts his operation to new trends such as reduced tillage and sustainable agriculture.

"The name of this game is dollars, and we must be profitable. But if you can reduce erosion, or contamination without taking a loss, it's senseless not to consider environmental alternatives," sums up Greenley.

David Hawkins
Plymouth County

Starting with 10 head when he was 12 years old, David Hawkins has been feeding cattle for 40 years. Today, Dave and wife Judy, who farm in northwest Iowa near Orange City, feed out 700 to 800 head per year. They farrow 75 sows and finish 600 head of hogs, too. Corn and soybeans are grown on 750 tillable acres. As testimony to the Hawkins' ability to organize their business and manage efficiently, this farm has done well with only part-time help – all in the family. "It takes total cooperation," notes Judy. "We work as a team. Our children are married and live and work away from the farm, but help when they can."

For many years, Dave farmed in partnership with brother Richard, now age 72 and retired. But Richard still helps out, as does Dave's father-in-law, Aaron Denniston, age 77. The part-timers work half-days, doing light livestock chores and working on machinery in the farm shop. A small amount of other part-time labor is hired for seasonal jobs. "The main helper is Judy," adds Dave. "She's a true partner in the management. She can run a tractor all day."

As innovators, the Hawkins family looks for and evaluates new ideas to put to work on their farm. They designed and built the livestock facilities over the last 25 years. Cattle eat from a 300-foot sweep-belt bunk. The system of bins and silos is designed so all feeding is push button. "It's homemade but it works," says Dave.

Likewise, the hog facilities were designed

Dave and Judy Hawkins

by Dave and built over the years. Fashioned out of renovated barns, they include liquid manure handling and automated feed handling features. Certainly not fancy, the facilities are economical and practical. During high school in the early 1950s, Dave was active in FFA and his livestock and crop projects were his beginning in farming. Dave gives a lot of credit to his vo-ag teacher. "He encouraged me when I needed encouragement."

Dave also worked for the Farmers Home Administration (FmHA) in Plymouth County many years ago. "Helping farmers with record-keeping and consulting with them about their management decisions was a valuable learning experience for me," he says. The Hawkins family has kept records with the Iowa Farm Business Association (IFBA) since 1966. Dave has served on the association's board.

Dave and Judy are conservation-minded. Over the years, they've built 15,000 feet of terraces to protect 130 acres of land and constructed grass waterways.

They farm on the contour and use conservation tillage. A 2-acre windbreak protects the farmstead.

Dave has earned recognition for achievements in FFA, Farm Bureau work, service to agriculture, and for church and local community activities. In 1968 he was named Iowa's "Outstanding Young Farmer" by the Iowa Jaycees.

Dave, Richard, and Aaron all like to tinker with a collection of 60 antique John Deere tractors. They've restored 40 of the old relics with loving care. Most of the tractors came from within 20 miles of their farm.

Last summer the Hawkins family invited the original owners of the tractors to a picnic to see, hear, and enjoy memories associated with the machines. "Our collection started when we restored dad's 1929 John Deere 15 years ago," says Dave. "We bought a few tractors from neighbors, then 10 years ago we got serious with our hobby. You meet nice people doing this."

Dave and Judy have four children and six grandchildren. Daughter Bonnie is an elementary school teacher in Sleepy Eye, Minn., and is married to Steve Klein. Daughter Roma works in LeMars for the Plymouth County ASCS office and is married to Todd Lancaster. Daughter Tammy works in the office at Wells Blue Bunny dairy in LeMars and is married to Todd Popken. Son Curtis Hawkins lives in LeMars, works for Wells Blue Bunny, and is married to Shannon Thieman.

Owen and David Kalsem
Story County

Excellent records, division of labor and management, and meticulous attention to detail are keys to success for Owen (John) and David K. Kalsem, Story County, Iowa.

The brothers, along with Owen's wife, Ann, and David's wife, Cheryl, operate 764 acres and feed out around 1,200 head of cattle a year in a corporation called Kalsem Farm, Inc. Both men started farming with their father, Orville, in the late 1940s and 1950s.

The Kalsem farm is an excellent example of how some degree of specialization can provide for highly efficient management of a family farm. Owen has an eye for cattle and uses this ability in the procurement of cattle as well as decisions relative to marketing. The health management program under Owen's watchful eye has resulted in minimal death losses.

David pays close attention to detail and, with Cheryl's help, keeps extensive records on the operation. He is in charge of nutrition and management. This attention to detail has resulted in a steady balanced ration and improved performance. Steer calves gain almost 3 pounds per head per day.

Computerized records are not new for the Kalsem brothers. David began using the TI-59 programmable calculator years ago, before the advent of the microcomputer, to do many of the things current computers do. The Kalsems were among the first farmers to test the Beef Feedlot Monitoring program developed at Iowa State University.

Beef cattle are fed with a feed wagon in concrete or wood feed bunks, placed in rows in the concrete lots, located next to open-front buildings.

Most of the cattle come from Montana. "We rely mostly on order buyers," explains Owen. "The last few years we have been buying heavy calves with a sound frame and growth potential. They are fast-gaining calves that reach Choice grade at a desirable weight for the packer. We like to get big, heavy calves then push them so they are ready for the early summer market before hot weather."

Scales are used extensively in this operation. "Since we installed the scales five or six years ago we weigh often," notes David. "We first weigh the calves when they arrive to check for shrink. Then we weigh periodically throughout the feeding period and when the cattle are ready to go to market. We can also use the scales to weigh grain, hay, etc., in fact, we weighed all of our hay last year to determine what it was yielding." That included 7,000 square bales and spot checks on 500 big round bales.

Owen and David were among the first to successfully incorporate snapped ear corn "earlage" into their feedlot rations. They also grind all big round bales in a tub grinder for more efficient utilization. "Management of their bunker silos is a model of how it should be done," points out Dan Loy, ISU Extension beef specialist.

Both families have been quite active in civic affairs, in church activities and in government. Owen is a member of Farm Bureau and Iowa Cattlemen's Association, served as vice president of Story County Cattlemen's Association, was on the Extension council, and has been a 4-H leader and county fair board member. He's also been a trustee of the Fjeldberg Lutheran Church in Huxley.

Owen and Ann have four children. Jeff lives in Ames. Sharon (Guilinger) lives in Savanna, Ill. Karen lives in Ames, and Clint is a senior in high school.

David has been a loan committee member of the Story County Farmer's Home Administration, past president of the Story County Cattlemen's Association, member of the Iowa Beef Industry Council research committee and a county Farm Bureau director. He has served as off-campus adviser to Alpha Gamma Rho fraternity at ISU. He is also active in the Fjeldberg Lutheran Church. David and Cheryl have two children. Mike is a sophomore at ISU and Jill is a high school junior.

Owen and Ann, Cheryl and David Kalsem

Vernon Beernink
Sioux County

For Vernon and Donna Beernink, Sioux Center, Iowa, the farm comes second. Family has always been first. The farm this family grew up on is becoming their family farm business.

Sons Brad, 33, and Mark, 26, are working their way into the operation. "There was never any pressure for them to come back to the farm," says Donna. "We thought it was important they do what they wanted, to make their own decisions."

Brad attended Iowa State University and South Dakota State University, and managed farm supply stores for a time. Three years ago he and wife, Pat, were drawn by the "independence" of making their own decisions—right or wrong. Along with children Riley, 5, and twin daughters Catherine and Aileen, they moved back to work for dad.

Vernon Beernink

Daughter Barbara, 19, attends Northwestern College, Orange City, Iowa. She enjoys the freedom of the farm and has a strong love for animals.

After graduating from ISU two years ago, Mark, a business major, was also pulled by the opportunity the farm he lived and worked on now offered as a career.

With the course set, the Beerninks are determined to offer their sons the same opportunity the century farm offered them in 1958.

Vernon started farrowing hogs as a 4-H project. After he was married he worked for his father, William, as a salaried employee, then formed a partnership and eventually bought him out.

"We still don't have a fancy hog setup," he says, "but it's been good to us." The farrowing house is a 26- by 90-foot structure that was updated in 1980.

The nursery has 21 pens. Portable buildings in open lots are used for gestation. Four groups of sows are bred every 35 days.

It works. Farm Business Association records show 1.97 litters per year per sow and 18.2 pigs weaned per sow per year. The 140-sow herd produces 2,500 head of feeder pigs a year.

It made sense that the sons follow the same path, moving into the diversified operation through its livestock enterprises. And, it fits the young men's interests and expertise. Brad is responsible for the feeder pig operation. To supplement that share of income, he recently has formed a partnership to produce pigs on another man's farm.

Mark is moving into the cattle side. The

four concrete feedlots handle about 1,500 head annually. "We've been in cattle a long time," says Vernon. "Being diversified has helped us through some tough times."

Typically, they purchase 600- to 700-pound calves in the fall and market in May or June. Average daily gains on last year's bunch was 3.25 pounds with a 9 to 1 feed efficiency for the full year. He has also had cattle custom fed in local feedlots and neighboring states. Complete closeout costs for cattle have been kept since the 1960s. "I've been with the Farm Business Association about since it started here," says Beernink. "Those records are important in our decisions. I especially watch the comparisons of similar operations in our region. You know where you stand in terms of management ability."

The family owns 400 acres and rents another 800 acres. They plant 750 acres of corn annually; yields average about 130 bushels per acre. There are 300 acres of soybeans planted; average yield is about 50 bushels per acre. In 1991 the Beerninks harvested an 80-acre field of corn that averaged 178 bushels and a similar sized field of soybeans topped 61 bushels.

Active in local and state organizations, Beernink is a candidate for the Sioux County board of supervisors. Other activities and honors include: Sioux County Outstanding Young Farmer, Sioux County Planning and Zoning Commission, Sioux Center Hospital board, Farmer's Co-op board, Rural Water System board, etc. He is an elder of the First Reformed Church, serving on countless committees.

Keith Hora
Washington County

This Riverside, Iowa, farmer has earned an impressive list of accomplishments in farming and farm organization work. Service to numerous local, state and national groups has always been a part of Keith's commitment to agriculture. His most visible leadership role was as president of the National Corn Growers Association in 1988. But his strong foundation of faith and family is what makes him tick.

Keith and his late wife, Celeste, were active participants in their children's education and activities, not only through their encouragement, but also giving of their time and leadership abilities. Together they built a successful farming operation making use of new ideas and technology along with old-fashioned hard work and long hours.

"The family displayed tremendous love and faith during Celeste's courageous battle with cancer and death in 1989. We've always admired the strength, dedication and integrity of Keith and Celeste. Their ideals and leadership abilities are evidenced in their children," say John and Martha Young, who have known the Hora family for many years.

Keith's family, four sons and two daughters, are all Iowa State University graduates. Raising six kids and being active in Farm Bureau, Iowa Corn Growers Association, National Corn Growers Association, Pork Producers, 4-H, church, school, and other community activities isn't easy. Keith gives a lot of credit to Celeste. They shared a special ability to manage time and make decisions efficiently and effectively.

Celeste and Keith were 4-H leaders for many years. Keith also served on the Iowa 4-H Foundation board and was a member of the State Extension Advisory Committee.

Keith graduated from ISU in 1960. He and Celeste moved back to southeast Iowa and started farming in partnership with his father, George Hora. On 320 acres, they raised crops, hogs and cattle. Today, Keith farms with sons Brian and Kurt, raising around 600 acres of soybeans and 1,600 acres of corn. Keith and sons share in the decisions for responsibilities in production and marketing. They also have a 70-sow farrow-to-finish hog operation.

In 1986, the Horas bought a no-till drill. The results of using that soybean production system have paid great dividends over the years. The overall soybean yield average for the farm has risen by nearly 15 bushels per acre, reaching 65 bushels per acre last year. No-till saves soil, fuel and labor. Equipment repairs have declined, so has machinery investment.

Keith says keeping good records has helped him make profitable management decisions. Keith's dad, George, started keeping records with the Mississippi Valley Farm Business Association in the late 1930s. The Horas now use the Iowa Farm Business Association's computer recordkeeping system. That 60-year commitment shows the importance the family places on the financial analysis of their farm operation.

Keith has attended Harvard University's Agribusiness Study Course. "As farmers, we're concerned about producing corn, soybeans, hogs and cattle," he notes. "When a processor gets hold of 5% to 10% of your production and makes as much money off of that as you do on the entire production, you have to ask yourself – what else should I do?

"That's a key reason I became active in the Iowa Com Growers and National Corn Growers," he adds. "As farmers, it's up to us to help find and develop markets for our products."

Keith is a member of St. James Catholic Church. His oldest son Gregg, 31, works for Iowa Farm Bureau and lives in Fort Dodge with wife Liddy and their three small children. Keith's youngest son, Darren, 25, farms near Fort Dodge. Sons Brian, 29, and Kurt, 26, farm with Keith near Washington, Iowa. Daughter Dana Wenstrand, 27, and her husband, Pete, farm at Essex, Iowa. Daughter Heidi, 23, lives in Kansas City.

Kurt, Brian, and Keith Hora

Howard Johnson
Osceola County

The sign in front reads "Lazy Acres." To illustrate, a wooden cutout profiles a stretched out soul leaning against a stump. Adorned in straw hat and overalls, you see he's "relaxed" country.

It swings from a pipe near the driveway which leads to the Howard and Leila Johnson home. "That's our farm name and motto," grins Howard. "We like to do things the easy way around here."

Maybe they do it easier now than before, but the lazy part doesn't fit this Ashton, Iowa, couple.

Start with 600 acres of row crops to plant every spring. The 24-stall farrowing house cycles three groups of sows a year. The finishing house sends 1,500 head to market. In the machine shop there's welding to be done, equipment to be serviced and repaired.

Next door an old feed store moved from town houses woodworking tools. Here, craft items are often mass-produced to give away in nursing homes, to groups, and to friends.

In the house there's an office. It's in a corner of the bright, open addition Howard built on the end of the family room he remodeled. There's a screen to track markets, a desk and files to work on farm records.

A remodeled barn serves as a 10 pen, 60-head gestation building. He cut out the north end of the barn, dug a pit in the center, laid concrete slats over it, and poured concrete down both sides. Equipped with automatic feeding, he pulls two cables to put rations in the drop feeders. "I told you I was lazy," he says. The 24-crate farrowing house handles six sets of sows a year. Pigs are weaned at about four weeks, 18 pounds and moved to the nursery. The nursery was expanded by adding a second deck of pens. Pigs are moved from nursery to finishing house at about 60 pounds. The 500-head facility is a modified open front with grower slats. Like the other buildings it has an automated feeding system.

Leila and Howard Johnson

"I also do my own welding and fixing whenever I can, but I also enjoy the challenge and diversity. I decided several years ago I couldn't replace the kind of help my family gives." He is talking about daughter Jodi, 24, (Mrs. David Srebrecht) with Pioneer Hi-Bred, Johnson, Iowa, and son Kirk, 23, a 1992 Iowa State University graduate.

Johnson grinds his own feed. Conversion is 3.48 pounds of feed per pound of gain, cost per hundredweight is $29.30. Return per dollar fed was about $1.55 the past year. Death loss is 1.70% with a weaning average of 8.14. He was named Master Pork Producer in 1984.

These figures are from recent Farm Business Association records and are just a sampling of what Johnson uses to keep his operation on track. "I've been a member since it was organized in the early 1960s," he recalls. "It's been an invaluable guide." The enterprise guide helped him make a major change in his operation in 1980.

"I was doing a much better job with hogs and crops than feeding cattle," he says. "The feedlot bunks were shot, the silo needed repair. After visiting with Tom Thaden, area FBA fieldman, we decided this was a good time to get out of the beef business. It was the right decision, to cut losses-add profits."

His philosophy is to keep costs down without sacrificing production or efficiency. Most of the farm buildings are renovated, the 42-by 100-foot machine shed was built by him.

In his spare time Johnson goes to meetings – meeting after meeting – to "keep up to date." He has served on countless community boards and committees. Included on the list are ISU Extension council, 4-H leader, fair superintendent, FmHA county chairman, Northwest Iowa Experimental Farm board, past president Osceola County Pork Producers, Sheldon Civic Music Association board, etc. He is clerk of the board of Bethel Reformed Church in Sheldon, Iowa, and sings in the bell choir.

Kenneth Strohbehn
Tama County

When you have four sons and a daughter who are interested in farming you have to have a plan. Kenneth and Barbara Strohbehn, Gladbrook, Iowa, apparently have such a plan and it appears to be working well.

Their oldest son, Scott, 29, joined the operation as a salaried employee about 10 years ago. Since then Scott has been able to rent land on his own to the point where he now can support himself with the profits from his own operation. He farms about 400 acres of row crop and has a small cow herd. He still farms with his father, though. They share machinery and labor.

Grant, 27, and wife, Susan, came back to the farm in 1990. Grant was able to rent 145 acres of cropland which he manages entirely on his own.

"Last year was his first year farming so he's still on the payroll and uses my machinery as part of his salary," explains Strohbehn.

"One of the points I stress is that I want the boys to make their own decisions. I've seen too many operations where one person, the father, made all the decisions. That usually makes for a bad situation."

Even though the two sons have their own operations, they are still connected to Kenneth and Barbara's operation. For example, Scott is interested in cattle, so he feeds cattle for them at the farm he lives on. Grant buys feeder pigs from them to feed out himself. In addition, Grant likes to work with machinery in the shop, which helps out, too.

Another son, Shawn, 22, is currently at Iowa State University majoring in political science and mass communications.

David, 20, has completed one year at Mankato Tech, Mankato, Minn., in swine production management. He is currently employed by Swine Graphics Enterprises at ISO Pork, Iowa Falls, Iowa.

Daughter Noel, 26, is married to David Fisher. They farm near Garwin, Iowa.

Strohbehn started his own farming operation in 1958 when he rented 160 acres from his father. Today, the operation consists of 350 acres of corn, 300 acres of soybeans, 125 acres of seed corn, an 80-sow farrow-to-finish hog operation and 200 head of feeder cattle.

Strohbehn has been drilling soybeans for about 10 years. He plants on 15-inch centers and does not cultivate. He likes the potential for better yields and less erosion with the drill.

On corn ground, Strohbehn applies dry P and K in the fall and anhydrous ammonia in the spring. "We have to watch erosion," he notes. "If you put anhydrous on in the fall, the water will run down the tracks left by the applicator."

Strohbehn buys feeder cattle (heifers) in early fall, usually from southern Iowa markets. "Local calves don't move until later in the year."

Calves are carried over winter on 160 acres of cornstalks and fed corn silage and high moisture corn. When it comes to marketing his finished cattle (1,000 to 1,150 pounds), Strohbehn's philosophy is "never hold cattle waiting for a better price."

In the hog operation, Strohbehn farrows two times a year, January through March, and again in June, July, and August. Some of the pigs are fed out and some are sold as feeder pigs. Trophies earned by their own children, and by other 4-Hers who have purchased pigs from them, attest to the quality of the product they produce.

Besides raising a farming family, Strohbehn has also been active in off-farm endeavors. He was named a Tama County Master Pork Producer in 1982 and also won local corn and soybean growing contests that same year. He was a 4-H leader for many years, and is a member of the Tama County Fair Board, Iowa Soybean Association, Tama County Pork Producers, Lions, and Farm Bureau. All the Strohbehns are active members of the Gladbrook United Methodist Church.

Kenneth and Barbara Strohbehn

IOWA MASTER FARMERS

~
June 1993

Master Farmer. It's a singular term that, first, and foremost, means the collective family–the family farm.

It's the men, the women, the children, all in the traces together, pulling as a team, pursuing success and happiness through the times of heart-wrenching hail and heart-lifting sunshine.

The recognition seeks to acknowledge what is right with agriculture, as a profession, as a way of life. It points to the accomplishments of a family in their farm operations. But, in a large measure, the family honored is a representative of the countless deserving Iowa families.

Varel Bailey
Cass County

His neighbors know him as the "Eastern Cass County Extension Office" and for good reason. Varel Bailey is always willing to share his knowledge and talents – in farming innovations, computer programming, agricultural policy, public speaking and leadership roles.

Bailey readily takes time to help friends and neighbors,

in spite of his own 1,335-acre operation southeast of Anita, Iowa. When he isn't farming or volunteering locally, Varel is often on the road attending state, national and international meetings to offer his considerable expertise in consensus building and problem solving.

"It's fascinating trying to figure out which way agriculture is headed. I enjoy the challenge of studying the driving forces that will revolutionize the pork industry in Iowa, or the best way to convert CRP lands to other uses," says Bailey.

Bailey farms with his wife, Jacqueline, and their son, Scot, and his wife, Cheryl. Their oldest daughter and son-in-law, Sue and Michael Drew, live in Minneapolis, Minn. Daughter Sara lives at home and is a student at Anita High School.

The Baileys' diversified operation includes 500 acres of corn, 240 acres of soybeans, 100 acres of hay, 160 acres of oats, and pasture for a 150-head purebred Angus and black Simmental cow herd and 110-head crossbred Rambouillet-Suffolk ewe flock. Annually, about 400 calves and yearlings are fed out,

Jacqueline and Varel Bailey

and a farrow-to-finish hog enterprise produces 1,600 to 1,700 hogs.

Bailey has always been a strong believer in recordkeeping. He joined the Iowa Farm Business Association (IFBA) in 1966 and helped develop record systems for programmable calculators. He graduated to an early Apple computer and now keeps general accounting for the farm with IFBA's Mac MARS program on his Mac computer.

He developed his own spreadsheet from other computer programs to monitor feedlot cattle. A sow productivity index spreadsheet is used for hogs. Weights are recorded for the cow herd, sheep flock and farrowing groups. All grain and feedstuffs are weighed prior to storage or feeding to livestock.

An innovative farmer, Bailey keeps costs down while increasing production to profitable levels. In 1991, his direct costs for corn was $60.06 and $25.21 for beans, well below IFBA averages by $29 and $17 per acre respectively, says Pete Tallman, IFBA consultant in Atlantic, Iowa.

"Varel has given endlessly of his time and talents over the years. He served on the committee to develop an early ag accounting software. The split check and deposit on-screen was his innovation that is now common on Ag software. In 1980 he wrote the computer program used to prepare W2s for employees. He wrote a program for the PIK alternatives that was used all over the Midwest.

"Varel has tremendous abilities and resourcefulness. He has made a difference for us in agriculture," says Tallman.

Bailey has devoted thousands of hours to commodity groups. He has served as president of the Iowa and National Corn Growers Association. As national leader, he helped develop strategies for the 1985 Farm Bill, Farm Credit law and GATT trade discussions.

An original thinker with a photographic memory, Bailey is sought for his opinions and debate skills. He's been involved with Iowa International Development Foundation, Wallace Technology Transfer Foundation, Iowa Beef Improvement Federation, Iowa State University Presidents Council, Federal Reserve Bank of Chicago, U.S. Feed Grains Council and USDA Export Enhancement Program.

"The next trend that will greatly affect Iowa and agriculture is information flow. We need to get a fiber optics system in place to have access to information worldwide. It will be like going from mud roads to the interstate highway system," predicts Bailey.

Frequently asked to lead international trade delegations, Bailey traveled to Europe during the corn gluten feed quota issue; to Brussels for negotiations during the Spain-Portugal accession; to Hungary, Czechoslovakia, Poland and East Germany for business opportunities, and to Japan, Taiwan, Hong Kong and Korea for trade policy discussions about beef.

Although his resume reads like one of a career diplomat, Bailey finds time for his community. He helps with 4-H and county fair, community development and has served as trustee of the Anita Methodist Church.

Robert Jardon
Fremont County

Robert Jardon, 79, started farming with his father in 1933 in Douglas County, Kan. He recognized early the need to conserve the soil and built his first terraces in 1939. He and his wife, Lucille, moved to Iowa in 1947 so she could be closer to her family. Most of his land in Fremont County, Iowa is now protected with terraces–broadbase, bench and narrow-based –and with two tile-outlet diversion structures near a creek. The terraces and reduced tillage have increased organic matter in the soil.

In 1980, the Jardon farm was one of the first in the area to use no-tillage crop production. Minimum tillage was used even before that. "In 1991, we decided that herbicides had progressed to the point that no-till soybeans would be practical, so in 1992 a large portion of our soybean acreage was planted with no-till drill," says Jardon.

The Jardons normally grow around 700 acres of corn and soybeans, around 120 acres of alfalfa and 90 acres of pasture. First cutting alfalfa is usually chopped for haylage to fill a 20- by 80-foot Harvestore. Subsequent cuttings are baled, letting the hay overdry and baling at night to preserve the leaves on the forage.

Corn silage is chopped to fill an 8- by 60-foot stave silo and the Harvestore. The remainder of the corn is combined, stored on the farm and dried with unheated air.

Jardon uses "natural fertilizer" from the livestock to the greatest possible extent.

The 88-cow dairy herd is the mainstay of the operation. "I was born under a cow," Jardon often quips, remembering how he was handed a bucket and assigned a gentle cow at age six. Today his registered Holsteins have a rolling herd average of 22,946 pounds of milk, 801 pounds of fat and 710 pounds protein. The cows are fed a basic total mixed ration of

Lucille and Robert Jardon

soyhulls, dried distillers grain, corn, haylage, corn silage and blood meal. A computerized feeding system is used to get more energy into top producers. Embryo transplant has become an important part of the breeding program with eight to 10 flushes performed per year.

Cows are housed in free stalls and milked in a double four-herringbone parlor. Pipeline milkers deliver the milk to a 1,500-gallon milk tank. Milk is marketed through Mid-America Dairyman, Inc. Dry cows and heifers are kept on pasture and fed supplemental grain to maintain body condition. A unique fence line feeding system utilizes self-locking headgates. "This makes it easy for herd examinations and for artificial insemination work," explains Jardon, who got the idea while visiting large dairies in California.

The Jardon hog operation starts in a seven farmer-member, 400-sow co-op. One hundred 30-pound pigs are moved to the Jardon facilities which consist of a semi-confinement system on concrete, taking advantage of existing buildings. The ration is balanced with concentrate and homegrown corn. Feeding from 30 to 250 pounds requires an average of 140 days, giving an average daily gain of 1.57 pounds with 3 pounds of complete feed required. About 700 head are marketed annually.

Lucille does the recordkeeping, handposting the accounts. Dairy Herd Improvement Association records are utilized for the cows.

The Jardons have 11 children. Three sons, Frank, Joseph and Carl are involved in the farm operation and have farms of their own.

Another son, Edward, is an accountant for the Defense Mapping Agency, St. Louis, Mo.

John is a systems analyst for Bellerophon Corp., La Grange, Ill.

Marie (Redig) is administrative assistant to the vice president of research and planning, Drake University, Des Moines, Iowa.

Kathryn (Palmcook) is health and physical education instructor at Farragut Community School, Farragut, Iowa.

Louise (Untiedt) is a business teacher at Jefferson High School, Conception, Mo. Julia (Gee) is a candidate for the Master of Fine

Arts, University of Nebraska, Lincoln, Neb.

Norma (Troxel) is assistant manager and buyer for a children's specialty shop in Shenandoah, Iowa.

Phillip is a veterinarian in dairy production, teaching, research and clinical work at the University of California, Tulare, Calif.

The Jardons have been, and are, active in many organizations. Bob is currently assistant soil commissioner and is on the Fremont County Board of Supervisors. He is a member of the Kiwanis, the Dairy Shrine, and a charter member of both the Holstein Foundation and the Wallace Foundation. The Jardons received the Iowa Distinguished Dairyman award in 1983.

Ken Kassel
Palo Alto County

His calling card reads "Ken Kassel—farmer, conservationist, grandfather."

This likeable, lanky fellow and his wife, Janice, farm in Palo Alto County in northwest Iowa. On the mantle in their family room today is a toy tractor and threshing rig Ken played with as a youngster. "I came home from the Iowa State Fair in 1934 with that toy," recalls Ken, a twinkle in his eye.

Those were the Dust Bowl Days, and the importance of soil conservation left its mark on Kassel at that young age. Ken, now 66, served Iowa for the past 30 years either as a soil conservation district commissioner, officer in the Iowa Association of Soil and Water Conservation District Commissioners or as a member of the State Soil Conservation Committee.

Ken recently retired from the state committee, an advisory board which sets policy for wise use of land and water resources in Iowa. Appointed first by Gov. Robert Ray in 1977, Ken served on the panel for 16 years, longer than anyone ever has. He chaired the committee in 1981-83 and 1990-91. "Some of Iowa's most significant conservation programs have been established during this time," notes Dale Cochran, Iowa Secretary of Agriculture.

"Ken used his ability to work with people at all levels to help build the conservation coalition that made these programs possible and workable."

The 165 miles to Des Moines were never too far to attend a meeting or hearing. Ken always made it clear that conservation is a priority in his life and he could be counted on when needed.

After graduating from Iowa State University in 1951, Ken worked for DeKalb Seed Co. in Illinois. He started farming on rented land near Emmetsburg, Iowa, in 1959. Moving to the Ayrshire area in 1961, Ken and Janice farmed the land where he grew up. Ken's 91-year-old mother still owns that original home place, located about a mile from the farm where Ken and Janice now reside.

David Kassel, eldest son of Ken and Janice, now lives with his wife and family on the original Kassel farm – where the hog operation is located. Ken and Janice have cattle facilities at their farmstead, but currently aren't feeding cattle.

Cropping 1,000 acres, the Kassels use conservation tillage. Janice is responsible for keeping the financial records. Attention is paid to recordkeeping, containing costs and figuring break-even levels on each commodity they market. Ken and David do a nice job of machinery maintenance and skillfully purchase used equipment.

In 1975 when David graduated from college and came back to farm, Ken and Janice expanded the operation. The family struggled financially when tough times hit agriculture during the 1980s. "We had to give up some land we bought," says Ken. But the Kassels weathered those problems, and today count their blessings. "It's very important to us that young people return to the land and have a place in agriculture in the future," adds Janice.

Together, the Kassels continue to serve their church and community in leadership roles. They've worked to maintain a strong 4-H program in the county, have served on hospital and school boards and are active in other organizations.

The Kassel children have all followed in the footsteps of Ken and Janice by graduating from Iowa State University. Son David farms with his parents. Son Paul is an ISU Extension field crops specialist at Spencer, Iowa. Son Jim recently received his PhD in psychology and is a psychologist in Louisville, Ky. Daughter Karen (Hutto) works as a media specialist and lives in Atlanta, Ga. Ken and Janice Kassel have seven grandchildren.

"Ken and Janice have been involved in a family farming operation with their children during a period of time when it hasn't been easy to establish such a business," notes Sally Puttman, a farmer and conservation leader from Kingsley, Iowa. "Despite the time and management effort required by the farming operation, Ken has provided valuable leadership on conservation matters for many years. It has been my privilege to serve with him on the state committee. His leadership has been vital for the conservation effort in Iowa.

Janice and Ken Kassel

"We are fortunate to have Ken and Janice in our state," adds Puttman. "They are so willing to give their time and talent to serve other people. Ken has been a strong advocate for soil conservation and has never been reluctant to exert his leadership when it's needed. His business card identifies him as farmer, conservationist and grandfather. I'd add Servant to Iowa to that description."

Ralph Manternach
Jones County

Ralph and Rita Manternach oversee 870 acres of cropland and almost 500 acres of pastured forest land south of Cascade in eastern Iowa.

They normally raise around 600 acres of corn, 70 acres of oats and 50 acres of hay. "And in 1993 more soybeans than we really care to on our highly-erodible land because winter kill wiped out 125 acres of hay," says Ralph.

In addition, Ralph and Rita feed out 1,100 to 1,200 cattle per year. They farrow and finish 3,500 to 4,000 hogs a year. Plus the Manternachs ride herd over about 25 stock cows and a 40-ewe flock.

The farm is a large, diversified operation. But to keep size in perspective, consider the families the Manternach family farm corporation, Manco Farms, Inc., is supporting.

First there's Ralph and Rita. Plus oldest son Brian, 30, his wife, LuAnn, and their two children. Second son Dale, 25, his wife, Sharon, and their three children. Youngest son, Ross, 15, will be a high school junior this fall.

"We're all in this together," explains Rita. "Our sons and their wives are all involved in our operation. I couldn't have found better daughters-in-law if I would have picked them out myself."

Besides the family, the Manternachs employ Dan Trenkamp full time.

Focusing on efficiency, Ralph and Rita started farming modestly by renting 140 acres on shares from Ralph's father, Joe in 1960. They bought their first land in 1968. Over the years, they gradually built to their current size. And they're still expanding.

A new farrowing house is going up which will replace some outdated facilities and pasture farrowing. It will boost farrowing capacity 4 litters at a time. They're shooting at an all-in, all-out system to farrow on a five-week cycle.

Why expand into the sagging price phase of the hog cycle?

"We're in farming for the long haul," says Ralph. "Our goal is to be low-cost producers. We think we can compete with anyone if we're efficient. To find ways to be efficient, we use records." Those records include:

• Cenex Land O' Lakes New Era Personalized Swine Records

• Iowa State University Extension's Beef Cow Business Record

• Feedlot Performance and Cost Monitoring reports from Land O' Lakes

• Iowa Farm Business Association monthly cash flows and annual performance summaries

"Our hog strategy is to breed enough sows and gilts to keep our buildings at full capacity all the time," says Ralph. "That spreads our costs for facilities over the most pigs.

"Next, we're striving to feed efficiently," he adds. "Working to wean big litters spreads feed cost for the breeding herd over more pigs. We're currently averaging about 8.1 pigs per litter. We strive for efficient gains.

"Finally, we aim to market our hogs to the packers who are willing to pay premiums for the type of hogs we produce," he says.

The Manternachs use a similar strategy for cattle. Buy them right. Make them grow. Hold down costs. Sell to packers who want the type of cattle they produce.

Most of the land the Manternachs farm is highly erodible, like much of Jones County. To keep erosion in check, the Manternachs use combinations of strip cropping, minimum tillage, no-till, contouring and terraces.

"I don't know how many terraces we have on our land," says Ralph. "We've been building them since 1972. They're best measured in miles, rather than feet."

Ralph has won numerous awards for his conservation efforts.

In both 1991 and 1992 Manco Farms was listed in *Farm Futures* magazine's 100 best managed farms in the United States.

Rita and Ralph Manternach

Besides raising a farming family, Ralph and Rita are active in off-farm endeavors. Ralph has been chairman of the Jones County Pork Board and the Swiss Valley Ag Services Co-op. He was on the Jones County Extension Council. Ralph served as 4-H leader.

Ralph and Rita, Ross, Dale, Sharon and family are active in St. Mary's Catholic Church is Cascade. Brian, LuAnn and family are active in St. Peters Catholic Church, Temple Hill.

Besides the three sons involved in the farming operation, Ralph and Rita have two daughters. Pam Ockenfels, 31, lives in Wellman, Iowa. Jill Friedow, 28, lives in Kent, Ohio.

"Ralph, Rita, and their family exemplify excellence in modern farming," says Joe Legg, long-time Jones County Extension director.

IOWA MASTER FARMERS

June 1994

It was 1926 that *Wallaces Farmer* began a program to recognize exceptional farmers who also took time to serve community, church and others.

Called Iowa Master Farmers, these are the men, women and children who pull together as families in the pursuit of professional success and happiness in life.

The intent is not to glorify particular families. Rather, it is to focus statewide attention on the positive role of agriculturists beyond the farm fraternity. Those selected are much more than simply good farmers striving for personal gain.

Simply look to the new class of Master Farmers as examples.

Bill and Judy Ellerman
Dallas County

Bill Ellerman began farming with his father-in-law in 1962 in Webster County, Iowa. But the farm was lost when the Brushy Creek Recreation area was established in 1968. "We looked for a farm from Minnesota to Missouri," says Bill. He and Judy finally found a 140-acre farm to rent near Dallas Center in Dallas County, Iowa and still oper-

ate the same farm. Since then, however, they have purchased 485 acres and rent additional land for a total of 750 acres.

Diversification has been one of the keys to Bill and Judy's success. The Ellermans fed cattle until the late 1970s when they dropped that enterprise for health reasons. Arabian horses are still a part of the operation, however. "We got into Arabians when our oldest son started high school," says Bill. "All three of our children showed them."

The Ellermans plant about equal acreages of corn and soybeans, 80 acres of wheat and around 60 acres of alfalfa.

Why wheat? "I've always enjoyed raising small grains and want a rotation," says Bill. "Wheat enables us to diversify and it spreads out the workload. Plus, we have always had a good market for it locally," he continues. The Ellermans are also able to sell the wheat straw at good prices to area hog farmers.

Alfalfa is another good cash crop for the Ellermans. "We have always had around 30 acres of alfalfa but this year we increased that to 60 acres," says Bill. "In the past we have

Bill and Judy Ellerman

sold 80% of the crop and alfalfa right out of the field as small square bales. In fact, we usually know what we are going to get for a crop of hay before we even begin cutting," he adds. Local horse owners are the primary buyers.

Since they sell so much of their hay to horse owners, the Ellermans strive for top quality. "We soil test, apply lime and try to select good varieties," explains Bill. "We use a mower conditioner making wide windrows. Then we turn it once with a wheel rake in early morning or late evening to save as many leaves as possible. We also watch it closely to bale at just the right time – that's usually around 4 p.m."

Since the Ellermans annually put up nearly 5,000 small square bales each of alfalfa hay and wheat straw they have tried to mechanize as much as possible. A bale accumulator is pulled behind the baler. This unit stacks the bales in piles of 10, which are then picked up with an attachment on a front-end loader and placed on racks.

On the row crop acres, the Ellermans use conservation tillage. Stalks are chopped in the fall then the ground is disk chiseled and field cultivated in the spring. Herbicides are applied in one pass with the field cultivator utilizing a sprayer monitor. "The monitor enables us to vary rates according to soil type, ground speed, etc," notes Bill.

No fall tillage is done on soybean stubble. Herbicides are banded at planting time. Both crops are usually cultivated once, or twice if necessary.

Bill and Judy are always looking for new ways to reduce costs and increase profits. One of the ways they have done that is by utilizing a grid sampling service. This has allowed them to trim fertilizer costs by as much as half in some cases. "There hasn't been a time grid sampling hasn't paid for itself and most often, more," notes Bill.

Corn and soybeans are marketed locally as cash crops using forward price contracts. "I like to price one-third of the crop at plant-ing, another one-third during the season, and the final third after the first of the year," he explains.

The Ellermans give a lot of credit to the Iowa Farm Business Association. "Records have always been important to me. But the farm business association provides more than just records with their analysis, etc. It's really a partnership with the consultant even though he is a nonbiased person who is there to help you make the best decision. He can offer viable alternatives."

In off-farm activities, Judy is an occupational health nurse for John Deere in Ankeny. Bill and Judy built a home in town four years ago and now both are co-chairpersons of the Dallas Center Quasquicentennial committee. Bill is a member of the city council and Judy is on the school board. Both are active in the Dallas Center United Methodist Church. Bill sells ICI seeds.

All three of the Ellerman children live on Century Farms. Mark, who farms 800 acres of his own in addition to farming with his parents, and his wife Jennifer live on the home farm. Lori and Mike Thomas live in rural Dallas Center as do Carol and Travis Snyder.

Jerry and Jean Goldsmith
Cedar County

Benton County lost a good county Extension agent and Cedar County gained a top-notch farmer when Jerry Goldsmith moved back to the family farm south of Clarence, Iowa, in 1970.

Over the years, Jerry and Jean have boosted crop production to about 600 acres in a corn-soybean rotation. But farrowing and finishing hogs is their lead enterprise.

The Goldsmiths run their farm with a balance of management principles and philosophy on life.

Under management, Jerry and Jean strive to effectively use existing resources. Remodeling buildings is a technique they've used time and again to hold down costs and widen pork profit margins.

Under overall philosophy, they strive to carve some time out of the farming operation for important things in life. For example, on Mother's Day they attended St. John's United Church of Christ in Clarence. Then they went out to eat. The soybean seed had to wait another day to get planted.

Goldsmiths are innovators. "Almost every building in our hog operation is a prototype," explains Jerry. "At each stage as we've grown, we've tried to identify the most critical bottleneck impeding the flow of hogs through our operation. Next we've considered what's needed to remove that bottleneck. That analysis always involves a series of questions:

• Can we remove the bottleneck by remodeling an existing building?

• Should we add something new?

• If so, what should we add?

• If we build new facilities, how can we still effectively use existing facilities?

• What ideas are other hog producers using that we should incorporate into changes we're making?

•What ideas of our own do we want to include?

"Sometimes our ideas have really worked out well," says Jerry. "One is using a flush gutter system for handling manure from the grower, lactation and finishing buildings. Recycling lagoon water cuts the amount of water we need to pump while boosting lagoon capacity. Emptying the lagoon with irrigation equipment saves manure disposal labor."

"Other times we would have been better

Jerry and Jean Goldsmith

off had we called the jack hammer back before the concrete was fully cured," notes Jean.

Jerry agrees. "When we remodeled the dairy barn into a lactation unit, we put in concrete pens," he explains. "But we're losing too many pigs with our pen design. If we could do it over, we'd do it differently.

"Another mistake we've made is not working harder and faster to get all of our hogs indoors," he adds.

"With our own facilities, plus those we rent and contract through neighbors, we have capacity to finish about 3,500 hogs per year. But a bottleneck in our gestation and breeding program limits our production to about 3,000 pigs," he adds. "We're currently wrestling with how best to get farrowing capacity in line with finishing capacity."

Despite what Jerry sees as mistakes, Iowa Farm Business Association records show Goldsmiths rank in the top one-third of producers in the swine enterprise summary.

Both Jerry and Jean give Ray Vitense, their herdsman, ample credit for the success of their hog operation. He also farms some cropland on his own.

The Goldsmiths trade Ray the use of their high-capacity crop equipment for labor in their hog operation. "It's an arrangement that benefits both of us," says Vitense.

The Goldsmiths focus on contouring and residue management to protect soil from erosion. They chisel plow in the fall, then make one pass with a soil finisher in the spring. The Soil Conservation Service helped design and install a manure lagoon on the farm in 1974.

Off the farm, Goldsmith helped organize the Cedar County Corn Growers Association. He served as vice-chairman of the Iowa Corn Promotion Board and executive board treasurer for the National Com Development Foundation.

The Goldsmiths were named Master Pork Producers in 1980. Jerry also served on the U.S. Meat Export Federation's executive board.

Jerry and Jean have three children. Mike, 24, graduated from the University of Northern Iowa. He works for the Paralyzed Veterans of America as program outreach/service resource specialist in Omaha, Neb. Mark, 22, will graduate from the University of Iowa in December with a degree in sociology. Daughter Kelly, 15, will be a sophomore at Clarence/Lowden High School this fall.

Ralph and Joyce Neill
Adams County

Cattle and conservation go together. So do Ralph and Joyce Neill.

The Corning, Iowa, couple has spent their married life molding their Douglas Center Stock Farm into producing high-quality beef, while protecting fragile soils.

Ralph and Joyce Neill

They have accomplished that in the true spirit of Iowa family farmers. Neither has ever had "off-farm" employment. "And believe me, Joyce has shared all the trials, tribulations, heartaches, joys and successes of our joint agricultural career," says Ralph.

Their partnership is representative of many husband and wife teams across the state who work together on the farm, yet make time for community and other activities.

Along the way, the Neills raised daughters Marta, 28, a pharmacist in Ft. Collins, Colo., and Natalie, 25, a mathematician working in computer software development in San Pedro, Calif.

The Neills feel an obligation to try to "give something back" to agriculture. They do that in many ways, sharing successes enjoyed, as well as failures endured. The desire is to educate, to inform others, to help in some small way to improve the profession they love.

Presentations often focus on that favorite theme – cattle, soil stewardship and the environment. One talk meshes all: "Cows, calves and conservation equals cash."

"The environment is fragile, we must diligently take care of it for future generations," says Ralph. "At the same time, the reality is that to be in a position to accomplish this, farmers must turn a profit."

One 40-acre parcel of the farm dates back to 1858. Their family represents the sixth generation to manage it. The Neills have spent 30 years building the operation around those traditional family values.

There are 1,300 tillable acres of the 1,700 now owned. The intensive cropping system of corn and soybeans is confined totally to bottomlands where erosion poses little problem. Neill hasn't used a moldboard plow since 1970. Though he no-tills some fields, heavier soils are still chiseled in the fall, field cultivated in the spring and planted in 38-inch rows. Average yield the past three years has been around 129 bushels per acre. That includes a slump to 90 bushels last year caused by the unusually wet season. By contrast, in 1990 the farm averaged 152 bushels of corn. Soybeans have been drilled since 1982. Again, yield averages the past couple of seasons have been reduced to around 37 bushels an acre because of weather. Top yields of nearly 60 bushels per acre were reached in 1989.

"Their hard work and dedication to farming have made the Douglas Center Stock Farm a working example of what is 'right' with American agriculture," writes Brian Peterson, district conservationist, Corning, Iowa.

Ralph and Joyce would rather talk conservation and cows. All marginal land is kept in forage, pasture or timber. Management of this land is just as, or more, important to them as row crops. The farm is frequently used for tours, from young farmer groups to foreign visitors. The Soil Conservation Service developed a slide presentation here on "Managing a Beef Cow Herd." The Neills welcome the opportunity to show how practices can work. Even individuals will get the "cook's" tour. Jump in the pickup and ride along. Their enthusiasm is infectious.

Hill pastures have been seeded to improved grasses and legumes for long rotations.

There are eight ponds for gully control and water supply. Tile-outlet terraces protect the bottomlands below and feed the ponds. There are short terraces in some waterways with tile inlets to "step" the water down.

The cow herd has been in or near the top one-third of the herds participating in Iowa State University's Beef Cow Business Record program. The normal 135 to 140 cows in the herd has been cut back because pasture is being renovated. All calves are weighed and tagged at birth.

Average weaning weight in 1993, adjusted to 205 days, was 548 pounds. All calves, not kept for replacements, are fed. The 1993 calves now headed to market averaged 3.22 pounds per day daily gain. Feed cost per pound was 36 cents. Projected weight was about 1,150 pounds per head.

The couple has been active in countless community activities, local, state and national organizations. 4-H activities have long been a priority, and they have held many offices in the Corning United Methodist Church. Ralph is a charter member of Iowa Cattlemen's Association. He spent six years on the Iowa Beef Improvement Association Board.

Dan and Diana Stadtmueller
Jones County

Dan and Diana Stadtmueller are committed to agriculture. Anyone who knows this Jones County, Iowa, farming couple is aware of that fact. There is no test like losing your home and building to a tornado that forces you to decide whether you'll take your financial resources and go elsewhere. Diana and Dan chose to reinvest in farming.

The twister left the farmstead in a shambles in March of 1990. Grain bins were caved in, machine sheds mangled, roofs were gone. Debris was scattered across fields. The house was severely torqued and twisted. "We pulled the door shut on what was left of our home and went to my mother's," recalls Diana.

"Luckily, we were able to save almost all our personal possessions," she adds. "That was a great comfort and relief. It was 5 p.m. when the tornado hit. By 9 p.m. friends, neighbors and relatives had helped us empty our house and pack up all the seed corn. They hauled everything to their sheds and barns to store it for us."

The Mennonite Relief Society also helped the Stadtmuellers put things back together again. "You read about such events, but you don't feel it until it happens to you," notes Diana. "We'll always be grateful for these people who reached out to help."

Dan and Diana got the crops planted that spring and moved into a new house in 1991. "You call on your courage and with the help of others, you rebuild," she reflects.

The Stadtmuellers have long been known for innovative cropping methods that save soil and reduce production costs. They have used ridge-till for 17 years, strip cropping six rows of corn next to six rows of soybeans for much of that time. The controlled traffic pattern allowed them to maximize yields and minimize the number of trips over the field. Today, the Stadtmuellers have switched to no-till on most of their acres although they still have some fields in ridge-till.

Dan has been a member of the Cedar Valley Farm Business Association since he started farming in 1962 after graduating from Iowa State University. Records show an exceptional low-cost per unit of production. "Dan was producing corn and soybeans with fewer chemicals, less fertilizer, less soil loss and less fuel usage when most of the industry said it couldn't be done," says Duane Murken, the Cedar Valley consultant who has helped Diana and Dan keep records for the last 20 years.

The Stadtmuellers are always willing to share their ideas. Dan once brought his no-till equipment to the church parking lot one Sunday. He stayed and answered questions until the last farmer went home.

Dan and Diana Stadtmueller

Dan and Diana are leaders in farm and commodity groups as well as church and community activities. Dan served as president of the Iowa Corn Growers Association and as a director of the National Corn Growers Association. He's also been president of the Jones County Farm Bureau and is immediate past president of the board that oversees Iowa State University's Northeast Iowa Research Farm at Nashua, Iowa.

Many times, Dan has taken equipment and redesigned it to better fit his operation. Other farmers have followed his lead. He has been a speaker on Soil Conservation Service and ISU Extension service programs, hosted tours and provided demonstration plots on his farm.

In 1980, Dan originated the first "un-tillage committee" to get farmers to leave soybean stubble alone in the fall. He has been president of Monticello Rotary Club. The Stadtmuellers are members of Wayne Zion Lutheran Church. Dan helped establish the Anna Husman scholarship fund.

Diana serves on the Iowa Agricultural Development Authority board, the state agency which works through banks and other private lenders to make loans to beginning farmers. Diana is an active participant in the farming operation.

Dan is consulted by politicians, farm organization leaders, ISU researchers and engineers at machinery companies. "Dan and Diana clearly represent first class leadership in today's agriculture," sums up Joe Legg, retired Jones County ISU Extension director.

"You can see the team effect of husband and wife working together in their farming operation," says Dave Lubben, a Jones County farmer. "For 10 years, we've had a marketing club in Monticello. We meet monthly, analyze the outlook and try to develop marketing strategies for our members. Dan has been an integral part of our group. His ideas are well-respected."

The Stadtmuellers have two children. Deborah, 26, is married and lives in California. Darren, 22, is a senior at ISU in ag business.

IOWA MASTER FARMERS

~ July 1995

Each year in Iowa a few outstanding farmers are selected as Iowa Master Farmers. These are the men, women and children who pull together as families in the pursuit of professional success and happiness in life.

Wallaces Farmer initiated the program in 1926 to recognize exceptional farmers who also took time to serve community, church and others. The recognition seeks to acknowledge what is right with agriculture. While the honor points to the accomplishments of the individual family, the intent is much broader.

These folks are representative of the many deserving farm families all across this great agricultural state. The intent is not to glorify particular families. Rather, it is to focus statewide attention on the positive role of agriculturists beyond the farm gate. Those selected are much more than just good stewards of the land.

In fact, they may not even be the best farmers in their areas. They make other contributions. They are leaders who display an unselfish, giving attitude.

The 1995 Iowa Master Farmers are Gary Ewoldt of Davenport, Paul Hill of Ellsworth, David Noller of Sigourney and Harold Peyton of Sac City.

On the following pages you will be able to read about each 1995 award winner in detail. You'll notice they aren't all "cut from the same mold." The similarity you will find in this group, however, is that the farms are well-managed, and all have given their time and abilities back to their community and state.

They join 358 others who have received the award since it began. This year's class is only the 58th, however. During the Depression years and World War II the recognition was interrupted.

In past "classes" you will find state senators, representatives, church deacons, Sunday school teachers, parade committee chairpersons. There are conservation board members, members of cooperative boards, members of countless committees.

Nominations come from many sources, including friends, neighbors, family, farm organizations, commodity groups and others.

Gary and Sally Ewoldt
Scott County

Tucked away in the hills not far from the Mississippi River is the picturesque farmstead of Gary and Sally Ewoldt. A winding drive leads to the white house and red barns. Green pastures and stately oak trees frame the grazing cattle.

Pulling up to the machine shed, I noticed a hitching rail. Gary greeted me with a question, "Can you ride a horse?" He saddled up Roxy and Rex and off we went. Bouncing along with my camera and notebook, I knew this was going to be a unique interview.

The Ewoldts farm 735 acres in the southeast corner of Scott County, Iowa. About 390 is tillable, the rest is mostly grazing land. Livestock pay the bills on this farm, making an efficient, conservation use of the rugged resources.

"We started with a cow pasture 25 years ago," recalls Sally. "That was it."

Gary was a widower and Sally a widow when they met and decided to marry. It was 1970 and Gary asked his soon-to-be bride, "How does 10 acres and horses sound to you?"

Gary and Sally Ewoldt

Recalls Sally, with a chuckle, "I was a widow with three teenage children. Gary's proposal sounded pretty good to me."

They built a house, barn, machine shed and a grain bin in those early years. Gary worked off the farm as an insurance adjuster. Gary and Sally raised a blended family of five children. "They are all super kids, supportive of each other," says Gary.

Gary grew up on a farm in Tama County and acquired an appreciation for agriculture. Gary and Sally's dream of 10 acres and horses for this family grew to more acres along with sheep, cattle and hogs as the Ewoldts became full-time farmers.

The Ewoldts now own 130 acres and rent the rest of the land they operate. They grow corn, soybeans, hay and have a 100-head beef cow herd and 115 sows. Recently they sold their sheep.

The main hog buildings are on a leased farm down the road. Accurate recordkeeping is a must, as the Ewoldts have 14 different landlords. Located between the city of Davenport and the town of Blue Grass, Iowa, "most of the fields we farm are smaller than what most Iowa farmers farm," notes Gary.

Horses are used regularly to check the 100

crossbred beef cows. The cattle are rotated on several different pastures, some of which have hills that a four-wheel-drive pickup wouldn't want to roam. The pastures are well-managed.

Calves are backgrounded, then sold as preconditioned feeder cattle. The top end of the steer calves usually weigh 600 to 610 pounds. The farrow-to-finish hog operation cranks out 1,500 head per year. Several older barns were remodeled for hogs. Gary and Sally hire very little outside labor.

Gary has, for many years, been active locally in church, Farm Bureau, 4-H, Iowa State University Extension Service and the Cattlemen's Association. The positive direction of these organizations in eastern Iowa can be attributed in part to Gary's farming philosophy and his management style.

The concept of the whole family has been important to Gary and Sally. "Not only have Gary and Sally raised a fine family on their farm, but their hospitality has reached out to extended family, foreign students, a foster child, friends and neighbors," say neighbors Wilbur and Pat Moeller. The Moellers also cite the support Gary has given Sally in her activities.

Gary and Sally inspired their children to "do their best" from grade school through college. The oldest child is Susan (Mrs. Gary) Moritz, director of development for Wesley Retirement Services in Des Moines. James Craig is an attorney in Cedar Rapids. Major William Craig is a test pilot at Edwards Air Force Base in California. Ann (Mrs. Paul) Torbert, is the county Extension director for ISU at Oskaloosa. Robb Ewoldt is a student at ISU in Ames. Gary and Sally have seven grandchildren.

Paul and Mary Hill
Hamilton County

There's quite a story behind those long turkey houses that stretch along Interstate 35 in Hamilton County, Iowa. It's the old saga of the 1980s, but this one has a happier ending than many of them do.

After graduating from college in 1967, Paul and Mary Hill started farming in partnership with Paul's parents near Ellsworth, Iowa. When Paul's sister and brother-in-law joined the operation, a turkey barn was built.

In 1980, they were marketing 70,000 turkeys and 4,500 fed cattle a year, in addition to grain farming and buying land. Then, as happened to many young, expanding farmers, the Hills were hit by severe financial stress during the tough cattle feeding times and the land value collapse in the 1980s.

Leaving pride behind, Paul and Mary addressed the difficult situation with a positive restructuring plan that led to a sizable expansion of their turkey production. Their foresight, together with planning, management ability and dedication to long hours of physical labor, turned the struggling situation into a successful operation.

"In 1984, we decided to reduce our debt," says Paul. "We had expanded too fast, land prices were plummeting, cattle prices were poor, and interest costs were eating us up. I was determined to avoid bankruptcy. We were lucky. We got into trouble early and recognized we needed to make big changes. We were able to liquidate 40% of our land and get out of cattle feeding and no one lost a dime on us."

Then Paul designed a unique turkey operation and expanded to 300,000 turkeys. The turkeys allowed the family business to survive and grow.

The business was restructured as a family-farming corporation. Paul is president of Circle Hill Farms, Ltd. Paul, along with his wife Mary, father Hubert, mother Daisy, sister Faye, brother-in-law Noel Thompson and son Nathan Hill are the key family employees. They also employ eight full-time men and five to six women part time. Circle Hill Farms owns 800 acres and rents another 80. All of the tillable acres are in continuous corn.

"Paul is a true example of someone who works hard but also works smart," says a neighboring farmer, Merlyn Hegland. "Paul has a keen, analytical mind. When times got tough, he got going!"

Paul Hill created a niche for himself in contract turkey feeding. He relentlessly pursued many avenues of financing to expand facilities. He designed a building and ventilation system unique in the Midwest.

The family corporation owns and operates two separate facilities and also operates another two owned by Paul's aunt and family. They now market over 600,000 turkeys per year on all four operations. They contract to sell the turkeys to two processors.

Expansion of

Paul and Mary Hill

295

the turkey facilities created another problem – an enormous tonnage of manure created weekly. Paul Hill crisscrossed the country talking to experienced farmers and researchers to learn all he could about composting. In 1985, he built a fermenter to "cook" the manure. He's fine-tuned his composting facility and now is turning the manure into an asset.

This fertilizer is sold mostly to farmers. A specialty fertilizer called Ultra-Gro is marketed as a lawn and garden fertilizer that is 100% organic.

Paul, with Mary's support, has devoted much time to motivating young people. He's taught Sunday school for 27 years and coached grade school basketball as a volunteer for many years.

Paul has served on Farm Bureau's Environmental Advisory Committee, Farm Bureau's Poultry Committee, is a member of the Governor's Environmental Task Force, and does voluntary promotional work for the Iowa Turkey Federation. Mary is a member of the Iowa Turkey Federation Board.

Paul and Mary have three children. The oldest is Peter, a financial planner with Equitable of Iowa, who with wife Leah lives in Des Moines. Nathan, after graduating from college last year, returned to the farming operation. Daughter Rachel will attend Wartburg College this fall.

David Noller
Keokuk County

The old adage still applies. "Hogs are the mortgage lifters," says Dave Noller, leaning against the "Bulls for sale" sign in the farmyard.

The veteran livestock man from near Sigourney, Iowa, has watched both the hog and cattle markets cycle through the years. "About every 16 to 18 years, the two meet at a low point," he says. "Right now, the cattle market is in the pits." For the first time in a decade he still has several purebred Charolais bulls waiting for buyers. Normally most are sold by mid-June.

Noller blames the poor cattle market for the slow season. Folks are just making that old bull last one more year. The miserable spring planting season across Iowa's southern counties hasn't helped attitudes, either.

Like the weather, Noller has faith the cattle market will eventually "straighten out" and bounce back to profitable levels. "I believe there is tremendous opportunity ahead for both hog and cattle producers," he says. "The increasing demand for meat in many nations around the world makes me optimistic about developing our value-added product industry."

Noller continues working to improve Charolais genetics. Calving ease and efficient growth are the objectives. The herd is recognized as a breed leader in these traits.

About 180 cows and heifers are bred each year. With the help of a few twins, the calving rate has approached 99% the past three seasons. They sell about 45 breeding bulls and 30 bred cows a year. The remainder are sold as feeder cattle and open cows. Calving period runs from March 20 to May 31. Detailed records have always been a part of the routine including birth weight, weaning weight, yearling weight, weight per day of age, ratios, grade score, frame score, percent of fat, loin fat, ribeye, pelvic size, etc.

Noller describes the hog operation as focused on least-cost production. Pigs are farrowed in two 10-stall and one 24-stall houses. In the summer they are moved to pasture in groups of 10 and remain there until weaning at six weeks. Pigs are brought back into confinement for growing and finishing. Average cost of production the past three years has been $35.79 per cwt.

"I give my partners Judy and Wayne Frank a lot of credit for the success of the hog and beef enterprises, as well as crop production," says Noller. "She's not just the recordkeeper, either. Judy plays an equal role in the hands-on production. We work together as a team, along with two employees."

David Noller

The Franks joined Noller as employees in 1969. The relationship grew and from their earnings and an incentive program Noller offered, the couple was able to enter into a partnership in 1972. They started to purchase 370 acres of the 1,170-acre operation in 1976. Of that, 890 acres are tillable, the remainder is for grazing. In the early 1980s, the farm was incorporated.

Noller has been a member of the Mississippi Valley Farm Business Association almost since it was organized n the early 1950s. "The association has helped us in many ways," he says.

Noller's wife, Jean, died in 1992. Children include Nancy Jones, who operates Homestead Handcrafts, Spokane, Washington. Her husband David is a chiropractor. Jon Noller and wife Cheryl manage Sebergen Feeder Pigs, West Point, Iowa. They also own a swine finishing operation and were named Master Pork Producers in 1990.

Noller has been active in countless organizations and has served on many boards and committees. Some of those include: Master Swine Producer in 1952; National Livestock and Meat Board; president and director, Iowa Beef Improvement Association; charter member, Iowa Cattlemen's Association; Iowa Hog Cholera eradication committee; Sigourney Development director and chairman; president's council, ISU; and trustee, Sigourney United Methodist Church.

Harold and Sue Peyton
Sac County

Some people believe lightning won't strike twice in the same place. But Harold and Sue Peyton, Sac City, Iowa, know that isn't true with tornadoes. Twisters have hit their farm twice, first in 1970 and again in 1984.

In fact, helping rebuild many of the farm buildings after the 1970 tornado was one of the first tasks Harold took on when he returned to Sac County to farm full time in 1971. He had taught agriculture for three years after graduating from Iowa State University. While at ISU, Harold took ag business law courses and encouraged his father to incorporate the family farm operation. The ideas gleaned from his course work provided the framework for Peyton, Inc., which was incorporated in 1969.

Harold farms around 1,500 acres, most of which is planted to corn to provide corn silage and grain for livestock feed. A regular rotation has been followed with corn, oats and alfalfa. "Because of the declining market for seed oats, I have soybeans in the rotation for the first time this year," says Harold.

The farm's primary enterprises are hogs and cattle, however. All feeder cattle and feeder pigs are purchased. Cattle, mostly crossbred, are brought in at 550 to 750 pounds, primarily from western Nebraska or South Dakota. The cattle are confined in feedlots ranging from 225 to 400 head in capacity. Recently, Harold redesigned his cattle-working facilities to include an electronic scale, hydraulic chute and gates to make it easier to sort cattle by weight. This allows for better decisions about implanting and marketing. "One person can sit at the scale and open and close gates from that position," explains Harold.

Hog facilities are older, yet have had continuous repair and remodeling to keep them as efficient as possible. There are two nursery units for 40-pound feeder pigs and three finishing houses. Two older barns are also utilized for finishing hogs.

Harold was a pioneer in the use of computer recordkeeping for livestock enterprises. He wrote the computer program, which was the forerunner of ISU's Feedlot Monitoring program. Currently, the ISU program is used to record all rations, feed costs and other financial information for the cattle. It predicts average daily gain and break-even costs, which identify a window of opportunity for marketing. Harold has also created a bunk reading program which tracks consumption and prints daily feed sheets. The program provides a systematic method of adjusting rations.

Because Peyton, Inc. also owns and operates a county grain elevator to purchase corn from neighboring farmers, Harold developed a spreadsheet computer program to summarize corn records. Statements are printed from computer files to provide each farmer with a record of corn delivered and its current status.

Harold oversees the total operation. His father Rolland is an energetic 85-year-old who works on the farm daily and buys nearly all the feeder cattle. Peyton, Inc. has three full-time employees as well as seasonal part-time help. "We could not run this operation successfully without our high-quality employees," says Harold.

Harold has been active in a variety of community organizations, having served on the County Extension Council and local 4-H committee. He has been president of the Sac County Cattlemen, and currently serves on local bank and hospital boards.

The Peytons are members of the First Christian Church in Sac City where Harold has been elder, deacon, chair of the church board, stewardship chair and a Sunday school teacher for 23 years.

Harold and Sue have two children. Kevin is 8 and Amy is 5.

Sue and Harold Peyton

IOWA MASTER FARMERS

~ June 1996

Dennis and Janice Berger
Washington County

Visiting with Dennis and Janice Berger on their farm near Wellman, Iowa, you feel that learning is very much a two-way street. This southeast Iowa family has always been interested in farming their soils correctly. For 32 years, their overall management has been aimed at profit without creating adverse environmental consequences.

Now in partnership with son Steve, the Bergers crop a total of 2,227 acres, pretty much half corn and half soybeans, all no-till. Of that, about half is owned and the rest is rented.

Dennis started out farming part-time. He and Janice began farming full-time in 1964 when they bought the 80 acres where they now live. They've grown the operation to where it now includes a

Dennis and Janice Berger

DeKalb and Stine seed dealership and a swine enterprise.

The Bergers hire no full-time help, although part-time help is hired as needed in spring and fall. Sons Steve and Terry are both graduates of Iowa State University. Steve works with his parents on the farm and Terry works for Pioneer Hi-Bred at Johnston, Iowa.

A major strength is the Berger's attention to detailed recordkeeping. Dennis has belonged to the Iowa Farm Business Association (IFBA) since the early 1960s. He is past president of IFBA and the Mississippi Valley Farm Business Association. The Bergers have been using a computer for 15 years for bookkeeping, inventory, field records and financial analysis.

Dennis began experimenting with no-till in the 1970s and gradually shifted his entire acreage to no-till in 1989. He has hosted farm tours and twilight meetings for Iowa State University Extension and Monsanto. The Berger farm has demonstrated no-till methods, new crop protection chemicals and other practices. Dennis has drilled beans for 16 years. He has a high clearance sprayer and uses a smaller ATV sprayer to get over fields when soils are wet.

The fertility program includes soil testing every year and maintaining optimum levels of P and K. Nitrogen is both fall applied and sidedressed in June. Dennis made a spoke injector applicator to apply liquid N on sloping soils to minimize soil erosion. He is cooperating with ISU in on-farm research regarding fertilization in no-till. The Bergers have won the Washington County corn contest twice in the last six years and hold the record for the highest yield of 225.27 bushels

Joyce and Gary Holst

per acre.

The Bergers have built 100,000 feet of terraces (19 miles) and were the first in Washington County to install parallel tile inlet terraces in the early 1960s. Dennis was one of the first farmers in Iowa to build narrow base terraces. He's installed 25,000 feet of terraces on rented land. He maintains 15,000 feet of waterways, along with several levees and drainage ditches.

Son Steve owns a share of a newly built 1,200 head sow unit near Wellman. The unit is owned by farmers. The Berger partnership purchases feeder pigs from Steve and contracts with other farmers to feed them out.

Janice served on the Mid-Prairie School board for 12 years. Active in the Wellman Rotary Club, Dennis is the incoming president and a Paul Harris Fellow. The Bergers are active in Asbury United Methodist Church.

Dennis served three terms on the Iowa Soybean Promotion Board, and is a charter member of the Washington County Corn/Soybean Association. He's served on the board of the Farmers Cooperative in Keota.

"I've developed a real admiration for Dennis and his marketing skills," says John Roach of Roach Ag Marketing. "He has a strong working knowledge of spread relationships, basis movement and profit-based marketing. He's skilled at using marketing tools to maximize the prices he gets for grain. He never becomes emotional in the face of erratic markets. Careful in his use of futures, he limits it to re-

moving risk rather than speculating."

"I always knew he was a good farmer and caretaker of the soil," says Roger Borup, Dennis' longtime friend and former loan officer. "But it has become even more clear, watching how Dennis farms the land. All land is cared for in the same manner whether he owns it or not."

Gary and Joyce Holst
Scott County

Gary Holst is a fourth generation farmer. Son Kevin is the fifth. Gary went into partnership with his father, William, after graduating from Iowa State University in 1960. Kevin now farms full-time with him in the 1,000-acre operation near Eldridge, Iowa. "This is definitely a family farm," says Gary. He is quick to add that Joyce helps out wherever and whenever she is needed. "She is a good tractor driver." The farm achieved Century Farm status in 1989.

Soil conservation is uppermost in the Holsts' minds. "It's been top priority as long as I can remember," notes Gary. "The soil is ours to use and protect, not abuse – pass it on to the next generation in better condition than we found it."

Gary was one of the first in Scott County to buy a chisel plow. In 1992, a no-till grain drill was purchased to no-till soybeans, rye, oats, grasses and alfalfa. No-till coulters and trash wheels have been added to the corn planter over the years. "We currently no-till more than 50% of our corn acres," says Gary.

The Holsts recently purchased a Tye Paratill to battle subsoil compaction yet leave surface residue relatively untouched. Nearly 4,600 feet of contour terraces have been constructed over the years to help curb erosion.

The cropping program includes nearly 600 acres of corn, 175 acres of soybeans, 135 acres of hay ground and 35 acres of permanent and rotational pasture. Alfalfa and oats are usually sown each spring with the oats either chopped for silage or combined for grain. About 40 acres of corn silage is harvested in the fall. In 1995, the Holsts raised 180 acres of seed oats for two companies. The oats served as a cover crop for alfalfa, sweet clover and bromegrass establishment on land rented from the Department of Natural Resources.

Gary's real love, however, is beef cattle. "I really enjoy good quality cows." Unfortunately, the Holsts lost nearly 85% of their pasture land recently to a DNR 2,500-acre recreational project known as Lost Grove Lake. The name seems appropriate to the Holsts. "It was ideal land for raising cattle," says Gary. "It has lots of trees and a creek running through it." Some of the land lost to the project was Century Farm land.

The loss of the pasture land meant the Holsts had to reduce the size of their purebred Gelbvieh herd about a year ago. "The rest of our land is just too productive to convert to pasture," explains Gary. He wrestled with the problem for quite a while. "I really didn't want to have to have a liquidation sale but time was running out." Finally, the American Gelbvieh Association put him in touch with a rancher in Canada. After details were hammered out—health requirements, exchange rates, trucking, etc.—77 head of purebred cows, heifers and bulls headed for Manitoba.

Today, the herd consists of about 35 head of purebred cows and bulls. Nearly 200 head of feeder calves are purchased each fall and fed to market weight along with some of the home-raised calves. A number of yearling bulls are sold in eastern Iowa and western Illinois. Local 4-H members buy heifer and steer calves from the Holsts for their projects.

Artificial insemination (AI) has been used extensively since the 1970s to obtain the use of top quality sires in the beef industry.

Gary has, for many years, been active in the Bettendorf Presbyterian Church, serving as elder and Mission Concerns Committee member. He has been a 4-H leader, vice president of the Scott County Cattlemen's Association, member of the Gelbvieh Association, township trustee, Scott County Soil Conservation District assis-

tant commissioner and county president of the National Farmers Organization.

In addition to Kevin, the Holsts have a daughter, Connie, who lives in St. Louis, Mo., and manages a Wilson's leather goods store.

John and Mary Miller
Black Hawk County

Near Cedar Falls, Iowa, in an area rapidly being inhabited by nonfarm residents, John and Mary Miller quietly demonstrate a love for the land through their words and deeds. Their Black Hawk County farm has carefully terraced fields, a newly established native prairie and neatly kept livestock buildings. One feels a natural synergy between people, land and livestock.

This synergy has existed in the Miller operation for a long time. Their goal is to leave the land better than they found it and provide a strong foundation for the next generation.

John Miller operates 600 acres and has a partnership with Larry Green in a 140-sow farrow-to-finish operation. G & M Pork, Inc. has survived and prospered through 19 years.

"It's been successful because Larry is a heck of a hog producer," says John.

The house and many of the buildings were put up in the late 1800s by John's great-grandfather. The pig nursery is an old hay barn and the farrowing building is a converted chicken house.

The facilities are utilized to their full po-

Mary and John Miller

301

tential and the hog enterprise is integrated effectively with the farming operation. John wanted to farm 600 acres to utilize the waste resources from the annual production of 2,800 hogs. A professional agronomist helps manage crop production with the use of soil testing, fertility planning and crop scouting – it's a complete Integrated Crop Management program. The managed manure program reduces the need for major purchases of phosphate and potash. Nitrogen needs are reduced by almost 25%.

"Back in the days of my great-grandfather, you conserved resources without even thinking about it," says Miller. "The fields were smaller and fencerows helped minimize erosion. Also, crop rotations were standard procedure."

His father was a science teacher, and as far back as John can remember, there was an appreciation for the environment. The row of trees that he planted at the age of 13 is now an effective windbreak along the driveway. His first broad base terraces were built in the late 1960s long before such practices became common. He also developed a farm pond at this time for water management and wildlife.

When John was a junior in high school, he received a book called "Round River" by Aldo Leopold as a Christmas present from his father. "This book talked about the country being the personality of the land," recalls Miller. "We are the best at producing crops but we don't know as much as we should about the country. It's not just production – it's commitment."

It's appropriate that Miller served on the first board of directors of the Leopold Center, an educational and research foundation devoted to sustainable agriculture. He helped establish the center's focus and direction, and is still involved with its activities and programs. John also served on the Iowa State Soil Conservation Committee for 12 years and helped develop the Northeast Iowa Research Farm at Nashua.

In their quiet, unassuming way, the Millers show how farmers can live in harmony with their urban neighbors. Mary has given piano lessons in their home for nearly 35 years and is a member of local, state and national music organizations. "It's a career that works well with living on the farm," she notes.

John has not sought media exposure, but he's been in the "right place at the right time" on a number of occasions. The Miller family was featured in a USDA brochure more than 20 years ago, called "People on the Farm: Corn and Hog Farming." John and Mary hosted the Today Show on their farm and were interviewed by Barbara Walters during a bicentennial special in 1976.

The Millers' thoughtful, articulate answers helped build a positive image for farmers and agriculture in 1976. They continue to do so today by demonstrating their belief in the value of sustainable agriculture.

The Miller children are: Julie, who lives in Lees Summit, Mo.; Brad, Daytona Beach, Fla., and Brian, Portland, Ore.

Alvin and Mary Wright
Cedar County

Next to markets and weather, one of the most difficult challenges facing farmers today is finding a way to bring the next generation into the operation. Alvin and Mary Wright have, for several years, been turning increasing amounts of authority and responsibility over to their sons, Kevin and Kerry.

That's the way Alvin and Mary started out in 1957 – slowly. After returning from the Navy, Alvin was able to rent 120 acres near his father and brother. "We started out very humbly with small equipment, a few sows, a few cattle and one cow," he says. Mary taught school to tide them over until the first paycheck – 10 cent hogs.

Today the Cedar County operation consists of 680 acres, mostly corn and soybeans. Father and sons work together nearly every day. However, both sons own and rent land of their own. Kevin and Kerry trade labor for the use of some of Alvin's equipment.

Alvin buys around 1,000 head of feeder

pigs from his sons each year. "I decided to let the boys do the farrowing," he quips.

He also buys 400-500 head of yearling feeder cattle. A converted barn handles one lot of cattle. A new cattle shed and an old corncrib are used for another lot of cattle. All lots are cement. The Wrights sold their cow herd earlier this year.

Alvin uses mostly minimum tillage in his cropping program. "Our John Deere 7200 planter is set up for no-till, but that doesn't mean we no-till all the time," says Alvin. "Sometimes we have to disk stalks when the residue is heavy."

Alvin uses Rawson coulters on his planter for minimum tillage. "We added a third coulter in the center of the row this year," he explains. "It really helps in those high residue situations."

Alvin has the local co-op apply liquid nitrogen and herbicides in a two-part program. In some fields it is applied preplant

Mary and Alvin Wright

and in pre-emerge in others. His tractor is also fitted with saddle tanks to apply liquid nitrogen close to the row at planting time.

He uses the same planter for planting soybeans into com stubble. "We typically chisel cornstalks in the fall followed by a light discing in the spring. We have successfully no-tilled beans into cornstalks, but sometimes we need to disc the stalks first."

Alvin is a member of the Mississippi Valley Farm Business Association. Both corporate and personal records are kept on PC Mars, a computerized recordkeeping system.

Not only did Alvin help his sons get started farming during the difficult 1980s, but a few years ago a young neighbor had just decided to return home and farm when his father died suddenly. "It was hard for him," explains Alvin. "I helped him by giving him some advice

when he needed it. He's doing fine now."

Alvin is director of the Mercantile Bank in Tipton, was a 4-H leader for 10 years and has been a member of the Lions Club for 23 years. He helped found, and is still a director of, Senior Park, a housing project for senior citizens which is sponsored by the Lions Club.

Alvin served as a director of the Cedar County Cooperative during the difficult 1980s. "During the recession of the 1980s, our cooperative experienced steady growth in sales and savings. Alvin's fairness and foresight during these years certainly was an asset to our co-op," says Robert Young, manager.

Alvin and Mary are active in the United Methodist Church in Tipton. Both sing in the choir.

The Wrights have three children. Kevin, who farms with his father and brother, and his wife Betty live nearby. They have two children, Alisha, 3, and Ryan, 3 months.

Kerry, who also farms with Kevin and Alvin, lives on a rented farm near Tipton. Daughter Amy and her husband Scott Kenworthy live in Rowlett, Texas. They have a daughter, Micaela, 2, and are expecting another child in July.

Exceptional Service Award
Garren Benson
Story County

For over 30 years, Garren Benson has been helping farmers solve the problems associated with the production of Iowa's largest cash crops – corn and soybeans. The longtime Iowa State University Extension agronomist has been selected to receive the Iowa Master Farmer Exceptional Service Award.

Wallaces Farmer has presented Master Farmer awards to farmers since 1926. But Benson is only the sixth person to be honored for exceptional service to the state's farmers.

Iowa farmers and agribusiness professionals have relied on Benson's expertise because they trust it. What distinguishes Benson from other experts in his field is that he is so practical. He "thinks like a farmer." His research and Extension information are presented in a useful, easy to understand manner.

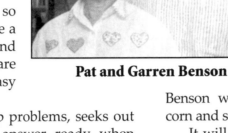

Pat and Garren Benson

"He anticipates crop problems, seeks out solutions and has an answer ready when farmers or industry people call him," says Regis Voss, Benson's longtime colleague at ISU.

The reassuring calm in Benson's voice, his reasoned, well-mannered personality, and his careful explanation of crop phenomena have squelched the panic of more than a few farmers worried about a weak stand of corn.

Benson is stepping down July 1 as Extension agronomist after having served 32 and one-half years. He will continue working in the ISU agronomy department at Ames on a part-time basis, doing corn research and helping teach a new crop problem-solving course. This will be the first time in his career that he hasn't had an ISU Extension appointment.

Benson never told farmers how to grow corn and beans. "No one set of recommendations fits all producers or all circumstances. I give farmers the information and they make the intelligent decisions for their situation."

Benson started as a professional agronomist almost by accident. After graduating from the University of Minnesota with bachelor's and master's degrees in soil science, he was working for an elevator in southeast Minnesota. He went to an Extension meeting in Decorah, Iowa, and heard Virgil Webster, an Iowa State area agronomist, talk about soil testing. "I asked him quite a few questions," recalls Benson. Webster contacted E.R. Duncan, leader of agronomy Extension at Ames, and recommended that Iowa State hire this young man.

Benson's first position began in January 1964 as an area Extension agronomist for seven counties in southeast Iowa. He joined the campus Extension staff in 1967 and started work on the Ph.D. in crop production he earned in 1971. Benson was ISU's only state-level Extension corn and soybean specialist from 1983 to 1993.

It will be difficult for him to leave Extension work, but the time seems right. "You can't work part-time at Extension," notes Benson. "This is a way to control my schedule and yet not be completely out of the profession."

He enjoyed the diversity of duties and the chance to get out in the field and talk to farmers one-on-one. He will miss that part of the job as well as the contacts with Extension staff.

"One of the reasons I stayed this long in this job is the tremendous group of scientific minds you get a chance to work with," says Benson. Much of his time has been spent working in the fields doing research and teaching at field days during summer months and at Extension meetings around the state during winter.

Iowa has 22 million acres of corn and soybeans, notes Benson. "This is a unique place to work if you're going to be an agronomist."

His wife Pat has been a big part of his successful career, as he looks back at the countless meetings and many miles he traveled. "We met at the University of Minnesota," says Garren. "Pat grew up on a farm in southwest Minnesota, so she knew what this was all about. She's the glue that held everything together." Pat taught school and worked in retail. The Bensons raised two children. Daughter DeeAnn is a medical doctor. Son Kent is working on a doctorate in electrical engineering. Pat's activities include volunteering at church.

1997 IOWA MASTER FARMERS

March 1997

With the 1997 selections, only 370 Iowa farm families have received the Master Farmer award since its inception in 1926. That points to the fact that it is a prestigious honor, given only to the most outstanding farmers in the state. On the next few pages you will read about the 1997 recipients. They are Donald and Grace Hertz, Laurens; Duane and Ilene Petersen, Sumner; Richard and Shirley Snyder, Cambridge and Ronald and Florine Swanson, Galt.

The program focuses on honoring a "select few" each year who assume leading roles in agriculture, citizenship and good family living. Those chosen for the award are recognized for their achievements in "Good Farming, Clear Thinking and Right Living." It is a sincere effort to honor top Iowa farmers who have devoted generously of their time and energy in building stronger communities and a better agriculture.

Note that it is a family award. We recognize farming is a true partnership between husband and wife. In fact, all members of the family contribute to each other's success.

While the honor points to the accomplishments of the individual family, the intent is much broader. These folks are representative of the many deserving farm families all across this great agricultural state. We do not intend to glorify particular families. Rather, we want to focus statewide attention on the positive role of agriculturists beyond the farm gate. Those selected are much more than just good stewards of the land.

As you read about the 1997 winners in detail you will notice they are not all "cut from the same mold." The similarity you will find in this group, however, is that their farms are well-managed and all have given their time and abilities back to their community, state and nation.

Don and Grace Hertz
Laurens County

Young people used to be able to get started in farming by using sweat equity and little else – raising hogs in a low-investment, no-frills operation. That's how Don Hertz did it. "We wore out a lot of scoop shovels," recalls the 56-year-old Hertz, who grew up on the family farm near Laurens, Iowa.

Today's hog business is no longer simple, and the farming operation of Don and wife Grace has continued to adapt, survive and grow in sophistication over the years. After graduating from Iowa State University in 1962, Don worked for a co-op in southwest Iowa. In 1964, he returned home to northwest Iowa and farmed with his parents, Amos and Helen. In 1974, Amos retired and Don took over. Don built a central farrowing house and a nursery on slats in the early 1970s. He added raised decks for the nursery in 1981.

Today, the Hertz farm markets 2,000 head of hogs per year farrow-to-finish, and sells 200 to 400 feeder pigs per year. Sows are pregnancy checked at 35 days. Farrowing is scheduled in groups – five times a year. Reflecting that focus on reproductive efficiency, the sow herd has a respectable 80% to 90% conception rate. Also, number of pigs weaned per litter is higher than average. "We use a computer to keep sow herd records and to manage farrowing schedules," explains Don.

Grace and Don Hertz

The Hertz's farm 950 acres, with 175 acres owned by Don and Grace and 775 acres rented. "Two-thirds of the land we farm is family-owned, which we rent from the family members," explains Don. Don and Grace derive 100% of their annual income from farming.

Don and Grace raised two children. Son Bill and wife Vicki have three children and live in Laurens. Daughter Deb is married to Todd Wingler. They have two children and reside in Arizona. Still producing hogs, corn and soybeans on that same land where Don began 33 years ago, Don and Grace are now helping another Hertz get started – Don's nephew Greg. "Our children went on to other careers and chose not to enter farming," explains Grace. "So it's a good feeling to hopefully keep the farm in the family."

Raised in Des Moines and Sioux City, Greg Hertz is 35 years old and has been farming with Don and Grace as a full-time employee for 11 years. "After spending time with us each summer through high school and college, Greg eventually moved from the city to the farm to pursue his farming career," explains Don. "Our farm was his summer job. After Greg graduat-ed from ISU, he worked in another job for awhile. But eventually we needed an employee. Greg did some figuring and decided he really wanted to farm."

Greg and his wife Deb have three children. It's a big step for Greg and Deb to buy into the operation. "I'm certainly not ready to retire," says Don. "But to start farming today, it takes a lot more planning. We're working with an accountant and a lawyer to decide how to structure this financially."

Can a family-owned farm compete with the huge corporate-owned hog confinements? "You have to make an investment in costly facilities and it takes a lot of financing to compete with the big hog outfits," says Don. "We have to figure out how we can compete. That's a monkey wrench in the decision-making process today that we didn't have 10 years ago. You always knew your hogs would be the mortgage lifters, if you worked hard and managed wisely. That's not a sure bet anymore."

Neighbors who wrote letters of support for Don's nomination for the Master Farmer Award cite his honesty, hard work and community service. "He is very conscientious, a leader in Pocahontas County," adds Nancy Jenson, county director for ISU's Extension Service. "Asking Don Hertz to be on a board or on a committee guarantees an outstanding end product."

Duane and Ilene Petersen
Bremer County

Listening to Duane and Ilene Petersen is inspiring indeed. It's the quintessential story of a young married couple starting out with nothing and, over time, building a successful farming operation along with several related businesses.

Their story begins in 1970 shortly after the couple were married. Both came from farming families but neither offered an opportunity for them to farm. Duane had returned from a tour in Vietnam and was employed by the co-op. A local farmer was looking for someone to enter into a 50-50 crop-livestock share agreement on a farm he had purchased. With the help of an FmHA loan, an agreement was reached and the rest, as the saying goes, is history.

Twenty-six years later, there are two full-time and seven part-time employees along with two brothers who exchange labor for custom work. "It's a case of the older brother helping younger brothers get started," explains Duane. Brother Don is 10 years younger and Dale is eight years younger. Including land the brothers farm, 5,300 acres are involved in the operation.

Duane and Ilene operate around 3,200 acres near Sumner, Iowa, in Bremer County. Most of the land is rented, however, as the Petersens only own around 600 acres. They have 15 landlords to deal with. Most of the land is cash rented, but some is crop-share as well as some custom farming.

Keeping that many landlords happy could be a nightmare, but not for the Petersens. "I never hold anything back from my landlords,"

Duane and Ilene Petersen

says Duane. "They are always welcome to ride in the combine cab and they get to see yield records. Communication is important when renting land." Duane also does other things to build relationships with landlords such as moving snow, etc.

The Petersens try to stagger rental contracts so they don't have to renegotiate all at the same time. Some are two or three year agreements.

Duane and Ilene also believe it is important to have strong relationships with their employees. "At our level we have to hire extra help. The most important thing is to keep them motivated," explains Duane. "It doesn't necessarily have to be done with wages. For example, if we have to combine all night, Ilene and I are out there with the employees. Don't ask anybody to do something you wouldn't do yourself." Duane shares information with employees to keep them informed.

In 1996, the Petersens had around 1,950 acres of corn and 1,100 acres of soybeans. Duane was one of the first in the area to use a no-till soybean drill and for the past four years he has used it on all of his soybean acres. He also does considerable custom work in the area as he now owns three drills.

Two deep-till machines are used for fall tillage except where soybeans will be drilled the following spring. Two 16-row planters are used to plant Duane's corn as well as that of his brother.

The livestock program consists of a 285-sow farrow-to-finish hog operation, marketing 3,000-3,500 hogs per year. In 1989, Duane was named a Bremer County Master Pork Producer and an Iowa Master Pork Producer. Duane has been a seed dealer since 1972 and a Northrup King dealer since 1987. Son Craig is a student at North Iowa Community College in Mason City. He has begun farming on his own, will come back to the farm and also play an important role in the seed business.

The Petersens have a daughter, Ranae, who is a graduate of Iowa State University.

"Twenty-six years ago I never thought we'd be where we are today," continues Duane. "My dad taught us to work hard and be honest. We've been fortunate all along the way. Land was available to rent and things worked out."

"Duane's foresight enabled him to survive the farm financial crisis of the 1980s as he was the first to recognize a problem," says Stan Laures, vice president, First National Bank, New Hampton, Iowa. "He came to the bank early on and said, 'this isn't going to work.' We worked out a survival plan that included selling some land and machinery which was done before prices dropped sharply."

The Petersens are active in the Grace Lutheran Church in Tripoli, Iowa.

Dick and Shirley Snyder
Story County

By today's standards, they operate a small farm that produces a lot of hogs. It's backed by a continuing heritage of strong family ties.

Meet Dick and Shirley Snyder who operate about 500 acres and market 3,800 to 4,500 hogs a year near Cambridge, Iowa.

The pleasant, unassuming couple say, "we truly haven't done anything that sets us apart from lots of our friends and neighbors. We have worked hard to be good at what we do, to give something back and to maintain our integrity."

Son, Lee, joined the farming operation in 1976 and has gradually assumed more and more of the responsibility. Two years ago, son, Mike, who also works full-time as a purchaser for Casey's convenience stores, joined the farming operation. The brothers share the crop enterprise, while Lee also raises hogs with their father.

"We've tried to help them as much as we could because that's how we started," asserts Dick. Shirley's great grandfather homesteaded the farm in 1866. His son assumed the reins, building it into one of the area's best beef enterprises.

"Now it's our turn to help and, hopefully, our sons will give another family member their chance someday," adds Dick. He still remembers their first big purchase, 30 gilts for $1,000, $33.33 per head. "It was like spending a million dollars," he says. "As the years moved on, it turned out to be a wise choice."

By the late 1960s, the cattle were all but gone as the hog business grew. It now claims nearly 80% of their labor time.

Today, the 400 acres, rotated between corn and soybeans, won't begin to handle their feed needs. "We buy more corn than we raise," says Lee, "and that was painful when it was $5 a bushel last summer."

The balance of the farm is in pasture and farmstead. The grassland is as important as the field crops because here's where the Snyders farrow-to-finish hog operation begins. They farrow twice a year, in April and September. The 50 acres of pasture is divided into separate lots with permanent fencing. Some 300 to 325 sows are grouped 15 to 20 head per lot. Litter average ranges from about 7.5 to 8.5 pigs. Weather is their worst enemy.

Bred sows are moved to pasture seven to 10 days before farrowing. The Snyders' goal is to have the farrowing in a particular lot completed within 10 days. Sows come out of the pens about six weeks after they farrow. At about 45 pounds, the pigs are divided into converted cattle sheds, barns, two Cargill buildings and an open-front finishing unit the Snyders designed.

The growing ration is a step feeding program, increasing the protein with weight. Feed is all premixed on the farm. "I've always tried to keep costs down, so I haven't put money in fancy buildings," he smiles, then quips, "they tell me I'm conservative. I've probably been too conservative. Lee calls me downright tight."

Dick has hired Iowa State University students to help part-time for several years now. Usually one or two students work an afternoon a week and a full day on Saturday. "They've been just terrific," says Dick. "I try to teach them some things about the business, and I always learn from them. I think they really like working here to get a taste of Shirley's cooking."

Dick has always taken time to serve on boards and commit-tees. They include the FFA Alumni Board and Scholarship committee, Polk County Federal Housing Administration Board, Alleman Cooperative Board secretary, Farm Mutual Insurance Association and others. Dick and Shirley are active in the Fjeldberg Lutheran Church of Huxley, Iowa. Dick has served as congregational president, a deacon, on the building com-mittee and pastoral call committee.

Shirley and Dick Snyder

The Snyder family includes daughter Robyn Engstrom, a medical practitioner in Davenport, Iowa. She has two children, Jennifer and Eric. Mike and Julie, Cambridge, are parents of Noah, Shawna and Zachary. Lee and Denise, also of Cambridge, are parents of Reonna, Brandon and Colton.

Ron and Florine Swanson
Wright County

Few, if any, farm couples are as active as Ronald and Florine Swanson in local, state and national leadership roles. Yet, while unselfishly devoting time and resources to make agriculture better, they manage a successful farming operation and have provided an opportunity for a son, Stuart, to begin farming. He is the third generation of Swansons to farm in Wright County. Stuart and Lori manage 500 acres and have a 60-sow farrow-to-finish hog operation, utilizing facilities on both the home and rented farms. They have two children.

Two other sons have off-farm employment. Kendell is in charge of quality assurance for the Iowa Turkey Growers Cooperative at West Liberty, Iowa. He and his wife Vicki have one child. Steve is a graphic designer in Minneapolis, Minn.

Ron began farming in 1962 after graduating from Iowa State University. He rented 160 acres from his father, Wendell, and traded labor for machinery. When Ron married Florine in 1964 the couple rented 320 acres near Woolstock. In 1974, they moved to their present farm near Galt.

Today Swanson Farms is family owned and operated with two separate sole proprietorships. One is Ron and Florine Swanson, the second is Stuart and Lori Swanson. Ron and Florine own 160 acres where they reside. They rent 750 acres in both 50/50 crop-share and cash rent arrangements.

Ron and Stuart farm together sharing labor and one line of equipment. They each own individual pieces of machinery with the goal of each owning a share of the total equipment base that is proportional to the acreage operated by each.

The Swanson farm is typical of many flat, fertile farms in north central Iowa. To reduce wind erosion, the Swansons were early adopters of mulch tillage, which they use in their corn-soybean rotation. On one of their rented farms they worked with the landlord to establish a permanent conservation area on a hilly field. They also re-established four acres of wetland working with the same landlord.

Ron and Florine were also early adopters of soil testing. They recognized the importance of controlling input costs by banding herbicides. In recent years, they have been using poultry manure as an alternative source of P and K. In 1996, they had 426 acres of corn and 420 acres of soybeans.

Florine and Ron Swanson

Ron and Florine have made many personal sacrifices while working for the good of agriculture as a whole. "There is more to production agriculture than just making money," notes Ron. "We also have a responsibility to help our industry."

Ron is currently on the Iowa Corn Promotion Board and is past chairman. He is a member of the U.S. Feed Grains Council as well as several other boards. Probably most noteworthy is the leadership Ron provided as president of the Iowa Corn Growers Association and research chairman of the National Corn Growers Association. He has been active in grain quality initiatives having served as chairman of the National Grain Quality Workshops. His efforts were directed at reducing the amount of foreign material in grain and promoting the concept of value enhanced grains.

Ron is currently on the board of the Farm Financial Standards Council. "The goal of this group is to standardize farm financial analysis reports so farmers can interact more easily with all agencies," explains Ron. In addition, Ron also serves on the board of Brenton Banks.

Florine is executive director of the Iowa 4-H Foundation where she has worked for 10 years for the benefit of Iowa's 4-H youth. Even though she grew up in a family of boys and had three of her own, she has always been an advocate for women. She served as state president of the American Association of University Women (AAUW), and is a board member of the National AAUW Education Foundation and board of Virginia Gildersleeve International Fund for Women.

Ron and Florine are active members of St. John's Catholic Church in Clarion.

IOWA MASTER FARMERS

~ Mid-March 1998

The Iowa Master Farmer award was established more than 70 years ago – in 1926. With the 1998 selections, only 374 Iowa farm families have received this prestigious honor.

This year we are also honoring an educator with the Iowa Master Farmer Exceptional Service Award. This award recognizes individuals who are not actively engaged in farming but who have made significant contributions to Iowa agriculture and helped individual farmers become more profitable.

Exceptional Service Award
Regis Voss
Story County

In his career as an Extension agronomist in Iowa (1964-1997), Regis Voss was the person in charge of nutrient recommendations for crops. He spoke at what must have been a couple thousand meetings and answered innumerable questions.

During that period, Voss undoubtedly was the most quoted person in Iowa and the entire Corn Belt on topics of soil testing, fertilizing and liming. "His suggestions and advice were always given with the goal of looking out for what was in the best interest of the farmer," says Garren Benson, an Iowa State University colleague who worked alongside Voss for many years.

Voss, who retired from his Extension position last July, has been selected to receive the Iowa Master Farmer Exceptional Service Award this year. *Wallaces Farmer* has presented Master Farmer awards to a number of Iowa farmers since 1926. But Voss is only the seventh person to be honored for exceptional service to farmers.

As the leader of ISU's Agronomy Extension staff for many years, Voss oversaw the crop subject matter content for all educational program activities of area and county Extension personnel. His leadership style was to be as helpful as possible and not to bring attention to himself. Authoring and co-authoring numerous Extension publications, papers and articles, Voss worked hard to make sure Iowa farmers were getting the best information. "He has a broad knowledge and practical understanding of Iowa agriculture and always worked well with disciplines outside his own area of expertise," says Benson.

Known to many farmers and fertilizer dealers as simply "Reg" or "Reggie," Voss is a humble person. "He is very deserving of this fine award," says John Pesek, who headed ISU's agronomy department for many years. "Reg has the reputation of being honest, loyal and a hard worker. In the 35 years I've known him, I can't name anyone who worked harder to make sure a job was done right."

Serving on various government, university and industry advisory committees over the years, Voss has also volunteered his time to professional agronomy organizations. He has supervised the advance degree work of graduate students, has done his own research in the field, and has worked in international activities in Argentina. He's won several professional awards and honors.

After receiving his bachelor's degree in agronomy from ISU in 1952, Voss put in a stint as a fighter pilot with the Air Force in the Korean War. He returned to ISU in 1956, where he completed his master's and doctorate. After two years with the Tennessee Valley Authority introducing new fertilizer options to farmers, Voss was hired at ISU. After he retired as Extension soil fertility specialist in mid-1997, he moved on to a new frontier in agriculture – precision farming. He's now working part-time for ISU, coordinating research on a precision farming project.

Voss and his wife Mardi grew up on farms in western Linn County near Cedar Rapids, Iowa. They still have family and farm ties to that area. They are active in church and community affairs in Ames, and are very devoted to their children and grandchildren. Regis has served as president of the Iowa Farm House Fraternity Alumni Board and was past chair of the Ames Kiwanis Agriculture Committee. Regis and Mardi have three grown children – Lori, John and David – and six grandchildren.

Pesek was Voss's major professor in the late 1950s and served as agronomy department chair for 26 years. Pesek says Voss has done an outstanding job serving Iowa farmers. "Reg was one of the first people to begin telling farmers that just because they needed a certain amount of fertilizer applied in the past didn't mean they still needed it," recalls Pesek. "Reg realized many farmers were putting on more fertilizer than was being used by the crop and he started speaking out."

Voss developed the Field Extension Education Laboratory (FEEL) on a research farm near the ISU campus. This outdoor lab gives ISU and private agronomists and crop consultants a chance to learn so they can give better advice to Iowa farmers regarding how to solve crop production problems.

"Regis Voss 'trained the trainers,'" says Kay Connelly, a former ISU crop specialist who now has a consulting firm at Cedar Falls, Iowa. "He taught us to provide the best possible help to farmers as they plan their soil fertility program in a way that is both profitable and environmentally sound."

David and Marlys Fisher
Hardin County

In the farm home of David and Marlys Fisher south of Hubbard, Iowa, hangs a framed black and white photo of David, his brother Bob and their father, Oswell Fisher. The photo was taken in 1958, and shows the three smiling farmers standing next to a white wooden barn, the typical kind of building hogs were raised in 40 years ago.

The person who shot that photo was none other than Neil Harl, now a well-known professor of economics and agricultural law at Iowa State University. Back then, Harl was a field editor on the *Wallaces Farmer* staff. He visited the Fisher farmstead to interview the family and take photos for an article on Oswell, who was named a Master Farmer, class of 1957. Oswell, now age 91, remembers that long-ago day of Harl's visit. "It was real muddy, just like today," Oswell said recently.

While Iowa still gets muddy in the early spring, plenty of other things

Mardi and Regis Voss

have changed in the farming business between 1958 and 1998, and the Fisher operation reflects the modern era. Now, David Fisher is a new Master Farmer.

David started farming in 1956 with his dad and brother. They farmed 480 acres, and farrowed sows in a converted barn that's still standing on the home place. Several years later, the partnership split, on friendly terms, and each son began to farm independently. Today, David and wife Marlys farm 1,050 acres. Their equipment is also used on an additional 480 acres farmed by an employee and a son-in-law. "We use conservation tillage, and typically plant 80% of our acreage to corn and 20% to soybeans," explains David. "The corn is in 30-inch rows and up until recently we've used a no-till drill for soybeans. In recent years we've been fine-tuning our use of swine manure to replace more of the commercial fertilizer."

About one-third of the crop ground is terraced and many grass waterways have been installed. David seeds some of the poorer land to oats, which provides a place to apply manure in the summer and build up that soil.

Hogs have been "hard work but rewarding" for the Fishers over the years. They have a 900-sow farrow-to-finish operation. Sows are bred and gestated in outside lots. Farrowing is in confinement, then pigs are moved to newer off-site nurseries on another farm. From the nurseries the pigs are finished in curtain-sided, fully-slatted finishing buildings.

Marketing over 15,000 hogs a year and farming all those acres is a lot of work. The Fishers get it done with the help of four full-time employees: Lon Smith, Rick Gustafson, Curtis Schwartz and Mike Nessa. A son-in-law, Paul Cook, has just taken over the finishing and will work into joint ownership.

David and Marlys use the Porkformance recordkeeping system. "It tracks each phase of production, from individual sow records to whole herd performance data," explains

Marlys and David Fisher

David. Accurate crop records are also maintained. A grain cart with a scale on it is used to check yields and evaluate variety and hybrid performance.

The employees have worked for the Fishers for a long time – starting in 1972, 1983, 1984 and 1986. "The longevity of David's employees speaks highly of what kind of a manager he is," says Ken Cook, a neighboring farmer.

How do you get and keep good help? "I've probably violated all the rules myself at one time or another," answers David. "You have to treat people with respect. The people we've hired are all capable of doing a lot of things. They are responsible and respected in the community.

"Communication is a key. If something isn't being done right, we talk to the employee individually, not as a group. You also have to pay a salary commensurate with what the employee could make working elsewhere in the community. And, we try to be flexible with our employees. They have family obligations, too."

Doug and Lynne Johnson
Jefferson County

Doug Johnson has wanted to farm ever since he was a small boy. He didn't even want to go to college, preferring instead to stay home and farm. But his parents strongly encouraged him and he enrolled in the farm operations curriculum at Iowa State University.

While in college he rented his grandmother's farm – 110 acres. After he earned his four-year degree from ISU he farmed in partnership with his father, Don, who was named a Master Farmer in 1959. That partnership has evolved into a farming corporation.

Today, Doug and Lynne operate more than 1,900 acres (about 1,600 tillable) northeast of Fairfield in Jefferson County. Some of the acreage they farm on their own, the rest is in the corporation. Part of that acreage has been owned by the Johnson family for 109 years.

The cropping program involves about 700 acres of corn, 700 acres of beans, 100 acres of small grains – oats and wheat – and 100 acres of hay. Around 250 acres of land are in pasture.

Cropping is mostly no-till. "We first no-tilled corn in 1979 and soybeans in the late 1980s," explains Doug. Last year, because the weather was cooler and wetter than normal, Doug tried to help warm the soil by tilling with a field cultivator. "After you've no-tilled a number of years, you start seeing a mat of corn and soybean residue," notes Doug.

The Johnsons are firm believers in soil conservation. In fact, they received the Southeast Iowa Regional Conservation Award for tiling and terraces they installed on their land -nearly four miles of terraces. "When there was a farm program, we'd try to set aside land where we could build terraces," says Doug. In the early 1980s, he bought a small dozer and a

Doug and Lynne Johnson

dirt scoop with a neighbor. "We built a lot of terraces that way," notes Doug. "It's his favorite thing to do," adds Lynne.

There are 12 farm ponds for water for livestock and erosion control. Some of these were built by Doug as well.

Doug and Lynne are willing to try new things to supplement income. For example, in the mid-1980s they planted one-half acre of raspberries. "It was a you-pick situation," explains Doug, "and it was very successful."

As for livestock enterprises, the beef herd consists of 45 cows. The Johnsons usually buy some calves in the spring to put on grass. Those are fed out on self-feeders in the fall. They also buy calves in the fall to go in the lots with home-raised calves.

The Johnsons, who will market about 4,500 head of hogs this year, are members of a far-rowing operative. Part of the reason was to have a supply of pigs for their new state-of-the-art 1,200-head hog finishing building, which was constructed last spring. "Finally, somebody looked at what the pigs want," says Lynne. "The pigs are so happy in this building. It's temperature-controlled. The hogs don't know if it is cold or hot outside."

One of the other key features is the ventilation stem. Gases are exhausted from under the floor. "Air comes in from the ceiling, down through the slats and is exhausted out using pit fans," explains Doug. Curtains on the north and south walls also help make the ventilation system work better.

The pit under the building is divided into

sections so the Johnsons are trying different odor control products. "We want to see what is best for the hogs and best for controlling odor when spreading," says Doug. "One product we are trying is used in the pit, the other is in the feed. So far, the one in the pit works the best."

Doug and Lynne have given their time unselfishly to their community. Lynne is on the board of the Rural Electric Cooperative and Doug has served on many boards, committees and organizations. "We are blessed with good employees," notes Doug. "That makes it possible for us to spend more time in off-farm activities."

The Johnsons, who are members of the First Lutheran Church, have three children. Eric, a senior at Fairfield High School, will go to ISU this fall. Jami is a sophomore and Kristofer is in the fourth grade.

Lucille Matthey
Woodbury County

The blue letters on her white sweatshirt spelled out the enthusiasm behind the smile. "Agriculture – can't live without it," read the slogan, which encircled the colorful farm scene.

And from the beginning of the conversation, it was clear this lady has no intention of leaving the profession which she and her husband dreamed about so long and that fate so abruptly left her alone to manage.

Lucille, she'd rather be called Lu, Matthey of Sergeant Bluff, Iowa, is a new Master Farmer, but she's been farming for 30 years. Since 1983, this energetic mother of seven and grandmother of 18, has been calling the shots. Her husband, Al, died of a heart attack that spring helping calve as a snowstorm raged. To farm was a goal they had shared and finally attained in 1967.

In the years before, Al became interested in flying while serving in the Air Force. He pursued that desire, taking private pilot lessons. Following his discharge, Al held several commercial aviation jobs, landing one as chief pilot for Terra Industries, Sioux City, Iowa. When Terra officials realized how much this couple and their seven children wanted to farm, they were hired to operate and manage the 1,800 acres which surround the agri-chemical company's plant.

Lu remains the farmer-manager. "There was never a doubt. I wanted to try to continue what we started 15 years before," she recalls. "Yes, of course, I had some apprehension. We were partners, we talked things over, but it was Al who ultimately made the production decisions."

She lived that first year a "minute at a time" and continues to follow that basic philosophy. Her family still provides a lot of support. Sons David and Mike, are professional pilots. They live nearby and when schedules permit, work around the farm.

Paul Iverson has been a full-time employee for five years. He gets a lot of credit for contributing to the operation's success. "I'm lucky to have him, he loves farming and can do just about anything," says Matthey.

While she helps in the field when needed, Matthey now considers her role as more of a manager/decision-maker, and unabashed promoter of agriculture.

Matthey's son, Bruce, helped her computerize the farm records in 1985. She does all the bookkeeping, tracking cash flow and making income and expense projections. A business plan is written in September and revised in February. "One change made this year was to temper our early excitement about Bt corn," she explains. "We backed off a little on the number of acres because of some concern about dry down. We'll run some of our own comparisons."

Matthey learns by observing, reading, attending meetings, visiting with other farmers and talking with experts. A friend describes her as a "serious student." She was quick to install a global positioning system (GPS) in a combine to collect data. Fields have been grid sampled and reams of historical information scrutinized to make production decisions.

GPS information has been used to alter seed corn populations between two different rates. A new system now being installed will allow the on-board computer to vary rates across the fields. Conservation tillage is used and a combination of preplant and post-emergence weed control chemicals are applied. Fertilizer rates are adjusted according to specific soil needs and yield expectations.

Lucille Matthey

A member of St. Joseph's Catholic Church in Salix, Iowa, her faith has been a big part of her life. A friend writes: "She walks the talk – believes and practices good citizenship. She's a 3-F person: family, farming and faith!"

Her family includes: Paula Matthey-Tott, lab technician, Sioux City, Iowa; Bruce Matthey, Terra Industries computer systems, Sioux City, Iowa; David Matthey, Great West Casualty pilot, Sioux City, Iowa; Mike Matthey, Terra Industries pilot, Sergeant Bluff; Phil Matthey, UPS pilot, Lansing, Mich; Anne Matthey-Mackey, artist, Alamo, Calif.; and Alison Matthey-Pigott, MCI Resources, San Ramon, Calif.

David and Marylu Watkins
Muscatine County

In order to be a successful dairyman, you have to concentrate on the cows. That's David and Marylu Watkins' philosophy regarding their business – Misty Vu Farms.

The couple owns 260 acres near Moscow, Iowa, in the north central part of Muscatine County. However, they only row-crop 160 acres– 100 acres is rented to a neighbor. "We just need enough land for feed," explains David. "We really spend our time on the cows, not the crops."

Dairying is in David's blood. He grew up on a dairy farm in the Bettendorf area. He and Marylu started farming in 1963 by renting land near Bettendorf. David also took over milking his father's cows. Later, that farm was sold due to urban sprawl. It is now a golf course. In 1969, they purchased 160 acres at their present location.

Today they milk 65 cows twice a day – at 4 a.m. and 4 p.m. Three-times-a-day milking was the norm until recently when David was elected to the county board of supervisors. He says cutting back to two times a day has trimmed production 10% to 12%. Production currently runs around 19,000 pounds of milk and 650 pounds of fat.

All replacement heifers are home-raised and artificial insemination is used for breeding. Heat detectors on the cow's tail head helps pinpoint cows in heat. It turns red when cows mount.

The Watkins utilize computerized feeding. Each cow wears a transponder tag. When she enters a feeder the computer reads her tag and drops only a portion of her daily ration. "It's programmed so she can get only one-fourth of her daily allotment of feed at each entry into the feeder," explains David. "The computer automatically gives us a daily printout indicating how much each cow is eating. It can help identify sick cows, etc.

"Feeding is pretty much automatic except for silage which takes a half hour to feed. Every day or so we have to push manure," says David.

That manure has helped trim their fertilizer bill. Fields are mapped for soil testing on 10-acre grids. "We know where to spread the manure. Other than anhydrous ammonia, we haven't had to buy commercial fertilizer for quite some time," says David.

Milking is done in an eight-stall herringbone parlor with a 3-inch low line. "The low line helps on udder health and speeds milk going into the line," explains David. He and Marylu do most of the milking, but sometimes get help from high school students.

All replacements are raised on the farm and bull calves are sold to area farmers. Cows are housed in a barn with 80 free stalls and an H-bunk feeder in the middle. All calves are raised in individual stalls until weaning. They are then grouped according to age or growth rate and moved to a Virginia style heifer barn.

The Watkins are optimistic about the dairy business. "There is still room for the smaller producer because he won't have the labor requirements," says David. "Larger producers will have to manage people, not cows. We like working with the cows. Once you get to 100 or more cows, you spend more time managing your help, and you don't get to spend time with the cows and get to know them."

Nevertheless the couple believe dairy expansion is needed. "We need to attract large dairies to Iowa and to show existing dairies how to expand," says Marylu. "That's important if we are going to keep milk processing in Iowa."

David and Marylu raised three children. Son Dwight is with Waukon State Bank. He and his wife Michelle have five children. Debora, a buyer for Von Maur, is married to Perry Hartman. Christopher, a banker with Central State Bank in Muscatine, and his wife, Rachel, have four children.

David and Marylu actually discouraged their own children from coming back home to farm. "Due to the lack of dairying in this area there isn't the support from suppliers such as milking equipment manufacturers, etc.," explains Marylu. But nearly 300 school children a year for the past 28 years have learned a lot about dairying by visiting the Watkins farm.

The Watkins are members of the First Presbyterian Church in Wilton, Iowa, and have been very active in a number of youth organizations.

David and Marylu Watkins

IOWA MASTER FARMERS
~
Mid-March 1999

Ken and Helen Fawcett
Cedar County

A strange twist of fate put Ken Fawcett on the road to a career as a successful family farmer. After graduating from Iowa State University in 1971, he enrolled in law school at the University of Iowa while his father and uncle ran the century farm near West Branch. But, an accident laid up his father and the young Fawcett came home to help harvest evenings and weekends.

While helping his uncle bring in the harvest, Fawcett realized he enjoyed farm work much more than law school. "I found I really didn't have much in common with the kids going to law school," remembers Fawcett.

Helen and Ken Fawcett

So he came home to take over the family farm. "I've never regretted that decision."

Today the operation, a family farm corporation, consists of about 1,200 acres of corn, soybeans and pasture. Fawcett's nephew, Kent Stuart, has been farming with him since 1980.

"My goal has never been to become the biggest farmer," says Fawcett. "Other goals, such as family, are more important."

Fawcett was immediately involved in management decisions as soon as he returned to the farm.

"We started no-till and minimum tillage right away," he says. "We were about 50% no-till and 50% minimum tillage in the early years," he says. Today, it's more like 85% no-till. "We have to till some of the heavier soils on the creek bottoms."

Soybeans are drilled in 15-inch rows into standing cornstalks and corn is planted in 36-inch rows into bean stubble. "We are still on 36-inch row corn because I like to side dress nitrogen and I can't do that very well on some slopes that are in narrow, 30-inch rows."

In 1994, Fawcett began mapping all of his fields according to soil type. The maps are on computer disk and are used to determine fertility needs. "I decided it was more useful to soil test and map according to soil type than a certain grid size," says Fawcett. "Using the yield monitor, we have found that yield is influenced more by soil type and moisture than a certain level of fertility.

"One thing precision farming is going to do is show areas of farms that, year in and year out, aren't very productive. These are areas we should concentrate on not cropping. Those areas might be better off in the Conservation Reserve Program (CRP) or something like that."

Fawcett, an Asgrow seed dealer since 1984, also uses test plots extensively. "I have test plots partly because of the seed business. But over the years, we've done a lot of testing of experimental herbicides, too," he notes.

He adds that the yield monitor, which he has had for three years, takes data from test plots to the next level. "I have seen varieties do well in the uniform dark soils in the test plot, but not do as well on the variable soils on the rest of the farm. I found two varieties that had similar yields in the test plots, but there was a 20 bushel per acre difference in yield on the more rolling ground."

Always a conservationist, Fawcett plans to plant around 8,000 trees this spring in riparian buffers on creek pastures. "We ran cows on these pastures for years, but with the government payment it made more sense to plant the riparian buffers," he explains. Roundup was sprayed in strips last fall to burn down the sod where trees will be planted. The strips will be seven rows of trees and switchgrass. Around 25 acres of former pasture will be converted to riparian buffers.

In another project, Fawcett converted a gully to a recreational pond. "It was a waterway that always washed out close to the creek," he explains. "For years we battled that gully. Finally, we put in a grade stabilization structure, which created a pond." He also put land around the pond into the CRP and planted around 4 acres of trees.

Ken and Helen haven't limited their activities to farm and family by any means. Both are active in many community activities. There isn't space here to list them all, but among other things, Fawcett has been active in the Extension Council, Farm Bureau, Lions Club, Township Trustees, West Branch State Bank board and the Hoover Presidential Library Association. On the Hoover Library Association board, he was the prime mover in developing a scholarship program called the Uncommon Student. These $5,000 scholarships are offered to Iowa students who demonstrate unique talent and organizational skills.

Fawcett helped initiate the Southeast Iowa Research Farm at Crawfordsville. He has been a member of the Iowa Farm Business Association since 1973.

The Fawcetts have two children. Leanna is a sophomore at Northwestern University in Evanston, Ill., and Thomas is in high school. They are members of West Branch Conservative Meeting of Friends (Quaker Church). Helen runs a floral design business out of their home.

Curt and Carol Raasch
Sac County

Spend a day with Curt and Carol Raasch and family of Odebolt in western Iowa, and you come away with a clearer view of who will be farming in the next millennium. This couple has worked diligently to help their sons return to production agriculture. They weathered the farm financial crisis of the 1980s, put three sons through Iowa State University, and now have three sons farming with them. Their fourth son is a junior in high school.

Son Mark, age 30, is married and works with ACServices Inc., a field mapping, crop scouting and consulting business located at nearby Arthur, Iowa. The Raasch family was gathering and using "precision farming" information long before global positioning systems (GPS) came on the scene. In 1988, Curt and Carol and another farmer, Neil Pullen, started ACServices. In the past 10 years, over 400 clients have also seen the need for accurate field information.

Son Greg, age 28, manages Raasch Beef, Inc., a custom feedlot near the home farm. Besides custom feeding cattle, Curt buys feeder cattle. About 2,000 head of cattle move through the feedlot annually.

The family had a farrow-to-finish operation, marketing 1,000 hogs per year, but the old farrowing barn and equipment needed extensive repair. Curt decided to sell the sows in early 1998. He's now looking into the possibility of "networking" with another producer or investing with owners of a newer facility.

Son Scott, age 25, assistant manager for Raasch Beef, helps with crop farming and keeps equipment maintained and repaired. Jeff Raasch, age 16, also helps and will likely return to the farm after finishing high school and college. Presently, all labor is family labor. "We like to farm, and there's plenty to keep us busy," says Carol, who teaches Spanish at Odebolt-Arthur High School.

Each family member has access to computers, including one in the feedyard office. Some

Curt and Carol Raasch

are laptops for portable recordkeeping. The bookkeeping is "in-house" and computerized. All feed and grain is weighed. Extensive field records are kept–maps, crop scouting reports, soil test results, chemicals used, yields and plans for the coming year. Livestock records detail feed use, efficiencies, average daily gains, projected weights, costs of gain and breakeven prices. "Records are an important part of risk management," says Curt. "With tight margins in agriculture, it's extremely important to know whether you are getting a 3- or 3.2-pound gain, for example."

With a bachelor's degree from ISU in 1966,

Curt taught high school vo-ag at Boone, Iowa. In 1971, he rented a piece of land near Odebolt, his hometown. Sharing machinery with his father, Curt began farming. Curt and Carol now own 281 acres, rent 270 acres and farm another 610 rented acres with Curt's brother, Bruce. "We work closely as brothers," notes Curt. "We're fortunate our families work together well. One thing that's difficult about receiving this Master Farmer award is, why should I be recognized when I've farmed with Bruce for 28 years? Bruce and his family deserve recognition for their accomplishments, too."

Curt has served on the school board and as a 4-H leader. Active in the First Presbyterian Church of Odebolt, Curt has held county offices for Farm Bureau and the Cattlemen's Association. He was on the Iowa Soybean Promotion Board from 1985 to 1991. He's served on Iowa Soybean Association and American Soybean Association committees. In 1997, Curt was appointed to the United Soybean Board (USB) and is on USB's International Marketing Committee.

Carol also volunteers her time for community activities. Sharing their home with foreign visitors, the Raasches have hosted students and farmers from Venezuela, Ukraine and Germany. "World relationships are important as we look beyond the year 2000," says Curt. "We can learn a lot from each other in this global economy."

"Concerned about the future of agriculture and young people making a living on the farm, Curt has helped his children get involved in farming and helped them stay in the local area," says Roger Jensen, ISU Extension director in Sac County. Curt worked closely with his lender, Bob Butcher of American National Bank at Holstein, Iowa, planning the future farming structure for the family.

"Curt is genuinely interested in youth and the promise which a progressive ag community can hold for them, and the world which needs the food they can produce," says Charles Bulger, the Raaschs' pastor. "Curt and Carol are considerate of the opinion of others, willing to listen. They desire to move their community toward as fine a tomorrow as possible."

John and Beverly Schultz
Allamakee County

As he shows visitors around his farm, it is obvious John Schultz is proud of his conservation efforts. The soft-spoken farmer points out the grass backed terraces and strip cropping on his farm near Postville in northeast Iowa.

Schultz started farming in partnership with his father upon graduation from Iowa State University in 1960. The farming operation was a diversified dairy, beef, hog and crop farm with farrowing four times a year. In 1972, John and his wife Janice purchased their first land, a 200-acre farm.

Janice passed away in 1994. She was an integral part of the operation and was very active in the community, especially in school and church activities. Since her death John has cut back his involvement in the day-to-day operation of the farm. He now rents out the 425 acres of cropland on a 50-50 crop-share lease. He still insists, however, that the tenant continue to use strip cropping on the steeper slopes, a practice he started in the 1960s.

Soil conservation has always been a high priority for Schultz. No-till, terraces, grass

waterways, windbreaks and contour cropping are examples. In the early 1970s, Schultz signed a 10-year agreement with the government to build terraces on his farm. "Most of the more than 200 acres of terraces on this farm were constructed under that plan," he explains.

At one time Schultz bought feeder cattle at 500-600 pounds for finishing and had a cow-calf herd of around 70 head. He also custom fed Holstein dairy heifers. Now, the pastureland (about 120 acres) and feed storage facilities are leased to others for raising cattle.

Recently, they discontinued farrowing and

Beverly and John Schultz

began buying feeder pigs and finishing them. The hogs are finished in a naturally ventilated confinement facility.

Promoting soil conservation has been the hallmark of Schultz's community activities. He was elected a commissioner in the Allamakee County Soil and Water Conservation District in 1986 and still serves in that capacity.

Schultz was also elected treasurer of Resource Conservation and Development for Northeast Iowa, Inc., in 1987 and still holds that office.

He also serves on an advisory board for

the Northeast Iowa Demonstration Project. "John identified the need in 1992 to demonstrate crop residue management using various tillage systems options in operating tillage equipment. He hosted a spring field day and followed through to harvest to obtain yield data. He was also among the first to enroll his farm in the project-sponsored Integrated Crop Management program," says John Rodecap, project coordinator, Northeast Iowa Demonstration Project.

Schultz serves on the advisory board for the Hickory Creek Watershed – a trout stream in southern Allamakee and northern Clayton counties. He has received many soil conservation awards over the years including the Goodyear Conservation Award and the Iowa Soil Conservation Award.

Schultz has been on the board of directors of the Postville State Bank since 1977. In the early 1980s, he served on the board to develop the Allamakee Zoning Ordinance and stayed in that position until he became a district soil commissioner in 1986.

Church is a big part of Schultz's life, too. As an active member of the Community Presbyterian Church, Schultz is an elder and sings in the choir. "John Schultz is a master of life," says the Rev. Gary Catterson, pastor. "He knows the importance of faith, family and caring for God's creation. John is not merely involved with farming, he is involved with his community."

John and Janice raised four children. Kent, who works for Purina Mills, lives in Waverly with his wife Karen.

Deanna lives in Waverly and teaches at Waverly Shell Rock High School.

Margaret is married to Todd Barker and they live in Lenox, Iowa. Margaret is a homemaker and helps out at Barker Implement.

Kirk and his wife Nancy live in Urbandale. Kirk works for CDS in Des Moines.

Last September, Schultz remarried. He and his wife, Beverly, spend much of their time "keeping up with the activities of their grandchildren, participating in church activities and going to board meetings," he quips.

J. Kelly and Irene Tobin
Taylor County

J. Kelly Tobin grew up on his parent's farm near Burlington Junction, Mo. When Kelly was 18, his father died. He and his brothers took over many of the farm management responsibilities. He began farming on his own by renting land near the home farm.

J. Kelly and Irene realized their dream of owning their own farm when they purchased their present farm in 1968 near New Market, Iowa.

When the Tobins' four sons were at home, they provided much of the labor needed. Most of the farm work is now done by J. Kelly with part-time help as needed. In the early 1980s, son Kevin helped full-time which allowed J. Kelly to pursue his dream of earning a college degree.

The Tobins have a corn-soybean rotation on around 500 acres. He was one of the first in Taylor County to use no-till in the early 1980s. Most of the hilly ground is enrolled in the Conservation Reserve Program, some of which is seeded to switchgrass. The farm is completely no-till and Tobin actively encourages others to adopt this practice.

Always looking for ways to cut costs, Tobin has been using Roundup Ready soybeans to save labor and herbicide costs.

Tobin has been an innovator in the use of new ground cover and different types of terraces (broad base, narrow base and bench). He has aggressively tiled and terraced the farm to increase productivity and control erosion. He was one of the first to build bench terraces with tile inlets back in the 1960s.

More than 16,000 trees have been planted on land taken out of production due to its erodibility. All eligible acres have been enrolled in the riparian buffer program.

Tobin has always said he wants to leave the farm in better shape than he found it. "We feel we've improved the farm land structurally and environmentally for the next generation to take over," he says.

The Tobin farm has served as a demonstration farm for no-till, new recordkeeping systems and new grassed waterway to control erosion. Records are kept through the Southwest Iowa Farm Business Association, which Tobin helped found.

The Tobins raised both hogs and cattle until the mid-1980s. As the sons went to college and careers and the economics of farming and livestock changed, the hogs and then later the cow herd were phased out. Before that, the Tobins had a farrow-to-finish swine herd and a cow-

Irene and J. Kelly Tobin

calf operation with 80-100 crossbred cows.

In 1986 while Tobin was finishing his classes to graduate from Iowa State University in ag studies, he started working with Hertz Farm Management as a licensed real estate salesman in southwest Iowa. Since then he has continued with Hertz as an independent contractor specializing in farm management, farm real estate sales and farm appraisal.

Tobin has been a long-time district commissioner for the Taylor County Soil Con-

servation District and served as president of the Iowa Soil Conservation District Commissioners. He has served on numerous boards including trustee of Iowa State University Agricultural Foundation, Southwest Iowa Farm Business Association, Iowa Barn Foundation, Taylor County Extension Council and others.

Irene's service to the community includes more than 25 years teaching at New Market Community School. She taught home economics and served as school librarian.

J. Kelly and Irene are members of the St. Clare Catholic Church in Clarinda. J. Kelly is a lector and Eucharistic minister and has served as a parish council member and trustee. Irene is active in the Altar and Rosary Society.

"The most important commodity a farm family produces is their family and what they give back to the community in which they live," wrote Florine Swanson, executive director of the Iowa 4-H Foundation, in her letter of support for the Tobin nomination. "The epitome of that success is exemplified by J. Kelly and Irene Tobin."

Neil Harl, ISU professor of economics, also wrote, "As is often the case with farm families, their most important 'crop' is their family. J. Kelly and Irene Tobin have made an enormous contribution to the world through their family."

The Tobins have four sons. Jim is with Monsanto Co., in St. Louis, Mo. He and his wife Gina have three children.

Terry is with Principal Financial Group in Des Moines. He and his wife Maureen have three children.

Kevin is a project director with Catholic Relief Services in the Congo in Africa.

Bernie is with Eli Lilly Co., in Indianapolis, Ind. He and his wife Lisa have three children.

CHAPTER 8
~
2000 - 2007:
The New Millennium

The new millennium started with a jolt that shook biotechnology to its roots.

In 2000, farmers planted bioengineered StarLink corn on just 352,000 acres, representing a mere 0.5% of the U.S. corn crop. StarLink corn was supposed to be used strictly for animal feed or industrial use. Unfortunately, some slipped into the food chain ending up in taco shells. A few consumers had allergic reactions. StarLink developer, Aventis CropScience, eventually paid a very high price to Iowa farmers and elevators in premiums and compensation for losses tied to growing and handling StarLink.

StarLink brought several messages:

* Biotechnology companies must check and recheck safety issues of their products.

* Consumers are more aware and increasingly vocal on issues they see as food safety.

* Farmers have crucial roles in safeguarding food supplies.

Meanwhile seed companies began introducing stacked biotech traits--weed resistance, corn rootworm resistance and drought resistance in one plant. Researchers began hinting that 300 bushel U.S. average corn yields might be within reach.

Ethanol boom

The attacks on New York's World Trade Center and Washington's Pentagon on Sept. 11, 2001 launched the world wide war on terror. The ensuing groundswell for energy security amplified farmers' efforts to promote ethanol as an environmentally-friendly fuel additive. One result was political mandates to replace an increasing amount of imported oil with biofuels.

The number of plants producing fuel ethanol from corn in Iowa ballooned to 51 in 2006. Ethanol soaked up more than 2.1 billion bushels or 20% of the 2006 corn crop. In 2004, 2005 and 2006 ethanol demand drew down corn stocks despite big crops.

Autumn 2006 prospects for short Southern Hemisphere crops launched a corn price rally reminiscent of the early 1970s grain export boom. Crop income prospects soared, launching an upward surge in land values and cash rents also reminiscent of the grain export boom.

Competition for food

The United Nations estimated that world food production would need to double by 2050. Social advocates argued that devoting a greater proportion of crops to fuel would hike food prices. Higher global food prices would impact people in less-developed countries far more than people in the developed world who can more easily adapt to higher prices.

Policymakers rapidly realized ethanol from corn alone could not bring energy security. They pushed for research for a wider range of feedstocks and a wider range of bioenergy products.

Bioenergy industry participants sought technological breakthroughs. They favored letting the market spur extraordinary innovation that would bring significant improvements in yields, product quality, in cost to consumers and in the quality of life. In short, they believed new technologies, plus better yields, could produce more food and more fuel not just here, but throughout the world.

Understanding relationships and trade-offs

In mid 2006, $2 corn and crude oil rising to $70 a barrel made ethanol economics extremely attractive. All types of investors raced to grab a share. Almost daily someone announced plans for new and expanded ethanol capacity.

But as corn hit $4 and crude oil prices sagged to the low $50s, the economics changed. Suddenly the picture became far less attractive to those seeking quick returns, as well as those who were unprepared or unwilling to be part of what essentially is a commodity business subject to market-driven highs and lows.

Where to from here?

"We do not know if the ethanol boom can lift U.S. agriculture to a new level of prosperity as some farmers expected during the grain export boom of the 1970s," says John Otte, *Wallaces Farmer* Economics Editor. "Some, as yet unforeseen, force may trigger an income bust such as precipitated the financial crisis in the 1980s."

However, certain things are clear, according to Otte.

*When farmers see new demand they have a long-established track record of being able to gear up production to meet the need, and then some.

*Farmers also have a long track record of bidding most, often all, of their profits into prices of fixed resources—land values and cash rents.

"Most importantly, farmers are innovative resilient entrepreneurs. Those who correctly evaluate opportunities, get in the proper position at the proper time, produce the right products and do it as efficiently as possible will reap handsome profits."

2000 Iowa Farm Facts

FARMS & INCOME

Number of Iowa farms	94,000
Crop production value	$4.9 billion
Livestock production value	$5.8 billion
Iowa net farm income	$2.4 billion

LIVESTOCK

	Inventory	Average price
Cattle and calves	3.7 million head	$69.20/cwt (beef)
Hogs and pigs	15.1 million head	$45.05/cwt
	Production	Inventory
Chickens (Layers)	7.8 billion eggs	28.9 million birds
Milk	3.9 billion lbs.	

CROPS

	Harvested acres	Yield	Production	Avg price
All Hay	1.7 million	3.55 tons/acre	6.1 million tons	$82.00/ton
Corn	12 million	144 bu./acre	1.7 billion bu.	$1.75/bu.
Soybeans	10.7 million	43.5 bu./acre	465 million bu.	$4.49/bu.
Oats	180,000	67 bu./acre	12.1 million bu.	$1.19/bu.
Wheat	18,000	47 bu./acre	846,000 bu.	$2.15/bu.

IOWA MASTER FARMERS
~
Mid-March 2000

Dave and Theresa Anton
Larry and Judy Anton
Black Hawk County

At their year-end family meeting last December, Larry and Dave Anton and their wives sat down with the brothers' parents, Irving and Thelma, plus their accountant. They discussed plans for next year and determined employee wages and bonuses. It's a meeting the family has held annually since they all started farming together more than 30 years ago.

The brothers are the fifth generation of Antons to farm near LaPorte City. Today the family farms 1,500 acres in a well-managed cattle and grain operation. In addition to two employees, Dave's wife, Theresa, and Larry's wife, Judy, help with planting and harvest.

Cattle feeding is the Antons' forte. The corn crop is used to feed out about 1,400 to 1,800 head of feeder calves from Idaho and Montana which are marketed April through June each year.

Both men are recognized throughout the Iowa beef industry as dedicated leaders. Dave and Larry have held many offices in the Black Hawk County Cattlemen's Association. Larry has served at the state and national level, too.

"Dave and Larry and their wives epitomize progressive family farmers through their adaptability to change, their involvement in developing agricultural policies and their ability to communicate information about agriculture to our growing urban population," says Carol Balvanz of Hubbard.

"I've called on Larry and Judy often to take media calls from reporters and they've fielded interviews on everything from PETA to LDPs. They're true farm spokespersons and always do a great job," adds Balvanz.

Both Dave and Larry have a long resume of active service to farm and community organizations. For 16 years, Dave was on the board of directors at Members Mutual Oil Co.

"Dave is honest and open with his

Dave and Theresa Anton (left) and Judy and Larry Anton

viewpoints, supporting our local cooperative and helping to make executive decisions. Dave always balanced his good common sense with progressive ideas for change in the co-op," says Kurt Raymond of Waterloo.

Although none of their children are currently farming with them, the Antons are devoted to their families. They always take time for family events and reunions. Like their parents, all the children have college degrees. David and Theresa's two sons, Steven and Mark, both work for John Deere. Larry and Judy's three children, Brian, Nancy and Paul, have careers in music, teaching, and banking, respectively.

The Antons are highly regarded in the community for their work ethic and high ideals. "They work well together, each one carrying out his/her responsibilities to make their farm efficient and successful. They are also supportive of the needs of the area, volunteering their time and talents," says Thomas Zeleny of LaPorte City.

The Antons have all given hundreds of hours to the 4-H program. As a past superintendent of the beef department, Dave is involved with annual weigh-ins and the 4-H beef show. Anton Farms has also donated funding for an annual scholarship in honor of Ron Borton, a retired vocational ag instructor.

As a college student, Larry traveled to France through the International Farm Youth Exchange. As a result of that experience, the Antons have hosted many students/delegates as visitors and for work experience.

Their dedication to farming and family, church and community has touched many people through the years. The Antons are respected for their insightful wisdom and "hands-on" willingness to work on projects and see them through to the end.

Their involvement in promoting their industry and educating the public is highly commendable, adds Jeff Meyers of Waterloo. "They truly represent the farming profession in an honorable manner."

Craig and LaVon Griffieon
Polk County

It's easy to understand why Craig and LaVon Griffieon are concerned about urban sprawl if you simply look south from their cattle feedlots. Just one and a half miles away, a sea of homes is steadily creeping toward their farm.

Not long ago their Polk County farm was a "comfortable" three miles from the city limits of fast-growing Ankeny. They are three-quarters of a mile from the city limits now. A recent annexation proposal threatened to bring the city limits right across the road.

Urban sprawl is threatening ag land in many areas of the state. But this unique couple isn't taking it sitting on the back porch. LaVon was a prime mover in organizing a group called "1000 Friends of Iowa," which has taken on the battle of conserving Iowa's prime farmland against urban sprawl. In the last two years, she has presented more than 65 programs in 53 counties across Iowa on land use and urban sprawl.

The big gun in the Griffieons' arsenal is education. Over the past 12 years, Craig and LaVon have introduced agricultural literacy into Polk County classrooms by providing educational materials and by sponsoring tours on their farm for rural and urban youth.

More than 10,000 school children have toured their farm.

Both Craig and LaVon are ready at a moment's notice to receive international visitors or to be interviewed by local, state, and national news media on current ag issues.

Craig, who started farming with his father in 1972, is the fourth generation of their family to live in the farm home. LaVon grew up on 80 acres in northwest Iowa near Spirit Lake.

The couple gradually purchased and rented more land. Today they operate around 1,200 acres. It's a corn-soybean rotation with oats and hay. Seed corn and seed bean contracts have helped even out the cash flow for many years. Craig is also a Golden Harvest

Craig and LaVon Griffieon

seed dealer.

At least half of the commercial corn acres are planted no-till. The rest of the corn and soybean ground is chiseled in the fall and field cultivated in the spring, prior to planting.

Sludge from the waste water treatment plant in Ankeny is used to boost soil nutrients and trim fertilizer costs.

The Griffieons manage a cow-calf herd of 35 to 40 head. Herd genetics has been improved through artificial insemination. Calves are fed out with others purchased from area producers. Breeding cattle are kept on pasture and rotated between paddocks.

As part of their effort to educate school children, foreign visitors and urban adults about farm life, and as 4-H projects, the Griffieons keep a diverse selection of other animals including free-range chickens (broilers and layers), a horse, a pony, beef calves, lambs, pigs, a bunny, dogs and many cats.

Craig and LaVon's day doesn't end at sundown. Among other things, Craig has been active in Farm Bureau and the Polk County Cattlemen's Association.

LaVon has been an assistant commis-sioner with the Polk Soil and Water Conservation District for seven years, Polk County Farm Bureau Women's chair, secretary of the board of the Wallace House Foundation, president of 1000 Friends of Iowa and is a religious education teacher at Our Lady's Immaculate Catholic Church.

Along with their heavy civic, social and farm workload, the Griffieons are raising four children: Autumn, 16; Nick, 13; Phillip, 9; and Julia, 7.

Barbara Hug, ISU Polk County Extension, sums it up well. "A master farmer is more than making a profit in the business, it's also about being a positive and contributing member of the community. Craig and LaVon do this as well and perhaps better than anyone I know."

Ron and Judy Kielkopf
Keokuk County

Raising hogs and renting 120 acres, Ron Kielkopf started farming in 1959. Judy Kielkopf worked for a local doctor. Whatever success they have today came by adapting to changes that have take place in agriculture.

The livestock are gone now and the Kielkopf family farms around 2,000 acres, mostly no-till. They own 560 acres and rent the rest. The operation, near Fremont in southeast Iowa, is set up as a "C" corporation with their two sons, John and Todd.

John lives nearby with his wife, Lori, and young son. He owns part of the machinery and operates 400 acres under his own name. Todd and wife Ann and daughters reside in Indianola. Todd has an advanced degree in finance and is involved in financial decisions of the farm corporation.

Reflecting on changes over the years, Ron

observes, "What we believed to be fact becomes nothing but a paradigm, something that was fact only because we had limited knowledge. In the 1950s, we had to plow. In the '60s, we had to disk. In the '70s, we had to chisel. In agriculture, everything will continue to change except the need to constantly try to identify what is true at this given moment in economics and technology."

When the 1980s farm crisis hit, Ron and Judy had just bought their first 80 acres and built a new home. Not good timing. They adjusted to agriculture's tough times by sharpening their management. Seed corn replaced the livestock enterprises. Today, they grow some identity-preserved corn and seed beans and use risk-management tools. Almost all of the acres are genetically modified crops. Ron stays involved in dialogue with the buyers of his grain about this issue.

When he exited the livestock, Ron was in his 40s. He became a part-time student in accounting, computers and business at Indian Hills Community College and took courses in agronomy at Iowa State University (ISU). He attended seminars "to become comfortable using futures as a marketing tool."

ISU Extension remains helpful in keeping his family attuned to the changes in farming. For 30 years, he's kept records with the Iowa Farm Business Association. Ron's grandfather helped him build a desk 35 years ago. It has been the most important piece of equipment he has ever owned.

The family contributes to the community. Ron served on the Hedrick Savings Bank and Ottumwa Regional Hospital boards and is now on the boards of ISU's Southeast Iowa Research Farm and local senior citizen housing. Rotary, Iowa Corn Growers and the Methodist church have benefited from his time and support.

The Kielkopfs have hosted farmer groups from several countries and lasting friendships have resulted. Ron participated in a trade mission to China and last spring went to the Cer-rados in Brazil. He feels strongly that American producers have a poor understanding of our competitors. Having seen soils on four continents makes him feel that one of the nicest things God ever did for the Iowa farmer is the gift of beautiful dirt.

The Keokuk County Soil and Water Conservation District has recognized this family's stewardship of the land. Ron began no-tilling corn in the 1980s, bought a no-till soybean drill in 1992 and credits successful no-tillers for showing him how to make no-till work. He's convinced that slow-starting no-till crops may not look so good in June, but do protect the soil and improve the bottom line.

"Landlords in this area of tight land recognize Ron's farming ability and his personal integrity," says his banker, Robert Helgerson. "He has an inquisitive mind, is knowledge-

Judy and Ron Kielkopf

able about trends and is willing to share his talent to benefit others."

Ron and Judy's love of nature has made vacation adventurous. They enjoy downhill and cross-county skiing as well as snowshoeing. "We rode in a hot air balloon on our 25th wedding anniversary," Judy recalls. "Ron skydived on his 50th birthday. We've canoed, kayaked, biked, hiked and enjoy golfing."

Tom and Elsie Ryan
Winneshiek County

Tom Ryan is a great example of the old adage, "Actions speak louder than words."

From the neat and organized farmsteads to the contoured, residue-covered crop fields, the Ryan farm is an excellent model of a successful family operation. And, despite long days spent farming, Tom has always made time to help his neighbors and community.

Tom and his wife, Elsie (nee Schnur from Colo), have farmed southeast of Cresco for 46 years. Starting with 160 acres of rented ground in 1954, they milked cows and steadily increased the size of their operation. Today they own 800 acres and raise corn, soybeans, beef cattle and hogs.

Tom is an innovator, eager to assess new technology and put it to good use on the farm. He has always measured results of yield and conservation efforts on his cropland. In 1984, Tom was one of the first in his area to develop a soil-saving system of waterways and contour farming. A yield monitor was added to the combine in the mid-1980s and the 1990s ushered in a global positioning system.

Tom adopted production testing and artificial insemination (AI) in his dairy herd. In 1961, Tom's herd was the first to surpass the 500-pound annual butterfat production level in Winneshiek County. He gave up the dairy cows in the late 1970s as the crop operation expanded, but he continued with livestock innovations.

Started in the 1960s and now about 100 head of cows, the beef herd was improved

with AI, estrus synchronization, progeny testing and carcass data collection. His swine operation has also evolved, adopting techniques such as segregated early weaning, marketing through a cooperative network and high-quality genetics.

The Ryans raised four children and remain a close-knit family. Sons Roger and Jeff farm with their folks. Daughters are Roxann Ryan, Des Moines, an assistant attorney general, and Jean Gehling, Cresco, a computer network administrator.

Education has always been a vital part of their family life. After years of working on the farm as "Superintendent of Farrowing," Elsie now enjoys substitute teaching in area schools. She and Tom encouraged all their children to attend college. They continue to participate in Extension and other educational opportunities, seeking new ideas to bring back to the farm.

The Ryans readily share their knowledge and farming lifestyle with others. They volunteer on community boards and organization representing farming interests and they have taken the time to explain agriculture to people from urban areas.

"Before we visited the Ryan farm, I had no concept of a working farm. During their busiest time of the year for a farmer, Tom and his family took us individually for a ride in the combine and explained their farming operation to us. We experienced a working livestock farm.

"What struck me most about Tom was the love he has for farming. He is wise and resourceful, and enjoys farming beyond all measure. Because of my weekend on the Ryan farm, I have tremendous respect for the American farmer, and the Ryans, in particular," says Martha Boesen of Des Moines.

A tall, quiet man, Tom is sought often for his well-considered opinions and advice. He's been on the Farm Service Agency (FSA) county committee for many years, currently serving as chairman.

"Tom Ryan is a recognized community

Elsie and Tom Ryan

leader. His stabilizing influence over many years on the FSA board led to his being sought out for appointment to the Board of Adjustment where his calm judgment and leadership were needed to inaugurate – and instill public confidence in – the recently adopted, and contentious, county zoning process. His sense of fair play parallels his excellent judgment," says Dean Darling, Winneshiek County supervisor.

Tom's service includes committee work to pass two school bond issues. He was also president of the Cresco Industrial Development Corp. Tom is also an active member of the Service Corps of Retired Executives Association (SCORE).

Exceptional Service Award
Neil Harl
Story County

Neil Harl grew up on his parents' farm near Seymour in Appanoose County. His hope after high school was to farm. Fortunately, for farmers the world over, that didn't work out.

There is no doubt he has contributed more to agriculture behind a desk and in front of a microphone than he ever could have from a tractor seat. Because of the expertise he has developed in production agriculture, estate planning and tax law, probably no one individual has done as much to help farmers the world over.

When it became apparent he wasn't going to be able to farm, Harl enrolled at Iowa State University. After graduating with honors, he earned a commission in the Army Reserve. After two years of active duty, he enrolled in the Law School at the University of Iowa (U of I) with an emphasis in ag law. After graduating from the U of I, he returned to ISU to earn a doctorate degree in ag economics.

Harl even found time for a stint as a field editor at *Wallaces Farmer* in the late 1950s. He hasn't stopped writing since. His many publications and articles further accentuate this great communicator's stature.

Harl's writings include 21 books, more than 300 professional articles and bulletins, and more than 750 articles in farm and financial publications. He is the author of the 15-volume treatise, "Agricultural Law," as well as "The Agricultural Law Manual" and "The Farm Debt Crisis of the 1980s." He is co-author of "Principles of Agricultural Law" with Roger McEowen, an associate professor of law at Kansas State University.

It was the farm financial crisis of the 1980s that propelled Harl to national prominence. "Dr. Harl has the unique ability to spot problems before they develop by understanding and thinking through the implications of court decisions, IRS rulings and congressional policy as applied to the agricultural sector," writes McEowen, in support of Harl's nomination.

"His efforts with respect to shaping federal tax and farm policy in the 1980s led to the creation of Chapter 12 Bankruptcy which helped keep a large number of farm families on the farm. The impact of this legislation on rural communities is immeasurable," continues McEowen.

The list of Harl's honors (academic or related), organization membership and activities, state, regional and national committees, publications, videos, etc., is unending. In addition, he has lectured all over the world. He is the most sought after expert on agriculture by lawmakers.

"Dr. Harl is a tireless worker. His level of publications is unmatched. He has the ability to write technical academic articles as well as pieces directed to a lay audience. Attorneys, tax practitioners, as well as farmers know they can contact Dr. Harl with a question any time. He is always willing to assist others in any way he can with their legal, tax or economic problems," added McEowen.

Even in semi-retirement, Harl continues to write and lecture about current concerns in ag-

riculture – concentration in seed companies, contracting, the GMO controversy and vertical integration.

With all that, Harl's early and continuing love for the land is still apparent. He and his wife Darlene own 640 acres in Appanoose County. Forty acres have been in the family since 1863.

And just because he hasn't made his contribution to agriculture from a tractor seat doesn't mean he doesn't like them. "A few years ago when we visited the Harls at their home in Ames, we noticed the family car parked in the driveway," says Dave Kalsem, Huxley. "After the greeting, Harl asked if we would like to see what was in the garage. There was a beautifully restored John Deere tractor that had taken over the car's stall."

Neil Harl, at 66, is gradually phasing into retirement from ISU, where he has been a professor since 1964. But, it is doubtful he will fade into obscurity. This man is too dedicated, too energetic and too devoted to sit idly by and not help his fellow farmers.

The Harls have two sons, Brent and Rod.

Neil Harl

2001 IOWA MASTER FARMERS

~
Second March 2001

Dean and Sandra Amstutz
Davis County

He's described as a mechanic, carpenter, livestock man and general jack-of-all-trades. There doesn't seem to be anything Dean Amstutz is afraid to tackle. Modifying field equipment, erecting his farm buildings, remodeling the church building and organizing a farrowing co-op are just a few examples.

Dean started farming in 1966 when he purchased 180 acres. In 1972, he purchased another 280 acres and married Sandra. Shortly after they were married, the couple rented the entire farm to Dean's brother Keith and left for two years to do mission work on the Amazon River. When they returned in 1975 they bought more land, rented additional acres and have seriously pursued a farming career southeast of Bloomfield in Davis County ever since.

Today they manage more than 1,300 acres, market 5,000 head of hogs per year and maintain an 80-head beef cow herd. It's a corn-soybean rotation with some hay on areas susceptible to erosion. Dean and Keith have continued to farm together but each owns his own land. "We own all the major machinery together except we each have our own tractors," explains Dean. "We work together during the row-crop season but as soon as it's over, we each do our own thing with livestock, farmstead improvements, whatever."

Dean and Sandra incorporated in 1992 as Dean and Sandra Inc. Farmland is owned by the couple and leased to the corporation. "It has worked well, but you have to have a good accountant," notes Dean. Incorporation is one of the things that has helped give the Amstutzes financial independence and a strong equity position. But, more important perhaps is their philosophy: Pay cash! "We observed some of the problems farmers had with lenders in the early 1980s," explains Dean. "We haven't borrowed any money since 1983."

Conservation plays a major role in the total operation. Dean and Keith own a bulldozer, dirt scraper, tiling machine and back-

Sandra and Dean Amstutz

hoe. This past November, they installed more than a mile of terraces with 22 tile inlets. Other conservation practices include some no-till, minimum tillage, erosion-control structures or just a crop rotation with grass and hay.

It appears Dean and Keith have never seen a piece of equipment they couldn't modify — or build. Twenty years ago they designed and built three 375-bushel gravity wagons which are still in use today. They've even solved a proverbial problem — keeping good tires on well-used gravity wagons. "We put 22-ply recapped airplane tires on when we built them and the tires are still good today," notes Dean.

They also built their own 400-bushel auger cart and more recently designed and built a center-flex-hinge corn planter. Dean and his family built virtually all of the livestock buildings, including the manure pits, on the Amstutz farm.

In leadership roles, Dean helped organize the Davis County Pork Producers some years ago and more recently helped form Fox Ridge Pork, a 1,500-sow farrowing co-op with four partners. Dean and Sandra invested in the $2.2 million facility because of changing times and a son who wanted to farm.

Dean and Sandra are active in the Pulaski Mennonite Church and serve as a deacon couple. In 1998, Dean helped organize the complete rebuilding of new basement walls and a 16-foot addition to the church.

Twenty-one-year-old Aaron is starting to farm alongside his father. He is purchasing a farm, recently erected a 600-head confinement facility and is developing a beef herd.

Daughter Tara is married to Kevin Goering and lives in Cambridge, Iowa. Another daughter, Kristi, is a staff member of the Great Lakes Discipleship Center at Fort Wayne, Ind.

Maynard and Dorothy Lang
Poweshiek County

Maynard Lang is passionate about the dairy industry. After all, milking cows has provided a good living for him and his family for more than four decades. But his passion goes far beyond the farm gate.

Maynard rented his first farm more than 50 years ago from wife Dorothy's grandfather. He and Dorothy eventually purchased the 240-acre tract near Brooklyn in Poweshiek County in 1964.

For a number of years, the Langs fed cattle, hogs and sheep. But, in 1958, they entered the dairy business — partly because Maynard grew up on a dairy farm and partly because he saw it as an opportunity.

Along the way, Maynard quickly understood the economics of the industry and grew his business accordingly. "I couldn't have survived milking just 40 cows," he says. "It's all economics driven — you have to expand when the time is right. At the same time, I tell my sons they shouldn't be married to any enterprise. When I expanded I always had a

Dorothy and Maynard Lang

backup plan. Fortunately, I've never had to fall back on one of those."

That wise management paid off. Maynard and Dorothy have built a dairy and crop operation that today includes nearly 1,200 row-crop acres and a 450-cow milking herd along with around 400 bred heifers, dry cows and replacements. It's a three-way limited partnership with sons Craig and Eric. The Lang dairy herd boasts an impressive rolling herd average of 21,000 to 22,000 pounds of milk. Forty to 50 bulls are marketed each year in Iowa and northern Missouri. Eight full-time employees contribute to the labor force on the farm.

All crops are planted no-till and alfalfa is seeded on areas prone to erosion. Corn for silage is planted in 15-inch rows at around 39,000 plant population. "I'd heard about farmers in California harvesting 35 to 40 tons of silage per acre on 15-inch rows so we tried it and got 30 to 35 tons per acre," says Maynard. "In dry years, you could have problems with ear set but it's a permanent practice with us."

Milking cows are housed in five groups with freestalls and dry lots when weather permits. Around 200 bred heifers also have free stalls and dirt lots. Another 200 younger animals are kept in loose housing. Feeding is done on concrete and all bunks are either in buildings or under roof. "We try to get all of the young animals on pasture for two to six months," notes Maynard.

In addition to managing and growing the family business, Maynard has become extremely involved in the dairy industry. On the regional level, he serves as chairman of the Region 2 Central Valley Dairy Farmers Association and co-chairman of the Midwest Dairy Association.

As a member of the board of directors of Dairy Farmers of America Inc. (DFA), Maynard was instrumental in bringing 24,000 dairy producers together in 1998 to form DFA. He recently served on the board of the United Dairy Industry Association and as chairman of the National Dairy Board.

Maynard was chairman of the county zoning commission, Poweshiek County Farm Bureau president and active as a 4-H club leader.

The Langs are members of the Madison Church of Christ where Maynard has been an elder for 40 years.

Besides son Eric, his wife, Nicole; son Craig and his wife, Mary; the Lang's children include John and his wife, Nancy, Stoughton, Wis.; and Christine, who is married to Tom Turpin and lives in Lafayette, Ind.

Fritz and Jane Langguth
Adair County

Adair County is proud to be the birthplace of Henry A. Wallace. "We are also proud to have outstanding farmers like Fritz Langguth who carry on the principles of innovation and conservation Wallace is known for," says Deb Hall, in nominating Langguth for the Master Farmer award.

"Fritz isn't only an outstanding farmer, he's a good father and grandfather, a community and state leader, a caring neighbor," adds Hall, Iowa State University's (ISU) County Extension education director for Adair County.

Being good stewards of the land is of primary importance to Fritz and wife Jane, who farm near Fontanelle in southwest Iowa. The Langguths own and operate 550 acres, raising corn, soybeans, hay and beef cattle.

Adapting to changes in agriculture while contributing to the productivity and maintenance of the land has been the mainstay of whatever success Fritz has achieved in the past 40 years.

Always eager to try new innovations, "Fritz is a strong proponent of conserving soil and water as shown by his no-till and minimum tillage practices," adds Jane. "He has a positive attitude when trying new methods of farming, to evaluate them fairly."

Known for his helpfulness and cooperation in the community, Fritz has participated on many boards and makes sound, common-sense decisions. Modestly, Fritz gives credit to

Fritz and Jane Langguth

his support group — local bank, farmers' co-op, land improvement contractor, implement dealer and good neighbors.

Throughout his school years, Fritz was active in the family's diversified farming operation. After high school and the Army, Fritz married in 1958 and moved to the family homestead where he is today. He was a partner with his father, Arno, who emigrated from Germany. Together they farmed the land and fattened calves and yearling beef cattle. In 1970, Fritz purchased the home farm of 240 acres.

Set amidst rolling hills, the farm has terraces, contour strip-cropping, grass waterways and tile, along with no-till and conservation tillage. Highly erodible acres are kept in long-term hay and pasture.

Fritz has been involved in identity preservation of specialty crops. Through a program of Crestland Co-op, he has planted STS soybeans on some acres and marketed them at a premium. Roundup soybeans are planted on other acres where weed pressure dictates or where they work with conservation compliance plans requiring no-till.

The 75-cow beef herd, until calves are weaned, rotates between pastures. Calves at a weaning weight of 600 pounds are put in the feedlot until they reach market weight. Additional feeder calves are purchased from local auctions. About 250 head are fed annually.

Activities over the years include ISU parents' board, county fair board, farmers' co-op, county cattlemen, Iowa Soybean Association board of directors, Lions Club, Adair soil and water conservation district, etc.

"Fritz is a community leader," says Mike Cass, president of the First National Bank at Fontanelle and Greenfield. "He and Jane have become a source of guidance to young farm families in the area."

The Langguths have four children: Brad in Iowa City; Lisa in Overland Park, Kan.; Mark in Palatine, Ill.; and Kristen in West Des Moines. They have seven grandchildren. Continuing education is important; all of the children earned at least one degree from ISU. With a banker, engineer, attorney and CPA in the family, there is much discussion at family gatherings.

"I watched as the Langguths nurtured their children as teens and treated each one as a unique and special person," says Hall. "They were great 4-H parents, encouraging and supporting, but allowing the kids to do the work so they could learn and grow."

Jim and Shirley Svendsen
Linda and Doug Svendsen
Marshall County

Marshall County farmers Jim and Doug Svendsen are the first father and son to receive the Iowa Master Farmer award at the same time.

Considering the amount of capital it takes to begin farming, the Svendsens' start was unusual. Jim and Doug had good paying employment off the farm — retirement and health benefits, a regular paycheck. They both decided to come back to farm. Their decision to meet the challenges of farming — the investment, uncertain markets, ever-changing technology — required much dedication.

Jim has lived all his life on the 80-acre farm

where he was born. He married Shirley and held off-farm jobs before going to work for a neighboring farmer, Bill Shipton, in 1978. In 1983 when the Shiptons retired, Jim worked out an agreement to purchase Bill's equipment and rent the land.

As the farming operation expanded, Jim and Shirley asked their son, Doug, and his family if they were interested in farming with them. The Shiptons agreed to sell the Svendsens the farmstead so Doug and his family could live a half mile from his parents.

Doug graduated from Iowa State University (ISU) in agronomy and, with wife Linda, was living and working in Minnesota for Pillsbury/Green Giant. The opportunity to move home presented itself, so 1989 marked the start of a farming partnership that has continued to grow to 1,300 acres.

The Svendsens use no-till, working out problems with sound decision-making skills. Cost of production remains low due to their painstaking analysis of the system. In 2000, they received the Marshall County Conservation Farming Award.

"Marshall County is the recipient not only of the Svendsens' dedication to farming, but also their high community involvement," says neighbor Ward Handorf, who nominated them. "They are committed to and active in their church, school, Lions Club, Mid-Iowa Co-op, Heart of Iowa Telephone Co-op, Farm Bureau, Rural Electric Co-op and other organizations."

Jim and Doug manage to do all the farming without any hired labor. Using no-till has reduced the field time and labor requirements dramatically. Shirley is retired from the local bank but not from her family activities. Linda teaches food science at ISU.

Doug keeps all the farm records at home on computer. Income and expenses are tracked to the field level. Doug handles the general accounting and Jim pays the bills.

Doug is co-founder of Wolf Creek Business Solutions in Conrad, Iowa. He and a partner are working for the Marshalltown Area Chamber of Commerce as consultants, identifying value-added ag opportunities.

To save soil and nutrients, Jim and Doug started converting to no-till in 1992. Since 1996, they've planted 15-inch no-till beans using a custom-built splitter that mounts to their corn planter. They do some grid sampling and variable-rate fertilizer application. Waterways are maintained and turn strips are used on some fields. They recently established a buffer strip along a creek and installed fabric in a hard to maintain waterway.

As a volunteer director of Heart of Iowa Telephone Co-op, Doug is committed to ensure rural Iowans have access to the current and cost-effective telecommunications networks.

In addition to son Doug, Jim and Shirley have one daughter, Kristi. Doug and Linda have two children: Kevin, age 12, and Michael, age 9. Kristi and her husband Jeff Farrington live in Minnesota with their children, Cory, age 13 and Jacob, age 9.

Jim and Shirley (left) and Linda and Doug Svendsen

IOWA MASTER FARMERS
~
Second March 2002

Jim and Linda Anderson
Boone County

By the time he was a junior in college, Jim Anderson was renting 330 acres of farmland on his own as well as farming in partnership with his father, Jewell.

While in college, Jim also hauled cattle to the Chicago stockyards for extra income. When Jim graduated, he had not only paid for his education but saved enough money to pay cash for a new tractor as well.

Jim met his wife, Linda, while attending Iowa State University. "When we were married, living on a farm was a new experience for me," relates Linda. "I grew up in Storm Lake where my folks owned a drug store. Now I can't think of a better place to live and raise a family.

"Throughout our farming career there have been many struggles and hardships, as any farmer would understand," she continues. "But we have been blessed with much success and many things that make us proud."

Today Jim and Linda farm in

Jim and Linda Anderson

partnership with their son Tim near Boone in Boone County. Tim has land of his own but they share machinery. Tim is a full partner with Jim and Linda in their cow-calf and cattle feeding operation.

Calves weighing 500 to 850 pounds are purchased primarily from Montana and fed in confinement and open lots; the family finishes up to 1,100 head a year. Daily gains average 2.6 to 3.8 pounds per day. Fat cattle are marketed on the Iowa Beef Packers (IBP) grid program and to a specialty packing company in Pennsylvania.

"About three years ago we started marketing fat cattle to Moyer Pack (Mopac) in Pennsylvania because I was having difficulty marketing locally," explains Jim. "Since then IBP has introduced the grid system and that is working out well." Computerized rations are utilized in the cattle feeding operation. The cow-calf operation consists of 130 cows.

The Andersons raise seed corn for DeKalb. "I've been growing seed corn for them since the

339

plant opened in Boone in 1975," says Jim. He admits growing seed corn is labor-intensive but he says, "I don't have to buy seed and I don't have drying or storage charges."

"Every year after planting I say I won't do that again. But when the check comes in the fall I figure I'll try it again one more year," admits Jim.

A byproduct of the seed corn business is bees' wings. "We are paid by DeKalb to spread them on our fields," explains Jim. The Andersons are using grid sampling to determine what effect this has on the soils.

Jim is known in his community as a leader, friend and stabilizing force. He was a member of the local school board for 21 years and served as president for 13 of those years. "Jim came to the board after a bitter battle over a failed bond issue to build a new school," says Don Riemenschneider, former school superintendent. "He brought stability to a divided board and community."

Larry and Nancy Beyer

Jim is active in the Boone County and Iowa Cattlemen's associations, Extension council and Lions Club. He is a past board member of the Boone Farmer's Cooperative (West Central Co-op), County Soil Conservation Board, 4-H Youth Committee and Rotary Club.

Jim and Linda are active in the First Evangelical Free Church in Boone.

They have three children. Terri and her husband, Blaine Martin, live in Humboldt. They have two children, Lindsay (9) and Madison (4). Blaine helps out on the farm on weekends during spring and fall. Tim, wife Lisa and 2-year-old son Colton live in Boone. Cindy lives in Urbandale.

Larry and Nancy Beyer
Iowa County

Larry and Nancy Beyer have a clear picture of where they have been in their farming operation and where they are headed. That's because they have developed a detailed business plan that outlines the history of the operation and where they'd like to take it in the future. Most telling, however, is the mission statement for Beyer Farms.

It states the obvious goals of producing crops at a profit and growing the business for the future. It also declares that it will be done in an environmentally-friendly manner.

The operation was launched in 1968 when Larry returned, after 10 years of college and military service, and started farming with his father, Howard. Larry signed a note with his father to purchase 50% of his father's machinery and 20 head of stock cows. Nancy's father gave them 20 gilts to start the hog business. Base of the operation was a 200-acre Iowa River bottom farm that Larry's parents owned and another 230 rented acres.

The partnership existed until 1978 when Larry's father retired and Larry bought the rest of the operation. Beyer Farms has grown to a 1,640-acre corn and soybean cash farming enterprise headquartered near Marengo in Iowa County. It includes land in Benton,

Poweshiek and Tama counties. Son Mike is a salaried employee.

Stock cows were part of the operation until the late 1970s when more attention was focused on a farrow-to-finish hog operation. In 1996 the hog operation was phased out due to disease problems and extensive repairs needed on the buildings.

Row-crop acres were expanded in the 1980s. Corn is grown with minimum tillage unless soil loss requires it be planted no-till. Soybeans are planted with a no-till drill. The Beyers employ a crop scouting service. They also do grid sampling and yield mapping.

Specialty grain contracts are used to help capture niche markets. For example, high-starch corn is grown for delivery to a co-op dry milling, ethanol plant — Sunrise Energy in Blairstown. "We have the opportunity to deliver 20,000 bushels to them — about 10 miles from our farms. White corn is grown for Penford Starch in Cedar Rapids," explains Larry.

Beyer Farms also uses options in grain marketing. "We like to have about a third of the crop sold ahead of harvest," explains Larry. "The rest of the crop that is dried and stored on the farm is marketed through our local elevator, but hauled directly to a grain processor in Cedar Rapids or river terminals in Muscatine or Davenport.

"Our philosophy is to hire the expertise when we need it to make management decisions," notes Larry. "Being involved in commodity, community and church organizations gives us access to the latest government, industry and local situations as well," he adds.

In leadership roles, Larry has served as director on the Iowa Farm Bureau board. He served as a state and national director for the National Corn Growers Association and is currently a director on the Iowa Corn Promotion Board. He represents Iowa on the U.S. Meat Export Federation where he serves on the executive committee. He is a member of the American Soybean Association and the Iowa Pork Producers Association.

Nancy taught home economics for three years at Iowa Valley High School, Marengo, and was an Iowa State University Extension home economist for 15 years in Iowa and Benton counties. She is currently editor of The Involvement magazine published by Marengo Publishing Co. for the Heritage Area Agency on Aging in Cedar Rapids.

Larry and Nancy are involved in the First United Methodist Church in Marengo. Their son John is a software design engineer in Madison, Wis.

Wayne and Joan Demmer
Dubuque County

If there is one thing that bothers Wayne Demmer, it is that he can't find enough time to fight. Wayne and his wife, Joan, do a superb job of managing their 600-acre farming operation near Epworth in Dubuque County. But they would like to have extra time to be more involved with people or organizations fighting for the livelihood of rural America.

The Demmers have been outspoken in their efforts. They have stood on the steps of the capitol to lobby against House File 519, which "gave the green light to the corporate takeover of pork production in Iowa." They have met with politicians to promote the right of pork producers' vote to count following the reversal of the pork checkoff referendum.

Though at times frustrated with the way the political winds are blowing, they have been highly successful in their own farming operation.

In 1977, Wayne and Joan moved to the family farm when his father, Lawrence, moved to town. They purchased the machinery and half of the livestock and grain. They farmed on a 50-50 share basis with Lawrence. In 1983, they purchased the farm and the rest of Lawrence's farm assets.

Today they have around 550 acres of row crops and feed cattle and hogs. The crop rotation includes corn, soybeans and alfalfa.

Wayne and Joan Demmer

Always searching for ways to trim costs and protect the environment, Wayne was one of the first farmers in his area to use Landoil as a herbicide carrier. Landoil is made from soybean oil and allows him to trim chemical rates by one-third to one-half. "My goal is to use as few chemicals as possible," declares Wayne.

Nitrogen, phosphorus and potassium are applied with the planter along with insecticide, when needed. But Wayne hasn't had much need for insecticide due to a unique practice. He has been applying sulfur with the planter. It helps control rootworms and breaks down the nutrients in manure.

Wayne believes the sulfur improves root mass, which probably helps the plant resist rootworms. He has used test plots to prove his theory.

He uses the same approach to fertility — testing his theories and decisions in side-by-side comparisons in the field. Maximum rate of nitrogen used the past seven to 10 years has been around 100 to 110 units where no manure was applied. "I've found that using no nitrogen or only about 30 units on the corn where liquid manure was applied still provides optimum yields."

The Demmers ran a farrow-to-finish hog operation until 1997 when they switched to buying segregated early weaned (SEW) pigs. But finding those pigs has become difficult. So they are investing in a sow cooperative.

The Demmers also feed out 450 to 500 head of cattle a year.

One of Wayne's mentors early in his farming career posed this question: "There are two kinds of people in this world — the ones who eat dust and those who make dust. Which one are you going to be?"

It's clear Wayne and Joan are the ones making dust. Wayne is president of the Dubuque County Pork Producers Association and has represented Iowa pork producers at the national level. He's also active in the state and national corn and soybean associations, the National Farmers Organization and Iowa Citizens for Community Improvement, among many others.

Wayne and Joan are active members of St. Patrick's Catholic Church in Epworth.

The Demmers' four children live in the Epworth area. They are: twin sons, Ryan and Russell; Lynn and her husband Pete Besler and their daughter, Paige; and Jill and her husband, Dan.

Arnold and Audrey Odland
Hamilton County

Even after 39 years of raising crops, livestock and four children on the farm near Webster City, Iowa, Arnie and Audrey Odland still have a streak of daring and adventure.

Last year marked their 40th wedding anniversary. In honor of that accomplishment, they parachuted from an airplane with their skydiver daughter. Mom and dad listened, jumped and were thrilled. Daughter Lorna, who became a skydiver in college, is an instructor. "We really enjoyed our anniversary gift," says Audrey.

Arnie and Audrey dove into farming in 1962. He graduated from Iowa State University in 1960. She graduated from nursing school in 1961. They married and rented a farm in Hamilton County. Working with neighbors and exchanging labor for use of machinery, they rented more acres and added a small herd of beef cows.

Today they no-till soybeans, minimum till corn and have installed conservation buffer strips. Farming 1,500 row-crop acres and raising cattle and hogs, the Odlands own 240 acres and rent the rest from nine landlords.

Part of their cow-calf business is the Bucket Bottle Calf project in the Iowa 4-H program. It has provided a market for quality calves. The 4-H exhibitors over the years have kept many of the female calves as breeding stock.

The Odlands are quality pork producers, too. In 4-H, the children showed pigs. Audrey and Arnie were 4-H leaders. For over 25 years, they've camped at the Iowa State Fair, supporting Hamilton County 4-H and FFA.

While farming, the Odlands haven't lost sight of the need for a balanced life. The family enjoys each other. They've hosted foreign exchange students. Three of the four Odland siblings drove in demolition derbies. All children scuba dive. Arnie and Audrey like to golf. Arnie, his sons and sons-in-law take time for deer season.

All four Odland children are ISU grads. "The harmony and affection so apparent in this family is what you like to see — families working together, supporting and encouraging each other," says neighbor Wilfred Groves.

Garland Just has been an employee of the Odlands for 31 years. "Gar has been an invaluable help," says Arnie.

The Odlands, members of Central Iowa Farm Business Association, serve as secretary-treasurer of that group.

Arnie believes farming still has opportunities for young folks. "But you must be willing to change," he says.

Eldest son Brent spent five years working for Murphy Farms in North Carolina in that state's rapidly expanding hog industry. He returned to Iowa in 1995 and now farms with his parents and also has a farming enterprise of his own. Son Wade is studying for a doctorate in plant genetics/biotechnology at the University of Minnesota.

Daughter Lorna and her husband, Todd Meyer, live in Altoona, Iowa, and have three children — Alex, Aaron and Paige. Lorna is a computer engineer with Maytag. Daughter Allison has a master's degree in education and lives with husband Brian Wenck in Houston, Texas, with their two children, Kyle and Tyler.

Arnie has served on county fair board, church committees and local elevator board for a number of years. He's been a school board member and county Farm Bureau president.

"Arnie is easy-going and always smiling. His devotion not just to farming but to the community and especially the youth of the community make him a fine choice for the Iowa Master Farmer Award," says Dale Blue, chairman of the Board of Elders at St. Paul's Lutheran Church.

Arnold and Audrey Odland

2003 IOWA MASTER FARMERS
~
Second March 2003

Lee and Martha Faris
Ringgold County

Visiting the Lee and Martha Faris farm at Mt. Ayr, you're struck by the genuine interest this family has in taking care of those rolling hills in southwest Iowa.

You see terraces, grass waterways, tile, no-till, conservation tillage, ponds, hay in the crop rotation, improved pasture, rotational grazing, contouring, and other conservation measures. The farm is a model of natural resource protection.

With the help of son Rod, who lives with his family across the road, Lee raises cattle and crops. Cattle enhance the environment by providing a use for soil-saving grass and forages, but that beef enterprise pulls its weight financially, too.

Lee started farming in 1958, purchasing 80 acres and a tractor and renting land. He used his father's equipment. Today, 45 years later, the operation totals 1,040 acres, most of it owned. Rod has off-farm employment in addition to helping his dad.

Lee and Martha have 420 acres in row crops and 170 in hay. Around 450 acres are grazing or non-tillable.

Cattle and conservation

"Perhaps the most significant conservation practice Lee uses is making good land-use decisions," says Brian Peterson, state grasslands specialist for USDA's Natural Resources Conservation Service (NRCS) in Iowa. "He limits the continuous row crop to the flatter areas, such as tops of hills and the bottomland. Hillsides and marginal soils are used for pasture and hay."

The 175-head cow herd's beef production is boosted by using rotational grazing and seeding improved forage species. Lee keeps records and uses them to improve the herd.

To control gully erosion, he built ponds in pastures. They improve water quality, wildlife habitat and provide water for livestock. Lee has designed limited water access systems to let cattle get a drink without walking down the bank. Fences, gates and frost-free waterers keep the cattle out of ponds.

"Controlling cows' access to water lets us do a better job of rotating pastures, helps prevent bank erosion and improves water quality," says Lee.

"He puts land to its best use and is able to do that because he's established a high-quality beef herd," says Pe-

Lee and Martha Faris

terson. "Lee gets very good production from pastures. And by row-cropping only the better soils, he's maintained a good average yield on this land as well."

Lee has been a Ringgold County Soil and Water Conservation District commissioner for 16 years, serving as chairman several times. He's also worked with other units of government to implement soil and water programs to benefit the county.

A longtime, active member of the Iowa Cattlemen's Association (ICA), Lee has been county president, district director and state president. He's served on committees of the National Cattlemen's Beef Association (NCBA) and is vice president of the Iowa Cattlemen's Foundation. Locally, he's been active in organizations such as ISU Extension and the Ringgold County Fair.

Lee served on Iowa's State Soil Conservation Committee and the NRCS State Technical Committee, advising staff on farm conservation programs. He currently co-chairs the Iowa Grassland Alliance.

An original member of the Southern Iowa Forage and Livestock Committee (a multicounty group of farmers and others) Lee helped establish the nation's first project to demonstrate alternatives to row-crop production on highly erodible, marginal land. This project has been running continuously since 1991.

Very involved in 4-H and FFA in his younger days, Lee received the Iowa Farmer and American Farmer degrees. He's still most proud of his 4-H and FFA achievements. "That was the start of community involvement for me," he says. "4-H and FFA taught me leadership skills I've used in farming and in life."

Lee and Martha attend First Christian Church in Mt. Ayr. In addition to son Rod, they have two daughters — Jackie and Jennifer — and seven grandchildren.

David and Donna Kunde
Delaware County

The oldest of 10 children, David Kunde grew up on a Jersey farm near Zwingle, Iowa. David and his younger brother Gary took on most of the physical responsibilities on the home farm at a young age due to their father's health. As the boys grew older, they divided the management responsibilities — David looked after the cows (about 100 head) and Gary managed the cropland.

Donna grew up on a Brown Swiss farm near Manchester. She served as the Iowa Brown Swiss Princess and attended the University of Dubuque where she earned a degree in music education.

David and Donna Kunde

David entered the U.S. Army reserves after high school and while in the service saved money to buy cows. He first rented a farm for four years, however, all the while building a swine and dairy operation. He raised top-quality animals — one that at the time was the only animal of any breed to be designated "All American" five times (twice as a heifer and three as a cow). David sold this cow, designated "EX94," to make the down payment on the farm near Manchester in Delaware County they have now owned and lived on for nearly 25 years.

David and Donna continued the hog and dairy operation until 1978 when they decided to specialize in dairy. In 1979, they razed an old hog facility and built a 72-cow tie-stall barn in its place, which is still used for milking today. Fire destroyed a heifer facility and killed 54 replacement heifers in 1987.

In June 1989, the Kundes were milking around 90 cows with a rolling herd average of 18,000 pounds — one of the top herds in the state. Then disaster struck.

Since they had extra room due to the loss of the heifers, the Kundes housed some cattle that were in poor condition for a friend. Eventually it was determined these cattle had Johne's disease and some of David's cows had become infected. Many had to be sold. "We were soon milking only 50 cows with a rolling herd average of 10,000 pounds," notes David. "The loss of animals, genetics and long lines of cow families can never be restored and I can't even put a price on the loss," he adds.

Determined to succeed

But he wasn't deterred. "I didn't come that far to throw it all away when I hit the first mountain to climb," he declares. Determined to learn everything he could about the disease, David formed committees to set up testing in Iowa and fund research projects focusing on testing and vaccinations. He's given numerous informational seminars statewide helping dairy and beef producers find ways to eliminate the positive animals or possible contamination of their herds.

Even though they still face some challenges associated with Johne's disease, the Kundes are back on their feet today — milking 120 cows and the rolling herd average climbs each month. They farm around 250 acres of corn, beans, alfalfa and rye using a minimum tillage system.

Donna has been a member of the Maquoketa Valley School board for several years and for 18 years the Kundes have hosted school classes at the farm.

Both David and Donna have a long list of community and state leadership roles including 4-H, numerous dairy organizations, Extension and others.

Donna has a full-time job at Gibbs Engineering in Manchester.

The Kundes have four children. Jennifer moved home after earning a degree in Dairy Science from Iowa State University and is involved in everyday management of the farm. Carrie lives near Fairfield and works for Child Support Services. Michael is pursuing a dairy science degree from Iowa State University. Daniel is pursuing a technical dairy science degree at Northeast Iowa Community College in Calmar.

Ron and Judy Leistikow
Bremer County

Ron Leistikow loves the out of doors — working the land and feeding livestock. He knew he wanted to farm even as a small boy when he began farming with his dad. Now in his early 60s, Ron has farmed nearly all his life except for a short stint in the army reserve and an off-farm job for about a year when the dairy barn burned.

Today Ron and his wife, Judy, farm around 1,200 acres near Readlyn in Bremer County in northeast Iowa. They are also involved in another 900 acres that sons Kevin and Kurt farm in partnership with son-in-law Marty Marticoff.

Visiting with Ron, it's easy to see he's a family man and that this is truly a family operation, albeit a unique one at that! Not every farmer has a mechanic and attorney "on staff" — but Ron does. Kevin has a machinery repair business, L&L Ag Repair, right there on the farm. Kurt, an attorney with Rickert and Leistikow in Waterloo, does the legal work and grain marketing for the farming operation.

Ron ran a dairy until a couple years ago, milking as many as 100 cows in a parlor. He currently raises 200 to 250 head of feeder steers.

Crops consist of a 50-50 rotation between corn and soybeans. Ron believes in soil and water conservation and employs minimum tillage, grassed waterways, buffer strips and wildlife plots. Bean ground is not normally disturbed until just before planting.

He uses 30-inch rows for both corn and

beans. "I tried drilled beans (15-inch rows) but decided that for cost and yield, 30-inch rows are still the best for us," Ron declares.

The Leistikows use the services of a crop consultant who keeps an accurate record of what varieties were planted and where. The consultant also soil tests regularly and checks fields every two

Ron and Judy Leistikow

weeks during peak growing season advising the Leistikows on weed control, insect damage, emergence, etc.

Ron utilizes manure from his feedlot and two, 2,000-head hog finishing buildings on more than half of his acres.

Kevin and Kurt own the hog buildings and custom feed hogs. The manure is injected and Ron applies no commercial fertilizer on land where hog manure is used.

Community leader

In community activities Ron has been very active and willing to serve in leadership roles throughout the county, in his community and within the major agriculture and commodity groups, according to Darrin Siefken, Bremer County Extension Service.

Ron has served in leadership capacities in the following organizations: Bremer County Farm Bureau (38 years), Bremer County Cattlemen's Association, charter member Bremer County Dairy Promoters, Bremer County Corn and Soybean Associations, Wapsie Valley Education Association and Bremer County Fair Board, among others.

Ron and Judy are active members of St. Matthew's Lutheran Church in Readlyn.

"'Behind every successful man is a good woman' is an old cliche," says Ron, "but it's certainly true in my case."

Besides Kevin and Kurt and their wives Deanne and Jenifer, Ron and Judy have four other children: Kassie is a senior at the University of Iowa; Kerri lives in Omaha, Neb.; Kristi is married to Marty Marticoff and lives in Readlyn; and Kimberly lives in Weston, Fla.

"Our family supports our mom and dad who have given us a quality of life we could never find anywhere but on the farm," says Kevin.

"Our farm background has landed us the jobs that we all have," he adds.

Dick and Sharon Thompson
Boone County

Dick Thompson is an innovator, in every sense of the word, though you wouldn't necessarily get that impression upon first meeting him. He is soft-spoken and humble. He teaches by example, which could explain why he's so well respected by his peers.

Dick's credo is "get along, but don't go along" — in other words, keep lines of communication open with everyone, even those people who strongly disagree with your practices, but don't follow the path just because everyone else is taking it.

A sign by the driveway to Dick and Sharon Thompson's Boone County farm states "Thompson On-Farm Research with Wallace Institute." Another one says "Practical Farmers of Iowa Research." Both messages go to the heart of Dick's philosophy.

Through support from the Rodale Institute and Jean Wallace Douglas, the Thompsons began their on-farm research in 1979. It was elementary at first, he says, but it became obvious that on-farm research was more effective than university trials.

Dick feels fortunate to have been in the right place at the right time, and doing or saying the right thing. One of his most rewarding accomplishments is the creation of Practical Farmers of Iowa (PFI) in 1985.

He says PFI basically started on a shoestring, charging $30 per membership. Last fall, he and other PFI board members OK'd a budget of $623,000. PFI has grown steadily because the organization presents alternatives for producers, Dick believes. Rather than taking a stand against a certain practice or serving as an activist group, PFI simply provides ideas on other, more sustainable methods of production. In addition, PFI works closely with other groups to pool resources and find common ground.

Simple, but effective

Many of the cost-saving practices shared with PFI members are experiments from the Thompson farm. Here are some examples:

Austree windbreak. The tree originated in New Zealand and is a sterile male "so we wouldn't have to deal with seeds or sprouts," says Dick.

A 50-year-old chisel plow is used for control of Canada thistle. "You have to look at the biodynamics of using the chisel in the fall, following hay, in the last quarter moon phase," he explains.

A multi-width Norwegian plow allows Dick to get manure covered quickly for minimum odor. It also buries the weed seeds and allows for deeper fertility.

A flex harrow increased hay production by 4,000 pounds per acre. It also reduced horn flies and parasitic worms.

A heavy, but inexpensive towel replaces the cloth that came on a cattle rub (which lasted a few months before shredding).

An innovative, low-cost animal-friendly loading chute at the hog farm simplifies the loading process and saves hours of work.

Since 1988, records have been kept on two different cropping systems: the Thompson farm corn-soybean-corn-oats-hay rotation vs. Boone County corn-soybean rotation. The Thompson net return has been a positive $103.57 per acre per year while the corn-soybean return has been a negative $43.24 with a difference of $146.83. Premiums, government programs, profits or losses from livestock are not included in these numbers.

When asked where farming will be in 10 years, Dick responds, "We're not going to change the world, but at least there's an alternative out there for people who want it. The world cannot live like we do; the earth can't support that. Pretty soon, we won't have money to buy all those inputs," he says. "But you can't stand in front of the train, because a lot of farmers like the way the train is going."

All you can do is offer an alternative that is cost-effective and sustainable, sums up Dick.

Dick and Sharon Thompson

IOWA MASTER FARMERS

~
March 2004

Jerry and Judy Morey
Buchanan County

Jerry Morey is the fifth generation to operate the family farm in Buchanan County near Hazleton. His great-great-grandfather purchased the original homestead in 1874.

Jerry helped his father farm for a few years after returning from a stint in the United States Navy. He then bought land and equipment from his father, equipment from a neighbor and struck out on his own. His father, Duane, still lives on the farm and assists with crop production.

"Dad turned 80 in November and still puts in a full day's work," notes Jerry. "He combines all the corn, but doesn't like to harvest beans."

Today Jerry and his wife, Judy, farm nearly 1,000 acres, growing reduced tillage corn and soybeans in a 50-50 rotation. About 50 acres is in the Conservation Reserve Program, buffer strips and timber. More than 150 acres are farmed on the contour even though the land is not classified highly erodible.

Jerry raised swine but discontinued livestock when the buildings were destroyed in a 1982 storm. "Interest rates and reconstruction costs were too high at the time so I discontinued livestock production," Jerry explains. "There have been times I wanted to get back into livestock, but it just never penciled out."

Religious about machinery maintenance, Jerry spends a lot of time in his shop cleaning and greasing equipment. All equipment is put away in the fall ready to go to the field in the spring.

"I have a part-time job at the local Farm Service Agency and I like to work as long as I can in the spring. I want the equipment to be ready to go on short notice. Proper maintenance also helps control my costs and maximizes machine efficiency."

Jerry utilizes his home computer to keep track of records, write checks and analyze production costs. "I write my own computer programs to analyze my records. I really enjoy that," he notes.

"Jerry has run Fin Pac analysis through Iowa State University Extension for his farm business several times," says William Lotz, retired Buchanan County

Jerry and Judy Morey

Extension director. "He says this computer-assisted program has allowed him to evaluate expansion and the impact of a downturn in yields or prices."

Jerry has served his community in a variety of capacities, not the least of which is 33 years on the Hazleton Volunteer Fire Department—17 years as chief. Jerry was instrumental in improving training and securing modern equipment for the department.

During his tenure, Jerry sustained two serious injuries: a broken foot and an anhydrous burn to 20% of his body. "An anhydrous tank was leaking at a fertilizer plant. I was burned trying to get in to shut off a valve," explains the quiet farmer.

Since Jerry retired from the department last year, he has been devoting his time to opening a campground on his property as a retirement plan.

In other leadership roles Jerry has served on the Oelwein Area Ambulance Commission, the Buchanan County Extension Council and the AgVantage FS board. He was an advisor with the FFA program, and actively campaigned to expand the vocational agriculture program with the school board.

He served as a 4-H club leader and volunteer at the Buchanan County Fair. As a past Master of the Masons, he worked to raise money for the scholarship fund.

Jerry is a charter member of the Top Crop seminar group. This group of farmers has met over the past 25 years to strengthen their operation and be models for others.

Dean and Harriett McWilliams
Poweshiek County

Dean McWilliams has been a farmer in Poweshiek County for 56 years, starting in 1947 after serving in the Mediterranean Theater during World War II. He's raised corn, soybeans, hay, pasture, hogs, cattle and turkeys.

But beef cattle are his first love, and the beef industry is where he has really made his mark.

"I've always enjoyed cattle," states Dean. "I started feeding cattle when I was 12 years old."

He bought four crossbred calves for $28 a head, fed them out, and the rest, as they say, is history.

Today, he and his son, Robert (Bob), have a 200-head commercial cow herd, 30 head of purebred seed-stock and finish around 500 head annually. The family farm operation consists of 950 acres of corn, soybeans, hay and pasture.

Conservation is paramount. "More than half our farm is in grass and hay at any one

Harriett and Dean McWilliams

time," explains Dean. Crop rotation involves two years of corn (one year for silage), one year of soybeans, then hay and grass. The farms have several ponds and many terraces.

Manure plays a huge role in crop production. "Commercial fertilizer is merely a substitute for manure," declares Dean. A minimum amount of commercial fertilizer is used, enough to satisfy soil test requirements.

Dean became active in Poweshiek County Beef Producers early in his farming career, serving as president for a time. He was a charter member of both the Iowa Cattlemen's Association (ICA) and the National Cattlemen's

Association (NCA). He eventually served as director, treasurer and president of the ICA. He also served several years on the National Cattlemen's Beef Association (NCBA) board and the executive committee of NCA.

Dean is most proud of his work with ICA, NCBA and — most recently — with the Iowa Cattlemen's Foundation.

He led the drive in the 1990s to build a new ICA headquarters building in Ames. He led two campaigns for the beef checkoff: state and national — both very successful.

Perhaps his most significant accomplishment was helping form the Interstate Livestock Producers Association (ILPA) cattle-marketing program in the early 1970s after the Chicago Stockyards closed.

"We shipped our cattle to Chicago — as did most people at the time. When the Chicago yards closed, we had to develop a market," he explains.

"That program has worked real well. I sold the first cattle on that program in 1974 and haven't sold cattle any other way for more than 25 years, other than a few loads to the Tama plant," he notes.

Dean served 18 years on the IPLA board and when IPLA sold the cooperative to United Producers of Ohio (UP Inc.), he became a member of that board of directors.

Dean and Bob buy about 120 calves through UP in the spring, graze them in West Virginia, and then bring them home for finishing in late fall.

"There is nothing more I enjoy than driving the feed truck," says Dean. "It provides an opportunity to observe the cattle from the truck and it's satisfying to know that while I'm feeding them, they are producing a choice product to be enjoyed around the world."

He sums up his feeding philosophy by quoting something he once read: "The eye of the master feeds his cattle. I really believe that," he declares. "In other words, you have to observe your cattle to know what's going on. We like to see every animal every day."

Jack and Dee Kintzle
Linn County

Farming 1,400 acres of corn and soybeans near Coggon in eastern Iowa, Jack and Dee Kintzle get a lot of work done with a small inventory of equipment. They only have two tractors: one is 150 horsepower, the other is 110.

"No-till farming has allowed us to lower our machinery cost and operating expense," says Jack. "I think agriculture as a whole can do a better job of containing production and equipment costs. We have to control costs if we're to compete successfully in a global market."

The Kintzles use the Iowa Farm Business Association recordkeeping system and computer spreadsheets to analyze cash rent, grain marketing and other financial decisions. They farm some land on crop share, some cash rent and they own 520 acres.

Dee and Jack have been on their farm for 30 years and do all the work themselves except at harvest.

Jack grew up on a diversified livestock farm 10 miles east of where he now farms. His father, Carl, 91, "was a very successful cattle feeder," he adds. "From him I learned the value of manual labor and the importance of managing time wisely. That's extremely important in crop farming today."

Jack and Dee have farmed for 37 years. Jack's older brother Harold, who recently retired from a successful farming career, always farmed nearby. "Harry and I had separate farming operations," says Jack. "He's been a close friend and a person I shared ideas with."

In his younger days, Jack had a pilot's license and a small plane. He was a sky diver. He also took a plunge into the land market at what turned out to be the wrong time. But he and Dee were able to hang on to part of their farm through agriculture's financial crisis in the 1980s.

It was a humbling struggle for survival.

They sold some land, deeded some back to Production Credit Association, restructured loans and basically started over with 40 acres and rented land.

After watching other farmers lose their operations, Jack got involved in the Iowa Corn Growers Association to try to help.

Always quick to smile, his skills as a listener and speaker helped Jack rise through leadership ranks of the Iowa association and the National Corn Growers Association (NCGA). He became NCGA president in 1990. As the nation wrestled with recession, war and government deficits, he was seen in Washington and Iowa as a scrappy fighter for the minority of Americans who grow the nation's food.

Jack helped others learn from his mistakes. Going through the farm crisis made him a better manager, he says, and made him see the

Jack and Dee Kintzle

big picture better.

"I've always enjoyed being an independent farmer," explains Jack. "Dee and I were able to make a living and raise our children. Working with my wife on the farm has been very satisfying."

Jack served on a national commission on crop insurance that came up with alternatives and solutions. He is a board member of City State Bank, his local bank.

"Jack is an excellent decision maker and is very articulate in speaking up for agriculture," says bank president John Maurice. "He has an excellent business mind and a deep understanding of agriculture's problems and opportunities."

Active in St. Joseph's Catholic Church and in the community, the Kintzles are always ready to lend a helping hand.

"They're excellent examples of what's so good about Iowa. Good farmers, good citizens, good neighbors," says friend Sharon Murken.

Jim and Bev Amdor
Adams County

Master Farmers should share the talents that make them special. Jim and Bev Amdor do that. They've farmed for over 30 years near Corning in southwest Iowa. Bev has taught school for many years and currently teaches second grade.

"Most young farmers don't have a formal mentoring program but Jim has served as an informal mentor to many young farmers and youth in Adams County," says Brian Peterson, a soil conservation and grasslands specialist with USDA's Natural Resources Conservation Service.

Jim started with the Amdor/Heaton farming operation in 1972 after returning from military service in Vietnam. The partnership lasted 31 years, with the Amdor family operating on a livestock lease.

The Heaton family corporation, which owned the land, decided to sell the farm in late 2003. The new owners took possession March 1. The Amdors recently moved to another farm near Corning.

Jim and Bev raised hogs and cattle on the 600-acre rented farm. They own 500 acres themselves, so they farmed a total of 1,100— 620 tillable acres, 480 grazing and non-tillable. They had a 75-head sow herd, farrowing and finishing the pigs.

The Amdors are now raising hogs on another farm. They still have 150 beef cows and farm the 500 acres they own. They're also partners with Bev's brother, Ron Brown, raising crops and cattle.

The Amdor/Brown partnership is 25 years old.

An excellent livestock producer, Jim developed animal husbandry skills through 4-H. He used his skills extensively in the Peace Corps in Nigeria and has applied them for all of his 31 years of farming. They have been a foundation upon which to learn new skills along the way.

The Amdors were selected as Master Pork Producers in 2003. Jim uses his livestock recordkeeping system to enhance the quality of the pigs and cattle that are marketed. This is verified by the success of the livestock he sells that are entered in competition by exhibitors at shows throughout the Midwest.

Southern Iowa hills normally require multiple conservation practices to adequately protect the land. "These farms are no exception," says Jim. "We plant row crops on the contour. Many of our fields are terraced. Conservation tillage is used on all of our cropland."

Oats and hay are rotated with corn on the more sloping land. Many of the steeper hills are seeded to permanent pasture. The pastures are rotated to allow for better forage use. Ponds were built to provide water and protect land from gully erosion.

"There are farmers who farm more land and have more livestock," says Peterson. "But I know of none who make better use of the resources available than Jim."

Jim was a 20-year member of the Board of Supervisors in Adams County, serving as chair several times. He served on the Southwest Iowa Area on Aging Board, the Multi-County Landfill Board and helped establish and manage the county-run day care center.

Bev and Jim Amdor

Jim was a 4-H club leader. 4-H holds a special place in the hearts of the Amdor family. Jim has donated many hours of labor and equipment as well as financial support to the Adams County Fair to make it a good experience for youth.

Jim and Bev have given many hours to the school district and school activities, helping organize fund-raisers, etc. Bev has included agriculture in her classroom, giving students an opportunity to learn about farming. "I've taken many pigs to school over the years," says Jim.

Exceptional Service Award
Stewart Melvin
Story County

Raised on a family farm near Bloomfield in southeast Iowa, Stewart Melvin is still very much in touch with his roots. His brother Phillip and nephew Rob still farm that piece of Davis County. "In fact, my 92-year-old mother, Ethelyne, is still on the farm," he says.

For the past 32 years, "Stu" Melvin, as he is known by farmers, has been an Iowa State University Extension agricultural engineer. He became a part-timer on the ISU staff last September but is still "full-time busy." Full retirement from ISU is coming at the end of June.

The 62-year-old Stu is the winner of the 2004 Iowa Master Farmer Exceptional Service Award. The award honors his career of helping farmers through his Extension work and for teaching their sons and daughters at the university. He's always been involved in research, too, never shying from working on controversial environmental problems.

Staying involved in the family farm helps

maintain his commonsense approach to assisting farmers, teaching students and advising legislators. Stu has a financial stake in the Davis County farm, which has cattle, hogs, lambs and crops. "It's a livestock farm typical of southern Iowa. We have some rough land," he says.

He earned a bachelor's degree in 1964, master's in 1967 and doctorate in 1970, all in ag engineering, all from ISU. He was an assistant professor at Colorado State University in 1969-70, then returned to Ames to join ISU's ag engineering staff.

Stu's wife, Carol, started her career as a teacher and took time off to help raise their two children. Carol is now a graphic designer in ISU's Engineering Department. Their daughter, Catherine, and son, Chris, are ISU graduates.

"Stu embodies the concept of taking research-based information and interpreting and explaining it on a practical level for farmers," says Mark Hanna, a fellow ISU Extension ag engineer. "When you went to a meeting where Stu was presenting, you knew you'd learn something you could use."

Stu has been a catalyst in farmers' use of sound drainage practices, manure management, soil conservation and water-quality practices. "Stu was the major source for both the technical material in the Iowa Drainage Guide and the application of its recommendations," says Hanna. "He taught farmers and contractors how to use the information. Improved drainage has unlocked tremendous yield potential for Iowa cropland."

He's been a valuable technical liaison charting practical solutions to problems between livestock producers and the Iowa Department of Natural Resources.

Even while heading ISU's Ag and Biosystems Engineering Department from 1994 to 2001, Stu made a special effort to keep in touch with farmers and issues affecting them.

"Stu's research and Extension career focused on critical issues," says Dean Lemke, water resources specialist at the Iowa Department of Agriculture. "He's helped agriculture move forward environmentally and yet find solutions compatible with the needs of farmers and landowners. He's willing to tackle the tough problems."

"Stu Melvin leads by example," says Hanna, "inspiring fellow Extension staff and farmers to take a practical approach. He's humble, a nice guy and a team player. His career has helped lead Iowa agriculture to sound and profitable practices to help protect the environment."

Stewart and Carol Melvin

March 2005

Jerry and Leola Britten
Story County

You don't talk to Jerry Britten very long before asking yourself: What did this guy do before he started farming 30 years ago? Teacher, banker or an accountant?

Actually, he worked as a loan officer for the Production Credit Association at Rockwell City in northwest Iowa. Then in 1974, Jerry and Leola moved their family to the home community where he grew up, near Zearing in central Iowa, and they began farming.

Prior to the PCA job, Jerry was a vo-ag teacher at Aurelia. Leola taught school at Storm Lake. After marrying, they both taught at United Community School west of Ames.

Leola and Jerry Britten

A long-time member of the Iowa Farm Business Association, Jerry knows the importance of keeping good records and using them in decision making. Leola helps in the field as needed during the cropping season and assists with recordkeeping. Farming 1,055 acres of corn and soybeans, they hire a retired farmer, Carlton Karns, as extra help in spring and fall. The Brittens exited the hog business in 1996.

Whether in the field or in front of a computer, Jerry thinks through and tests ideas before putting them into practice. He succeeds in producing above-average yields with lower-than-average production costs.

To market grain, the Brittens use a combination of cash sales, forward contracting and options (puts and calls) in conjunction with a good crop insurance program. Their goal is to be in the top third of the price range the market offers each year. "We don't expect to hit the highest price," says Jerry. "But we typically get a fair share of our crop sold in the top one-third."

Jerry has learned how to put the tools together: marketing, crop insurance, financial management. He is an independent crop insurance agent, and handles that business as seriously as he does the farming enterprise. He spends time studying crop insurance products and developments so he can provide the best possible coverage for customers.

"Jerry's devotion to his customers' crop insurance needs is like having an agent in their back pocket," wrote neighbors Don and Nancy Ellingson, in a letter of support for the Master Farmer award. "Jerry is there when needed."

"I like working with farmers on crop insurance," says Jerry. "I try to help them be better marketers — not so I can necessarily sell them insurance, sometimes it's even less insurance. To be able to analyze their individual situation, to help them figure out what is their best buy so they can balance risk protection against insurance cost, that's what it's all about."

Karol and Rozanne King

Takes practical approach

The Brittens store about 65,000 bushels on-farm, but don't own a semi-truck. "We've farmed for 30 years," notes Jerry. "My job description never included hauling grain to market. We sell to several different grain buyers or we forward contract and arrange it so grain is picked up at our farm."

If you have time and labor, running your own truck is probably a good way to do it, he adds. "But I don't have the labor and I need to manage my crop insurance business. That's why we choose to market grain the way we do."

Karol and Rozanne King
Harrison County

Very professional in their activities, Karol and Rozanne King are quiet, humble and hardworking. Their history of helping and supporting their local community and serving agriculture and their state is inspiring.

It's not like they have time on their hands. They keep busy growing corn and soybeans on approximately 2,900 acres at Mondamin, along Iowa's western edge. This past year, 650 acres were devoted to producing seed beans

and 333 acres to popcorn. Located in the Missouri River Valley, they have water and irrigate over half of the land. They own 388 acres and rent the rest.

They also own and operate King Agri Sales, a local retailer of irrigation equipment, ag chemicals, fertilizer and short-line machinery. To help with the farm they have two full-time hired employees and seasonal part-time help.

The Kings are very supportive of 4-H and Rozanne has been involved in the local 4-H club for many years.

Karol has contributed much time and effort on behalf of the Iowa and National Corn Growers Associations and the Iowa Corn Promotion Board. Rozanne has served on several state boards and advisory committees. "Yet, they take time to do a lot here locally. They've opened their home and farming operation to 4-H, school and various groups for programs related to agriculture," says Dee Colwell, county youth coordinator for Iowa State University Extension in Harrison County.

Helped ethanol get its start

Along with seven other Iowa farmers, Karol helped get the legislation passed to establish the Iowa corn checkoff in 1977. He was one of the first people to understand the potential of "gasohol," now called ethanol. Serving for 10 years on the National Gasohol Commission, he focused on the dual benefits of energy security and value enhancements that this corn-based alternative fuel can provide for farmers and our country.

Karol's firm commitment to accomplish the goal to make ethanol a viable market for corn is one of the cornerstones of the ethanol success story.

Farming in the Missouri River Valley isn't easy. For a number of years, farmers in that part of Iowa were plagued by dry weather and poor yields. Yet, the Kings succeeded by effective use of skill, experience and wits.

All their farmland is not highly erodible, but they still use conservation tillage to control wind and water erosion. Recently, Karol helped NRCS in promoting a new water conservation program to convert high-pressure center pivots to low pressure.

Speaking up for farmers

Rozanne's involvement as a partner and co-owner of the family farm and business has provided valuable guidance and input for state regulators, legislators and others. For a number of years, she represented agriculture on the state Environmental Protection Commission. Her representation and expertise helped attain a balance between production agriculture and environmental interests on controversial issues.

Rozanne was one of the first women to serve on a district Federal Land Bank board, a county REC board and only the second woman to serve on the Northwest Iowa Power Cooperative Board. She is currently a member of the Iowa State Farm Service Agency Committee, which oversees USDA farm programs in Iowa.

Gary and Judy Burrack
Clayton County

Soil conservation is important to anyone farming the rolling hills of northeast Iowa, but it is Gary Burrack's passion. "My feeling is if you rent or own land, your first goal should be to try to improve it," he declares.

The Burracks' picture-perfect 1,400-acre farm near Monona utilizes many conservation practices including terraces, grass waterways and drainage tile. Gary and Judy have built more than 40 miles of terraces on both owned and rented land. These structures are enhanced with rotated corn and soybean crops planted on the contour with either minimum or no tillage.

Gary and Judy took over the family farming operation when Gary's father died in 1974. Gary was well prepared to run the farm. By the time he was 9, he was driving tractors and helping with chores on his parent's farm. "I always liked farm work and still do," he says.

The Burracks have been soil sampling with GPS for more than 12 years. They use variable-rate technology to apply fertilizer and lime. They have been using a yield monitor with GPS in the combine since 1999.

One thing they have learned from the data is that bean yields have been slipping the past few years. "Overall, bean yields in this area seem to be trending down," says Gary. To

Judy and Gary Burrack

357

overcome that the Burracks have switched to a two-year corn-on-corn rotation. "That seems to help improve bean yields," he notes.

Communication is the strongest part of this operation. Gary and Judy work closely with daughter Suzanne and son-in-law Joe Shirbroun, who returned to the farm in 1999. Their different skills complement each other, and similar interests and goals help grow the operation. Suzanne and Joe own a successful seed dealership. They farm separately but share labor and equipment with Gary and Judy. "Our goal is to eventually turn the entire operation over to Suzanne and Joe," explains Judy.

"Marketing is our biggest challenge," admits Gary. "There was a time when you just raised the crop and sold it when you needed cash flow. It's much more complicated now."

Gary says it takes a lot of discipline to market these days.

"I have a hard time forward selling my 2006 crop, for example," he says. "I'm old-fashioned. I want to know it's in the bin first — or at least in the ground!"

Gary and Judy have always been forward-thinking — looking for ways to make themselves and others more efficient. Since 2000 they have been involved with F.I.R.S.T., Farmers Independent Research of Seed Technologies. This involves 3-acre plots in their fields for corn and soybean yield trials.

Cutting-edge technology

They worked with Iowa State University researchers for many years with on-farm nitrogen/manure-management research to help determine best use of manure from a produc-

tion and environmental standpoint.

The Burracks have helped promote identity-preserved corn and soybean varieties for specific end-use markets by hosting plot days in conjunction with Pattison Brothers, Fayette.

Gene and Jean Wiese
Carroll County

Gene Wiese realized at an early age that cattle were his future. "I have known since I was 8 years old, without question, what I wanted to do. I saw it as an opportunity to work with livestock, land and expand our relationship with people interested in ag domestically and abroad," he declares.

He and wife Jean are the senior partners in a family farming partnership near Manning called Wiese and Sons. Gene is the third generation on this farm; his grandfather settled here in 1904.

The operation consists of nearly 2,000 acres of pasture, corn, and hay, but the Wieses are widely known for their development

Gene and Jean Wiese

and marketing of top-quality beef bulls. Gene's grandfather, Ed, and his father, Les, started the registered bull business in 1912. Gene and his brother, Sam, ran the business until Sam retired.

Gene, son Dave and daughter Helen Ohde now own the business. Dave is operational manager. Helen maintains the records.

"Genetic decisions to continually improve the herd are vital," says Gene. "Breeding decisions are a consideration that involves the entire family."

Records are one of the keys to their success. The first calf weight records were recorded in 1955 — also the first year artificial insemination was used on the farm. Fifty years of records provide a lot of useful data: calving ease, weaning weight, yearling data, rate of gain, etc. EPDs are used extensively.

Breeding herd is Hereford and Angus with 350 registered cows in the base herd. Commercial cows are bred for carcass and feeding records.

Approximately 100 Hereford and 50 Angus bulls are marketed annually in private treaty sales. Breeding stock from Wiese and Sons has been sold throughout the United States and 17 foreign countries through live cattle, semen sales and embryos. "But our best customers are neighbors and those within a 200-mile radius," notes Gene.

Manure is stockpiled in spring and spread in fall after naturally composting. "The benefits are less tonnage hauled and this schedule fits our farming practices," explains Gene.

The Wieses farm land in both Carroll and Guthrie counties, some of it fairly steep. "Forage is our most important crop and the quality and care of this crop is directly related to cattle productivity and efficiency," explains Jean.

Forage is principal crop

Plant diversity has been achieved by interseeding a variety of legumes and grasses. Rotational grazing has been practiced since 1982. Weed management is achieved through interseeding and clipping. Herbicides are carefully applied only when absolutely necessary. Contouring, strip farming, field borders and extensive use of grass outlets and waterways help decrease erosion.

For more than 20 years the Wieses have planted trees for shelterbelts, windbreaks and wildlife habitat. They have developed their own 600-tree nursery as a ready source of trees.

Terraces have been built on moderately and highly-erodible land, even in pastures. "We have made a concerted effort to conserve the land," says Gene. "We have hills here that could be in row crops but we've kept them in grass to conserve the soil."

Crops are grown on a meadow-based rotation: four to five years of continuous corn, then four to five years of alfalfa or mixed hay. Soybeans are not included in the rotation because soybeans are not part of the feeding program. "We feed what we grow," he notes.

"We enjoy sharing our business and our philosophy with guests, tours and students," notes Gene. The Wieses have hosted over 30 students from the United States and numerous foreign countries.

2005 MASTER FARMER PROFILES

JERRY & LEOLA BRITTEN

Hometown: Zearing
Farm: Corn and soybeans on 1,055 acres. Also, independent crop insurance agent and consultant.
Family: Three sons — Chad and family in Wisconsin, Jeff and wife at Story City, Mark and wife at Nevada.
Leadership highlights: Colo-Nesco School Board six years, two as president; Leola and Jerry served on numerous school committees; Jerry is an honorary FFA Chapter Farmer, past 4-H leader and precinct caucus chair. He served eight years on Story County Extension Council, five years as chair. He served on ISU Extension State Advisory Committee, is active in Lions Club and is an American Legion member. The Brittens were in the hog business for years and sold Specific Pathogen Free breeding stock.
Organizations: Minerva Valley Independent Telephone Co. board chairman, 2002 to present. Current chairman of Bethel United Methodist Church board, church activities.

KAROL & ROZANNE KING

Hometown: Mondamin
Farm: Around 2,900 acres corn, soybeans, popcorn and seed beans. Also own and operate King Agri Sales Inc., a local business that sells irrigation equipment, ag chemicals and fertilizer. Rozanne is a freelance interior designer.
Family: Daughter Alisha, age 16
Awards: Harrison County Farm Bureau Distinguished Service; ISU Friend of Extension, Iowa Corn Growers Distinguished Service Award, Honorary 4-H Member.
Leadership highlights: Karol and Rozanne serve on the Parent Advisory Committee at West Harrison Community School. Karol is treasurer of the First Lutheran Church Board. Rozanne is a state 4-H Foundation trustee.
Organizations: Karol's past positions include Farmers Co-op Board, president; Iowa Corn Growers Association, president; Iowa Corn Promotion Board, chair; U.S. Feed Grains Council board of directors; National Gasohol Commission, vice president; National Corn Growers Association, vice president; and ISU College of Ag Advisory Committee. Rozanne served on Harrison County Rural Electric Co-op board for 18 years, as well as Northwest Iowa Power Co-op board.

GARY & JUDY BURRACK

Hometown: Monona
Farm: Family corporation, G and J Burrack Acres Co., approximately 1,400 acres corn and soybeans.
Family: Daughter Suzanne and husband Joe Shirbroun, ISU graduates and farming; daughter Nancy and husband Jon Vonfeldt, ISU graduates, Nancy is a CPA and Jon is a chemical company representative. Three grandchildren: Tom and Andrey Shirbroun, Mick VonFeldt.

Awards: District Soil Conservation Award, Teddy Roosevelt Conservation Award.
Leadership highlights: 4-H, Clayton County Compensation Board, Iowa Corn Growers Association director, Strawberry Point Lutheran Home and Gernand Center director, AGRI Industries director, Luana Savings Bank director, Care Review Board of Great River Care Center in McGregor, Shepherd of the Hills food and clothing shelf.
Church: Active members of St. Paul Lutheran Church, Monona.

GENE & JEAN WIESE

Hometown: Manning
Farm: Approximately 2,000 acres corn, oats, alfalfa; registered Hereford and Angus breeding cattle, purebred bull sales.
Family: Son David and wife Diana, daughter Helen and husband John Ohde are partners in the family farm. Daughter Kathryn runs her own business in Hawaii. Four grandchildren: Chance, Shayne and Trey Wiese, Kierev Gibson.
Awards: National Cattlemen's Beef Association Region III Environmental Stewardship Award, NCBA Cattle Business of the Century Award, Alpha Gamma Rho Century Award for Service to Agriculture, Iowa State University Animal Science Department Hall of Fame, Iowa Cattlemen's Association Hall of Fame.
Leadership highlights: Presidential appointee to Animal Trade Advisory Committee, Iowa Cattlemen's Association president, American and Iowa Hereford Association president, Iowa Beef Breeds Council president, founder of Manning Community Foundation, 4-H, FFA, Farm Bureau. Local, state and national cattle judge; First Presbyterian Church, trustee and elder.

IOWA MASTER FARMERS

~

March 2006

Don and Marylou Ahrens
Mitchell County

Don Ahrens began his career not in the fields of Mitchell County but in the field of education.

While working toward advanced degrees at Iowa State University, he was an instructor in ag engineering and an adviser in the farm operations department. He was an assistant professor at Southern Illinois University (1970-72) and ag division head, Chippewa Valley Technical College, Eau Claire, Wis. (1972-80).

In 1974, while still at Chippewa Valley, he purchased a 160-acre farm near his boyhood home in Osage, which he farmed on weekends. His wife, Marylou, held a position in western Wisconsin and eastern Minnesota as a consultant dietitian for area nursing homes.

When Don's parents retired in 1980, he and his family decided to make a career change and moved to the home farm. He purchased an additional 40 acres from his parents and another

313 acres have been added since.

In 1983, Don was named area Pioneer salesman. He sold seed and farmed for 21 years. Three years ago he retired from Pioneer and rented out part of his farm ground. Today he farms part time and is a part-time sales representative for Progressive Planting Systems. Marylou, also an ISU graduate in dietetics, owns a health-care consulting business.

Over the years the couple has experimented with conventional tillage, ridge till and strip tillage. Don switched from conventional tillage to ridge till in the mid-80s. In his 18 years as a ridge tiller, Don banded fall fertilizer on the ridge. He also banded herbicides and applied starter fertilizer at planting time. Nitrogen was side-dressed while cultivating.

In 2003, Don built a twin-row planter using a Kinze planter as the foundation. "The twin rows allow for greater space between plants and yet allow a higher population to be planted," he explains. Don continues to experiment

Marylou and Don Ahrens

with plant population, nitrogen rates and manure management.

"A goal on our farm has been that all farm production, as it leaves the driveway, goes to a farmer-owned value-added entity which we are a part of," says Don. "Since the mid-80s we have explored many venues to add value to the raw materials we produce."

"As a farm-based dietitian, I have a real interest in how the consumer perceives agriculture and farm products once they leave the farm gate," adds Marylou. "We as farmers need to continue to educate the public as to our importance in the food, disposable products and energy chains."

"Don's life interests have allowed many 'circle of influences' to develop throughout the county, state, Midwest, nationally and internationally," says friend Randy Heitz. "His ethical standards shown in his lifestyle provide the example for a family known for their contributions to society. Don and Marylou's children recognize their close heritage with the soil and their parents' values of serving others."

Ernie and Virginia Sage
Black Hawk County

Ernie and Virginia Sage have had to deal with many adversities — a farm accident and poor health, for example — but it hasn't affected their faith, slowed them down in their farming or detracted from their leadership in local, state and national issues.

Ernie was struck with lupus disease in the early 1980s, which severely affected his eyesight. However, he has continued to be actively involved in management of the operation and in service to his community. Much of the physical workload has fallen to Virginia, but that hasn't put a damper on her volunteer efforts, either.

Following Ernie's graduation in 1955, he started farming full-time with his father. After Virginia and Ernie were married in 1960, they farmed on shares with his father and eventually bought him out.

Virginia and Ernie were farrow-to-finish pork producers at one time. But health issues and the 1998 price declines forced them to look at other alternatives. Today they raise around 900 head of replacement gilts per year on contract in confinement buildings. They also buy about 100 Holstein feeder steers each year and finish them in open lots.

Their cropping program consists of a corn-soybean rotation on about 700 acres. Fertilizer impregnated with herbicides has been used since the 1980s. The Sages have also tried to diversify the operation by experimenting with raising edible beans and waxy corn.

Conservation counts

Crane Creek meanders through their farm, so conservation is important to the Sages. Since the land has a less than 3% slope, grass waterways and buffer strips are adequate. "We had a cow herd until 1999 to utilize land along Crane Creek because we don't believe in row crop-

Virginia and Ernie Sage

ping too close to streams," explains Virginia. "During that time, our crop rotation included oats and hay."

Son Allen now helps with the farm on a shared-labor arrangement. "Allen has been involved with the farming operation since high school," notes Virginia. "It's because he wanted to farm and helped us that we were able to continue farming. At the same time, we were able to help him get his farming operation started."

Virginia and Ernie have opened their home and farm for tours for foreign visitors from New Zealand, Sweden and Mexico, as well as anyone interested in learning about a family farm in Iowa. As president of Black Hawk County Farm Bureau and chairwoman of Farm Bureau Women, Virginia has been a strong spokeswoman for agriculture, willing to present the farm picture to newspaper, radio and TV audiences.

Virginia and Ernie have served on the Republican Party Central Committee for Black Hawk County, and the couple has hosted many political events. They frequently travel to Des Moines to visit with state legislators on issues related to agriculture.

In 1992 Virginia ran an unsuccessful campaign for county supervisor. "It was truly an eye-opening experience into the world of politics," she declares.

Dave and Diane Petty
Hardin County

The Petty family has taken what might be considered a negative situation—farming along a river—and turned it into an environmental plus, as well as a profitable and productive farming operation.

Dave, Diane and daughter Dresden farm

Diane and Dave Petty

land along seven miles of the picturesque Iowa River near Eldora in Hardin County. Dave began farming in 1974 with 10 beef cows and a rented pasture. Over the years, he worked to rent and make improvements on marginal cropland and overgrazed pastures.

With the help of USDA's Natural Resources Conservation Service, the Pettys have put soil-saving practices to work. The operation has over 13 miles of terraces, 12 miles of tile drainage and 11 miles of shaped grass waterways. Four ponds and two miles of buffers also help control erosion, improve water quality and establish wildlife habitat.

Dave rented small pastures when commodity prices were high and "no one else was interested in grazing." Much of the land was hilly or easily flooded, not suited to row crops.

The Pettys have two employees and additional seasonal help. Dresden, an Iowa State University student, helps when she has time.

Use resources wisely

Dave has put the land and resources to their best use by establishing a high-quality beef cow herd. He gets very good production from pastures and by only row-cropping the better soils, has maintained a good yield average. Petty uses no-till and conservation tillage

Conservation practices are made productive by harvesting forage from waterways, contour buffers, filter strips and grassed headlands. "Our crop headlands are grass, which we bale once during the season to keep it growing," he explains. "Then in the fall our cows graze cornstalks and grass in the headlands, field terraces, grass waterways and buffer strips."

The Angus-based cow herd traces back to the original 10 animals Dave used to begin farming. Calves are finished through the farm's feedlot. Heifers are retained for replacement.

Through the feedlot Dave monitors his breeding program and tracks the calves with electronic ear tags. This has provided eight years of carcass data to help make decisions.

"Dave gives generously of his time, serving on a number of committees and boards to improve the cattle industry and the environment," notes Brian Peterson, state grasslands specialist for NRCS in Iowa. "Dave shows others how to farm in an environmentally-friendly way. The family hosts tours and field days. Dave makes presentations at meetings in Iowa and elsewhere."

Diane, an elementary-school principal, helps with visitors. The farm hosts people from federal and state agencies such as EPA, NRCS, Iowa Department of Natural Resources and Iowa State University Extension, farm groups and foreign visitors. ISU has conducted water-quality, stream bank stabilization and grazing research on the farm.

Howard and Velma Keitzer
Des Moines County

After farming for 50 years near Mediapolis in southeast Iowa, Howard Keitzer retired in 1999, but is still busy channeling his energy into volunteer activities. He and wife Velma rent their land to son Dan and have sold the hog facilities to Dan and a nephew, Bryan Keitzer.

Howard and Velma have another legacy: They helped several young people get started in farming or other careers. Howard hired youth to work on the farm and enjoyed teaching them about farming.

In particular, there are two young men Howard mentored. He gave them an ownership interest in a swine enterprise with him while they were employed by him during high school and college years.

One student, Steve Wilson, is farming in southeast Iowa today. Another, Dennis Breder, is a CPA. Both helped nominate Howard and Velma for the Master Farmer Award.

"I was a town kid but active in FFA," says Wilson. "Howard's instruction and knowledge enabled me to become a farmer with my grandfather and then on my own for the past 30 years. Even today if I needed help I know Howard would be there for me. You are never forgotten once you leave this extended family."

Takes pride in community

Howard has always had a passion for recordkeeping, starting out with a paper system of notebooks and the old "Better Farm Accounting" orange record book from Iowa State University.

The Keitzers are strong supporters of school activities.

Howard and a group of citizens started an organization, The Mediapolis Community Theater. It took 14 years and a lot of work to raise the funds from private donations and fund raisers. Now there's a $1.2 million auditorium attached to the school building for use by the school and community.

During Howard's tenure on the Des Moines County Fair Board, the fairgrounds was taken over by a new four-lane highway and was forced to relocate. The board decided to partner and pool funds with Southeastern Community College to build a mutual facility to serve both entities. Howard was very instrumental in leading this effort.

The Keitzers helped remodel the United Methodist Church they attend in Mediapolis. Pastor John Gaulke describes Howard as "one of the most giving and generous people I've ever known."

If you shadow Howard for a day or two, you'll be busy. If the work is finished on the farm, then you'll be helping someone else because that's Howard's way, says Gaulke. "For me, he epitomizes the qualities of a Master Farmer. I am blessed to be his pastor."

Exceptional Service Award
Alfred Blackmer

Iowa farmers lost a friend, ally and champion when Iowa State University agronomy professor Alfred Blackmer died Jan. 28. He is being honored posthumously with the Iowa Master Farmer Exceptional Service Award.

The award is given to a person who has given exceptional service to Iowa agriculture. Blackmer, 62, battled pancreatic cancer for two years.

Growing up on a dairy farm in Connecticut, Blackmer developed a desire to help farmers. He moved to Ames in 1973 and received a doctorate in soil microbiology and biochemistry from Iowa State University in 1977. He specialized in soils research at ISU and taught graduate courses in advanced soil fertility.

Blackmer worked directly with hundreds of farmers throughout Iowa to solve practical problems. A recognized expert on nitrogen, he developed better ways to manage this important crop nutrient. It wasn't always a popular stand with some of his colleagues and the fertilizer industry, but everyone knew where Blackmer stood.

His fight against excessive application showed how economic returns to farmers can be improved and losses of N to the environment can be stopped. It sometimes put him at odds with other researchers and agronomists, but over the years, more and more farmers, many participating in on-farm trials, have proven him right. His studies showed that N application rates could usually be reduced significantly without losing yield. His death leaves an empty office in the ISU agronomy building, but the work he began will continue.

Blackmer maintained an active research program with a primary focus on N management and precision-farming methods. He advised 17 masters and 19 Ph.D. students from eight countries as well as numerous international visiting scientists. He authored many publications, received 14 professional awards and represented ISU at many international conferences.

Tributes may be sent to the Fred Blackmer Ag Scholarship, c/o JSCS Foundation, Home State Bank, 115 State St., Jefferson, IA 50129. This fund will go to graduates of Jefferson-Scranton High School who are entering college.

A second scholarship will provide funding for ISU graduate students in agronomy conducting applied research. To contribute to the Alfred Blackmer Scholarship Fund, contact ISU Foundation, 2505 Elwood Dr., Ames, Iowa 50010.

Alfred Blackmer

2006 MASTER FARMER PROFILES

DON & MARYLOU AHRENS: Osage
Farm: 513 acres corn and soybean rotation
Family: Renee (Brian) Thomas is an associate professor of pharmacy at Shenandoah University, Winchester, Va.; Brad is an engineer at Trammel and Crowe, Dallas, Texas; Lisa (J.R.) Peterson is a consultant with Ag Business Group, Indianapolis, Ind.
Leadership highlights: Don: Mitchell County Corn and Soybean Growers Association, Iowa Corn Promotion Board director, U.S. Feed Grains Council, County Extension Council. Marylou: 2004 graduate of the first I-LEAD (Iowa Leadership Enhancement and Development) class, ISU Agricultural Endowment Board of Directors, ISU Extension Advisory Council, president of Iowa Consultant Dietitians.
Awards: ISU Ag Innovators, County Master Grower, Pioneer Top Sales Club, Friend of Extension, Honorary FFA degrees.

ERNIE & VIRGINIA SAGE: Dunkerton
Farm: Corn and soybeans on about 750 acres. Raise replacement gilts on contract in confinement, feed out Holstein steers.
Family: Eric (DeeAnn) manages TAMCO Pork LLC; Allen (Cassie) farms with Ernie and Virginia; Melinda (Alex) Cartwright is a computer systems analyst at University of Buffalo New York.
Awards: Virginia, first woman elected Black Hawk County Farm Bureau president and first female county voting delegate.
Leadership highlights: Both have held all executive offices in Black Hawk County Farm Bureau. Virginia: chairwoman, Farm Bureau Women's group. Ernie: church treasurer, finance chairman.
Organizations: Pork Producers, Iowa Cattlemen's Association, Corn and Soybean Associations.

DAVE & DIANE PETTY: Eldora
Farm: Half row-crop, half pasture and hay. Calves from Angus-based cow herd are finished in feedlot on farm. Diane is an elementary- school principal.
Family: Daughter Dresden is a senior at Iowa State.
Awards: State and national winner of National Cattlemen's Beef Association Environmental Stewardship Award, Spencer Award from the Leopold Center for Sustainable Agriculture, and the U.S. EPA's Regional Administrator's Award for Environmental Excellence.
Leadership highlights: Dave is a board member of Southfork Watershed Alliance, Hardin County Conservation Board and a representative to Prairie Rivers RC&D.
Organizations: Two terms as president of Hardin County Cattlemen and Iowa Cattlemen's Association. He's served on the Iowa Beef Industry Council and National Cattlemen's Beef Association board of directors.

HOWARD & VELMA KEITZER: Mediapolis
Farm: Howard and Velma own 370 acres. Family operation includes son Dan and Howard's brother Robert and nephew Bryan. They farm a total of 2,400 acres of row crop on rented and owned land. Howard is retired but helps with farm work.
Family: Son Dan farms with Howard and Velma. Daughter Jodie and family live in Cedar Rapids.
Awards: Honored for 18 years on Des Moines County Fair Board, Howard is active in Lions Club. Proud of FFA and 4-H honors he earned as a youth, he was an adult 4-H leader. Howard and Velma have spent countless hours volunteering for church, school and community projects.
Leadership highlights: Organizes big parade at Mediapolis Town and Country Festival each August. They've always been strong supporters of school activities and active in Mediapolis Community Theater.

IOWA MASTER FARMERS

~
March 2007

Four Iowa farm families have been named Iowa Master Farmers by *Wallaces Farmer* magazine. They were recognized during ceremonies in West Des Moines on March 15. The four families include: Bill and Nancy Couser, Nevada; David and Lisa Lubben, Monticello; Kenneth and Bethene Maass, Remsen; Curtis and Brenda Meier, Clarinda.

Henry A. Wallace started the Iowa Master Farmer program in 1926. The 2007 selections bring the total to 410 Iowans who have been honored since 1926.

Bill and Nancy Couser
Story County

Although he and his family farm a lot of ground, operate a cattle feedlot, employ five people full time and have part-time help—which all takes time and effort to manage—you'll find Bill Couser cooking beef at various local events and helping his community in many ways. A leader and a forward thinker, Couser remembers his roots and what got him to where he is today.

From the days of showing calves in 4-H, his interest in beef production grew. After graduating from Des Moines Area Community College, Couser worked for a local implement dealer, rented some land on his own and began farming and raising hogs and cattle with his parents, Dick and JoAnn Couser, north of Nevada.

Bill relies on wife Nancy to help him manage the extensive farming operation. He also credits employees and business associates for their help. Nancy works part time as a registered nurse. Eldest son Casey is now a student at the Brook Institute in California studying film production. Son Tim is a sophomore studying agriculture at Iowa State University and also works part-time for Couser Cattle Company.

Bill makes farm equipment available for FFA and other community purposes and has provided use of his farm shop for FFA projects at Nevada High School. He hires ISU students part-time to give them farming experience.

The Cousers use records to track each farm individually. GPS mapping combined with planting, fertility and harvest information is maintained for each field. The information can be shared with landlords and farm managers in addition to use by the Cousers to make decisions and maximize returns.

Common sense solutions

Experimenting with different rates and times to apply fertilizer, Bill has built equipment to apply liquid nitrogen from planting to tasseling. Most of the N is sidedressed with a cultivator. Other equipment he's engineered includes a portable unloading pit used in the field to dump and load seed corn to greatly speed up harvesting.

A couple years ago Bill contacted the Iowa Department of Natural Resources, Iowa State University Extension ag engineers and USDA's Natural Resources Conservation Service to see if they can come up with an alternative to an earthen catch basin for feedlot runoff. A field day at the feedlot last summer was attended by over 300 farmers and ag business professionals.

The engineers, cooperating with the agencies, have installed an alternative system and the study is ongoing. "We're doing this not only for our own benefit but to help other cattle producers who face environmental issues," says Couser.

Bill's conservation ethic was instilled by his father. The Cousers maintain grass waterways, terraces and buffer strips. Where cornstalks and bean straw are removed the ground gets bedding and manure from the feedlot. "Bill has great concern and does what he can to save soil and manage wisely. He applies no fall nitrogen and tries to find the right timing and amount of nutrients to produce a crop," says Dave Andrews, Story County Extension director.

"We've tried to mold our farming operation to be a progression of value-added activities, one phase leading to another," says Bill, "from corn to ethanol, to feeding the distillers grain to cattle, to using the manure nutrients to grow more corn." He is president of Lincolnway Energy, a 50-million-gallon-per-year ethanol plant at Nevada owned by 947 people—local investors in Story County and surrounding area. He was a driving force behind the idea to build the plant and has attended countless meetings to talk with shareholders and work with the board.

"Nancy can speak to this, too," says Bill. "Winning the Iowa Master Farmer Award is very humbling for both of us. We just wanted to farm and raise our kids and hopefully leave this place a little better than it was when we began. And enjoy it."

Nancy and Bill Couser

Lisa and David Lubben

David and Lisa Lubben
Jones County

The old saying "knowledge is power" certainly applies to David Lubben. Not only does he utilize on-farm test plots, track expenses and returns on every aspect of his operation and write an annual business plan, he shares this information with anyone who is interested.

This leadership style began to emerge in the early 1980s when Lubben organized a marketing club. "In 1982, I was experiencing anxiety about marketing so I invited a few farmers to a meeting to talk about marketing. The club continues to this day. We each develop a written marketing plan that is fine-tuned throughout the year. As the facilitator, I challenge our thinking by asking a question of the month and we have regular speakers to help broaden our knowledge."

In the early 1990s, Lubben began conducting replicated cropping experiments on his farm near Monticello in Jones County. Over the years he has studied a variety of tillage practices, crop varieties, fertilizer placement, etc. But the key was the detailed data he presented at Practical Farmers of Iowa field days showing how each practice performed in productivity and profitability.

Lubben is a consummate record keeper and spends many hours at his computer developing spreadsheets on cost of production, breakeven prices, etc. His annual business plan includes financial reports, enterprise analysis, marketing goals and objectives, cost of production worksheets, supply and demand reports, historical comparisons, crop production by field, etc.

He shares all this information with his banker. "It provides much more documentation than any banker would ask for," notes Lubben. "But, it is really helpful to see the whole picture."

Lubben is ready and willing to test new technologies on his farm. He and his father Robert have a family-owned corporation of around 1,700 acres owned and rented acres of corn, soybeans, hay and pasture. They have a commercial cow herd of around 210 head and finish around 400 calves in the feedlot.

This northeast Iowa farmer was an early adopter of management intensive grazing. "We started using this practice in 1989 and it has evolved into an integral part of our operation," notes Lubben. "We have 20 paddocks which we subdivide into 50 smaller paddocks. Our grazing system consists of four to five cycles through the paddocks," he explains.

Four major benefits are derived from the grazing program, according to Lubben. "The rest period we give our pastures has given new life to our forage diversification. I'm continuously amazed at new species of grass and legumes growing in the pastures."

Body condition of his cows has improved as well. "We rotate our cows daily to a fresh paddock, which greatly improves the palatability of the grass."

Stream bank stability has also improved over the years. "We have 5 acres of creek bottom pasture that was continuously grazed and showing wear and tear on the banks. Downstream I was using management intensive grazing and grazing the stream banks one day per month. We had massive amounts of vegetation. This taught me management intensive grazing also improves riparian areas, but there is a four to five year transition to get there."

Lastly, Lubben lists peace of mind as a benefit. "I thoroughly enjoy going out on my ATV and moving cows to the next paddock. I have two young daughters and I want to do things with them that don't require big machinery or pesticides. Management intensive grazing allows me to do that."

Kenneth and Bethene Maass
Plymouth County

The way Kenneth Maass and his brother Arnold began farming in 1959 probably isn't feasible for two young people today. After both served in the military, they started out in a 50-50 partnership with money they'd saved. They farmed together for 18 years until Arnold's sons were old enough to help their dad, then Kenneth farmed on his own.

Today Kenneth and wife Bethene are working son-in-law Jim Ruba into the operation and rent 700 acres to him. In exchange for labor, Jim uses Kenneth's machinery. Kenneth and Bethene recognize this is a way they can help the next generation remain in farming.

The Maass family had a beef cow herd and raised hogs for many years. Maintaining a flock of 100 head of Suffolk ewes rounded out the livestock program. When Kenneth quit raising livestock on the farm, he kept an interest by partnering with other farmers. He custom fed pigs in a partnership owning 6,000 head per year. Until 2003 he was into commercial cattle feeding having a 15% interest in groups of 1,800 head, feeding three groups a year.

Kenneth uses his on-farm records to track fertilizer, chemicals, planting and yield information, he says. "I look for good seed genetics and seek the advice of a local agronomist and rely on results from the Iowa Crop Performance Tests."

Using GPS, Kenneth was ahead of most farmers in having his ground mapped. He hired a local service early on. The data helps determine soil fertility, lime needs and manure application planning. He's used a yield monitor since 1998.

Soil conservation practices include terracing, contouring and minimum tillage. The windbreak he established the very first year he farmed in 1959 has been maintained, renovated and still does its job. He maintains 30 acres of CRP land. "It's good habitat for wildlife and is adjacent to streams. I support Pheasants Forever and realize the benefits of buffer strips for streams," he says.

Resourceful and seeking advice from others when making decisions, Kenneth also shares what he knows, particularly with young farmers. He says his partnership with his brother in those early years helped him greatly in life. "There were two minds to make decisions and two of us to share the financial risk. Today I still rely on Arnold--for additional help during planting and harvesting."

Kenneth uses the services of a CPA. "I initially went to the CPA because managing our financial records took more time than I had," he says. "After awhile, I realized the value of

children. Daughter Tammy Maass is married to Steve Portz and they live at Remsen. Lori Maass, married to Jim Ruba, Jr., is at Granville. Stacie Maass has a pharmacy degree and a law degree and works on the White House staff in Washington, D.C.

During his tenure on the county fair board, Kenneth was "mayor" of the fair's Pioneer Village, which depicts a small town of bygone

Kenneth and Bethene Maass

the CPA's expertise as an advisor."

Always available to help

Intellectually curious, Kenneth takes Iowa State University's grain marketing classes. Last fall he went to China. Active in Christ Lutheran Church in Remsen, Kenneth and Bethene raised three daughters and enjoy four grand-

days. He managed the stage and his knack for finding good entertainers and emceeing helped the village become a favorite of fairgoers. He carried out the tasks tirelessly and brought new additions, buildings that have historical significance so fairgoers can appreciate the county's history.

"As a fellow fair board member, I appreciated Kenneth as a leader," says Plymouth County Extension Director Carol Schneider. "If the board was faced with a tough decision, he gave the topic plenty of thought outside the meeting and contributed to good decisions that have made the Plymouth County Fair one of the leading county fairs in the state."

Kenneth believes farming today extends beyond the needed success generated by man-

the recipe Meier Family Farm Inc. has used to add a son and son-in-law to this 2,000-acre diversified operation in southwest Iowa.

It's a family run business managed by Curtis, Brenda, son Michael, who joined the corporation in 1997 and son-in-law Kevin who joined in 2002. Curtis and his father Rudy set up the corporation in 1981. All family members are employees of the corporation. Curtis

Curtis and Brenda Meier

aging acres and livestock. "You also should give some time to your community," he says.

Curtis and Brenda Meier
Page County

It takes foresight, planning and organization to successfully bring the next generation into most farming operations today. And that's

has two brothers who are also shareholders.

As part of the process to "bring the boys in," Meier Family Farms has nearly doubled crop acreage in recent years. The livestock program includes a farrow-to-finish hog operation, a cow-calf herd and cattle feedlot. Livestock numbers are being increased as well. Plans include doubling the current feedlot capacity. The availability of dried distiller's grain makes this plan even more attractive. "We have at least four ethanol plants coming on line within 60 miles," explains Curtis.

Mike and Curtis take care of the livestock and Kevin is in charge of crops and is the truck driver. To obtain the best prices, they haul their own grain to market, even as far away as Kansas City. "If we can make a buck, we have the truck," chuckles Curtis.

The Meiers rent nearly half of the land they farm. That's not easy these days with the tough competition for farmland. "Our philosophy is to take care of things, do things right and you'll be rewarded," notes Curtis.

Corn-soybean rotation

The cropping program consists of corn and soybeans rotated with alfalfa and annual rye grass. Curtis is willing to try new ideas and uses the latest technology. With the increased acres, they stepped up to a 16-row planter last year. Both the planter and combine are equipped with GPS. Mapping is done with the planter and the maps overlaid on yield maps to compare yields of various varieties.

"I view this as an on-going process," observes Curtis. "The more data we collect as we go down the road, the more useful it will be, particularly as we develop variable rate technology. At some point, we'll probably utilize VRT.

"We foresee the day when we'll have a total nutrient management system. We'll have to account for every ounce of nutrient applied to our land. With our GPS records, it will be easier to move into total nutrient management," he adds.

Soil and water conservation efforts include terraces, filter strips, windbreaks, cover crops, no-till and zone soil testing. He has installed nearly 21 miles of terraces on the family farm.

As many farmers will relate, "pigs have been good to me," declares Curtis. And the couple has paid back by being active leaders in the pork industry. They have promoted pork around the world in places like Japan, Vietnam, Thailand, Taiwan and Cuba. Curtis has been on fact-finding missions in Germany, England and Brazil. They continue to promote the industry around the United States as well. "Some of the best days of my life were promoting pork. It was work, but I enjoyed it," says Curtis. "We have met a lot of nice people."

LOOKING AHEAD
The future of Iowa agriculture

In 1926, when Henry A. Wallace launched the Master Farmer Awards program in Iowa, most farms were energy self-sufficient. Homegrown oats and hay "fueled" the "horse" power. Wood cut on the farm cooked the family food and heated the farm home.

Agriculture has changed dramatically over the past 80 years. But many issues, including our desire for energy self-sufficiency, or at least energy security, persist. But technology has created an entirely new renewable energy playing field. No longer does energy flow directly from the farm woodlot to the cook stove. Rather, it flows from Iowa grain and oilseed fields through processing plants then on to the nation's highways. It moves from Iowa's windy ridges into the nation's electric power grid. Research on cellulosic ethanol may one day bring the farm woodlot back as a major energy source.

Corn-based ethanol's recent rise to prominence seems meteoric. Yet ethanol's modern roots go back to events of the early 1970s. One was the grain export boom. U.S. farmers geared up production to meet ballooning world grain demand, particularly to the Soviet Union. Then came the 1973 oil price shock. Forward thinking farmers saw ethanol as a way to trim dependence on foreign oil. But high energy prices and attempts to control inflation, particularly in the United States, stifled world economic growth bringing a major world recession in 1981. Grain export demand softened. Oil prices retreated, eroding ethanol's price competitiveness. Burdensome grain supplies built up. Crop prices fell. Corn farmers repositioned ethanol to use surplus stocks and buoy prices.

Euphoria over the grain export boom plus expectations that inflation would keep accelerating drove land prices sharply higher. A farm income bust linked to faltering exports and efforts to wring inflation out of the economy precipitated the farm financial crisis of the mid 1980s.

Fast forward

U.S. farmers are again gearing up production to meet ballooning demand for corn for ethanol for energy security on and off the farm. New technologies, cellulosic ethanol and butanol for example, promise to open new market doors for farmers.

The bioenergy economy may be on the threshold of explosive growth just as the electronics industry was in the 1960s. Farmers will have opportunities to pocket handsome profits—in growing feedstocks for bioenergy and in processing those crops into fuel, food and feed.

But evolving technologies can rapidly flourish, then fade. Electric typewriters, beta video tapes, and 5¼ inch floppy discs are just a few. The fax supplanted mail, then e-mail trumped the fax. Profit opportunities in bioenergy will be fraught with risks for those who invest in the wrong technology, invest at the wrong time or fail to pick opportune moments to roll investments forward into the next emerging technology or market.

Some people worry that planting fencerow to fencerow for fuel will weaken conservation efforts launched during the dust bowl days of the 1930s.

Bioenergy could evolve into combined systems. For example, a fermentation unit running on corn or cornstalks produces fuel ethanol and feed co-products. The feed goes to a livestock facility. Manure flows to an anaerobic digestion unit. Gases from the anaerobic digester go to fuel cells that turn out electricity, heat and carbon dioxide. The latter two go to heat and fertilize greenhouses for vegetables.

Some sociologists fear fuel crops competing with food crops will boost food costs for people in developing countries who are least able to pay higher prices for food.

The length of the fuels boom depends upon three factors:

*Continuation of a U.S. energy policy that favors biofuels;

*The economics of conversion of energy from corn to fuel, which is highly dependent upon the price of corn in relation to the price of petroleum; and

*The paths of new technologies.

Economic concerns

Suppose bioenergy does lift grain prices to a new plateau. Historically, farmers have used profits to bid up the price of agriculture's fixed resource—land. Higher land prices and cash rents boost fixed costs, wringing profit back out of production.

High crop prices quickly attract more land into production. However, if a downturn comes, it would take a long stretch of low prices to get land back out of production.

We're not predicting that farmers will overproduce, resulting in sagging prices and a burst to the land price bubble. But we certainly would not rule out such developments. Everything in agriculture is cyclical—always

has been and likely always will be.

Keeping on the cutting edge

Still, coming generations of Iowa Master Farmers will size up agriculture's growing myriad of opportunities. They'll analyze the tradeoffs. They'll make decisions to invest or not invest, on what to produce and what not to produce. They'll find the most efficient ways to produce it.

Ethanol euphoria ran up grain prices, putting livestock producers in a cost/price squeeze. They began adapting. Dairy and beef rapidly incorporated ethanol co-products in rations. Researchers are seeking ways for swine and poultry to better use bioenergy co-products.

Information drives agriculture

Agriculture needs solid investment in public and private research to keep pushing back the frontiers of science, discovering new products and developing new production practices. Farmers need vehicles like *Wallaces Farmer* to keep informed and a rapid information disseminator like the Internet to transmit data and information so they can keep pace with the ever-changing times.

Putting those management tools in the innovative hands of Iowa's future Master Farmers will keep them on the leading edge of feeding and fueling people around the world, plus profiting on the farm.

ALPHABETICAL LIST OF IOWA MASTER FARMER AWARD WINNERS

*deceased

A

*Adamson, Whitfield, Cherokee (Cherokee), 1955

Ahrens, Don, Osage (Mitchell), 2006

Amdor, Jim, Corning (Adams), 2004

Amstutz, Dean, Bloomfield (Davis), 2001

*Anderson, Carl T., Wellman (Washington), 1927

*Anderson, J. Merrill, Newton (Jasper), 1958

Anderson, Jim, Boone (Boone), 2002

Anderson, Richard, West Branch (Cedar), 1985

*Anderson, William C., West Liberty (Muscatine), 1929

Anton, David, LaPorte City (Black Hawk), 2000

Anton, Larry, LaPorte City (Black Hawk), 2000

Autenrieth, Horace, Paullina (O'Brien), 1967

B

*Backhaus, H.D., Clear Lake (Cerro Gordo), 1927

Bailey, Varel G., Anita (Cass), 1993

*Baker, H.K., Beaconsfield (Ringgold), 1930

*Ballou, Bert, Monticello (Jones), 1964

*Barber, S.A., Kanawha (Hancock), 1952

Barker, Norman, Ireton (Sioux), 1966

*Barringer, H.E., Emmetsburg (Palo Alto), 1928

*Bay, Stanley L., Albia (Monroe), 1990

*Beck, Walter, Danville (Des Moines), 1931

Beernink, Vernon James, Sioux Center (Sioux), 1992

*Bell, Robert W., Coggon (Linn), 1970

*Bellman, G.D., Indianola (Warren), 1946

Benson, Garren, Ames (Story), 1996 – Exceptional Service

Berger, Dennis, Wellman (Washington), 1996

Beyer, Larry, Marengo (Iowa), 2002

Bjustrom, Charles, Whittemore (Kossuth), 1985

*Black, Hugh, Algona (Kossuth), 1965

*Blackmer, Alfred, Ames (Story), 2006 – Exceptional Service

*Blackwell, Dale, Bloomfield (Davis), 1949

*Blahauvietz, William, Harris (Osceola), 1957

*Blakely, A.J., Grinnell (Poweshiek), 1927

*Blinks, Roscoe, Marion (Linn), 1931

*Boatman, J.J., Montezuma (Poweshiek), 1930

*Bode, Harry J., Algona (Kossuth), 1929

*Bolte, Harvey C., Silver City (Mills), 1971

Boyd, Duane, Charles City (Floyd), 1975

*Boyer, W.H., Dallas Center (Dallas), 1929

Britten, Jerry, Zearing (Story), 2005

*Brown, Glenn R., Grundy Center (Grundy), 1964

*Bruene, Fred K., Gladbrook (Tama), 1940

*Buck, H.W., Greenfield (Adair), 1938

Burrack, Gary, Monona (Clayton), 2005

*Burt, Don, Marshalltown (Marshall), 1987

Busch, George H., Allison (Butler), 1973

*Byrnes, Louis, Cresco (Howard), 1968

C

*Cain, Larry, Mason City (Cerro Gordo), 1959 – Exceptional Service

*Calmer, Ralph, Manson (Calhoun), 1968

*Campbell, Herbert, Washington (Washington), 1951

*Christensen, Frank, Ogden (Boone), 1952

Christensen, Robert ("Bob"), Hastings (Mills), 1983

*Christiansen, Alvin, Nora Springs (Floyd), 1955

*Christophel, George W., Waverly (Bremer), 1926

*Christy, Glenn, Garrison (Benton), 1958

*Clampitt, R.R., New Providence (Hardin), 1927

*Clark, Robert M., Mitchellville (Polk), 1931

*Clause, A.R., Grand Junction (Greene), 1948

*Cline, Herbert, Bussey (Marion), 1960

*Coglon, Ray, Exira (Audubon), 1941

*Collins, Bernard, Clarion (Wright), 1959

*Collison, John, Arcadia (Carroll), 1931

*Conner, Carney H., Glidden (Carroll), 1947

Cook, Kenneth J., New Providence (Hardin), 1984

Copenhaver, Paul, Independence (Buchanan), 1987

*Core, Clyde M., Pleasantville (Marion), 1950

*Cornelius, Gerald E., Bellevue (Jackson), 1991

Couser, Bill, Nevada (Story), 2006

Curran, Leigh R., Mason City (Cerro Gordo), 1947

D

*Dall, Henry, Battle Creek (Ida), 1941

*Darbyshire, William, Rockwell City (Calhoun), 1957

*Davidson, William H., Stanwood (Cedar), 1947

*Davis, James C., Millerton (Wayne), 1929

Demmer, Wayne, Epworth (Dubuque), 2002

Doolittle, Donald F., Blairsburg (Hamilton), 1969

Doolittle, Donald L., Duncombe (Webster), 1982

*Dreeszen, Elvie, Cushing (Ida), 1964

*Dubbert, Fred, Laurens (Pocahontas), 1948

*Dunham, Z.T., Dunlap (Harrison), 1929

*Dunn, Leo, Clemons (Marshall), 1970

*Dunphy, Gene, Creston (Union), 1968

E

Eddy, Loren, Centerville (Appanoose), 1978

*Eldred, Russell, Anamosa (Jones), 1956

*Elijah, Earl E., Clarence (Cedar), 1928

Ellerman, Bill, Dallas Center (Dallas), 1994

*Elliott, Jack M., Mount Ayr (Ringgold), 1970

Engstrom, Edward, Kanawha (Hancock), 1990

*Entz, J.E., Waterloo (Black Hawk), 1950

Enyart, Gordon, Prairie City (Jasper), 1977

*Everett, Frank F., New Sharon (Mahaska), 1928

Ewoldt, Gary, Davenport (Scott), 1995

F

Faris, Lee, Mt. Ayr (Ringgold), 2003

Fawcett, Kenneth I., West Branch (Cedar), 1999

Feldman, Marlowe, Albert City (Buena Vista), 1972

*Fisher, C. Raymond, Grand Junction (Greene), 1956

Fisher, David H., Hubbard (Hardin), 1998

*Fisher, Oswell, Hubbard (Hardin), 1957

*Flint, David, What Cheer (Keokuk), 1974

*Foster, Burrell C., Wellman (Washington), 1928

*Foutch, Donald, Woodbine (Harrison), 1957

*Fox, Harry B., Odebolt (Sac), 1929

Fox, Ralph, Riceville (Howard), 1960

*Franzenburg, Herman, Keystone (Benton), 1931

Freese, Glenn, Vail (Crawford), 1973

*Frye, Wilbert, Independence (Buchanan), 1975

G

*George, Floyd N., Janesville (Black Hawk), 1959

*George, W.M., Denver (Bremer), 1929

Gilbert, Alvin J., New Hampton (Chickasaw), 1982

*Godfrey, George, Algona (Kossuth), 1926

Goeken, Walt, Monona (Clay), 1986

Goldsmith, Jerry G., Clarence (Cedar), 1994

*Goodhue, Wilbur E., Carlisle (Warren), 1949

*Grafft, Delbert L., Olin (Jones), 1972

Grau, Arnold I., Newell (Buena Vista), 1989

Gray, Farris, Bedford (Taylor), 1977

*Greaser, Lewis, Vinton (Benton), 1952

Greenley, Morris, Independence (Buchanan), 1991

Greiner, William, 1975 – Exceptional Service

Griffieon, Craig, Ankeny (Polk), 2000
Griffith, Paul, Lamoni (Decatur), 1969
*Gronna, Theodore, Waterville (Allamakee), 1928
*Groomes, Edmund, Menlo (Guthrie), 1961
*Groot, Merlyn, Manson (Calhoun), 1978
Groves, Richard F. ("Dick"), Webster City (Hamilton), 1984
Groves, Wilfred A. ("Bill") Jr., Kamrar (Hamilton), 1984
*Grunewald, H.J., Blairstown (Benton), 1930

H

Haahr, Leon, Newell (Buena Vista), 1965
*Hadenfeldt, Louis, Sioux Rapids (Buena Vista), 1931
*Hagen, Walter, Waterville (Allamakee), 1963
*Hagglund, Lenus, Essex (Page), 1926
*Hall, Lowell, Griswold (Cass), 1956
*Hamann, Elmer J., Eldridge (Scott), 1960
*Handorf, Ward, Gladbrook (Marshall), 1978
*Hanrahan, Ed, Creston (Union), 1968
*Hansen, Alvin, Mason City (Cerro Gordo), 1986
Hanson, Garland, Callender (Webster), 1972
Harl, Neil, Ames (Story), 2000 – Exceptional Service
Harvey, Irvin, Oskaloosa (Mahaska), 1969
Hasenclever, Frank, Fort Madison (Lee), 1973
Hawkins, David W., Orange City (Plymouth), 1991
*Hazen, Hervey E., (Lee), 1928
*Heath, Frank, Corning (Adams), 1927
Helmers, George A., Sibley (Osceola), 1980
*Helmick, James D., Columbus Junction (Louisa), 1953
*Helming, Edwin, Hornick (Woodbury), 1951
Hertz, Duane R., Laurens (Pocahontas), 1997
*Hill, Clarence S., Minburn (Dallas), 1954
*Hill, E. Howard, Minburn (Dallas), 1946
*Hill, E.L., Minburn (Dallas), 1927
Hill, Paul, Ellsworth (Hamilton), 1995
*Hinkhouse, Herbert C., West Branch (Cedar), 1967
Hoffman, George Jr., Ida Grove (Ida), 1985
*Holland, Frank, Milton (Van Buren), 1929

Holland, John R., Milton (Van Buren), 1950
Hollis, J. Gordon, Waterloo (Black Hawk), 1965
*Hollowell, W.A., Melcher (Marion), 1930
Holst Gary,, Eldridge (Scott), 1996
*Hood, Donald, Bode (Humboldt), 1971
*Hoopes, Mrs. J.E., Muscatine (Muscatine), 1931
*Hopp, R.C. Sr., Glenwood (Mills), 1930
Hora, Keith G., Riverside (Washington), 1992
*Houston, E.W., Dunlap (Harrison), 1930
Howe, Ralph R., Clemons (Marshall), 1989
*Hueck, John, Everly (Clay), 1929
*Hunt, John M., Ackley (Hardin), 1927
Huser, John ("Ted"), Sac City (Sac), 1981

I

Imlau, William F., Kensett (Worth), 1961
*Irwin, Orie F., Sac City (Sac), 1938

J

*Jager, W.F., Eddyville (Wapello), 1930
Jardon, Robert A., Randolph (Fremont), 1993
*Jensen, Roland, Ida Grove (Ida), 1974
Johnson, Don, Fairfield (Jefferson), 1959
*Johnson, Doug, Fairfield (Jefferson), 1998
Johnson, Howard Lee, Ashton (Osceola), 1992
*Johnson, Lester, LeMars (Plymouth), 1975
*Johnson, Oscar W., LeGrand (Marshall), 1927
*Johnson, Peter J., Inwood (Lyon), 1950
Johnson, Robert, Andover (Clinton), 1977
Jorgensen, James Jr., Hampton (Franklin), 1981
Jorgenson, Bud, Farragut (Fremont), 1973
*Joslin, Bob, Clarence (Cedar), 1977
*Juelsggard, Glen, Gray (Audubon), 1974

K

*Kaldenberg, Ollie, Albia (Monroe), 1976
Kalsem, David K., Huxley (Story), 1991
*Kalsem, O.J., Huxley (Story), 1928
*Kalsem, Orville N., Huxley (Story), 1952
Kalsem, Owen J., Huxley (Story), 1991
Kassel, Kenneth, Ayshire (Palo Alto), 1993
Keast, Edward F., Henderson (Pottawattamie), 1990

Keith, Edgar Wayne, Algona (Kossuth), 1988

*Keith, Wayne, Algona (Kossuth), 1954

Keitzer, Howard, Mediapolis (Des Moines), 2006

*Kennedy, Sam, Clear Lake (Cerro Gordo), 1929

*Keppy, Roy B., Davenport (Scott), 1966

*Kernen, Henry, Villisca (Montgomery), 1947

Kielkopf, Ron, Fremont (Keokuk), 2000

King, Karol, Mondamin (Harrison), 2005

King, Marshall, Boone (Boone), 1974

*Kinsley, R.G., McGregor (Clayton), 1930

Kintzle, Jack, Coggon (Linn), 2004

*Kirkpatrick, Charles D., Keota (Keokuk), 1926

*Kline, Allan B., Vinton (Benton), 1938

*Klodt, Edward, Ottumwa (Wapello), 1973

Kluver, Morris, Britt (Hancock), 1975

Knake, Albert ("Bud"), Bellevue (Jackson), 1984

*Knight, John S., Strawberry Point (Clayton), 1929

Koos, Ervin J.J., Shelby (Pottawattamie), 1959

*Korslund, Allen J., Eagle Grove (Humboldt), 1982

*Kruse, D.F., Sheldon (O'Brien), 1931

*Kruse, Donavan, Charles City (Floyd), 1960

Kuecker, Richard, Algona (Kossuth), 1979

Kunde, David, Manchester (Delaware), 2003

L

*Ladd, Edward, Rock Rapids (Lyon), 1971

*LaDoux, Fred W., Spirit Lake (Dickinson), 1926

Lang, Maynard, Brooklyn (Poweshiek), 2001

Langguth, Fritz, Fontanelle (Adair), 2001

*Lapke, Zeno, Dunlap (Harrison), 1949

*Larsen, Hans A., Spencer (Clay), 1950

*Leffler, George W., Stockport (Van Buren), 1927

Leistikow, Ronald, Readlyn (Bremer), 2003

*Lengeling, Joseph, Carroll (Carroll), 1930

*Linder, Arthur, Hartley (O'Brien), 1949

Livingston, John R., Bedford (Taylor), 1972

*Long, Ralph A., Mt. Ayr (Ringgold), 1957

Lubben, David, Monticello (Jones), 2007

*Lubkeman, H.F., Hampton (Franklin), 1930

*Lyon, Earl, Toledo (Tama), 1947

Lyon, G. Joe, Toledo (Tama), 1983

*Lyon, Howard H., Toledo (Tama), 1983

M

Maass, Kenneth, Remsen (Plymouth), 2007

Manternach, Ralph, Cascade (Jones), 1993

*Martin, H.S., Newton (Jasper), 1926

Martin, Loyd, Marion (Linn), 1986

*Martin, Sterling B., Melrose (Monroe), 1954

*Mather, Dayton W., Greene (Butler), 1939

*Mathis, Ralph C. ("R.C."), Elkhart (Polk), 1983

Matthey, Lucille ("Lu"), Sergeant Bluff (Woodbury), 1998

*McAllister, Keith, Mount Union (Henry), 1967

*McAlpin, Willis A., Villisca (Montgomery), 1964

*McArthur, William, Mason City (Cerro Gordo), 1926

McConohy, Walter, DeWitt (Clinton), 1951

*McElhinney, R.C., Waterloo (Black Hawk), 1929

McGohan, Les, Mt. Pleasant (Henry), 1964

*McGregor, Malcolm, Nashua (Chickasaw), 1976

*McGrew, Dallas, Emerson (Mills), 1954

*McKeegan, John, Rock Valley (Sioux), 1930

*McKeown, J.R., Harlan (Shelby), 1940

*McNutt, Paul, Iowa City (Johnson), 1966

McWilliams, Dean, Montezuma (Poweshiek), 2004

*Mehl, Ralph, Hornick (Woodbury), 1977

Meier, Curtis, Clarinda (Page), 2007

Menefee, Maynard, Fayette (Fayette), 1948

*Michel, Charles B.F., Marion (Linn), 1929

*Miller, Doyce, Osceola (Clarke), 1953

*Miller, F.L., Beaman (Grundy), 1930

Miller, John, Cedar Falls (Black Hawk), 1996

*Miller, Seth N., Indianola (Warren), 1928

*Misbach, J.D., Williamsburg (Iowa), 1939

*Mitchell, Fred, New Providence (Hardin), 1931

*Mitchell, Ray, Charles City (Floyd), 1957

*Moeckly, Harvey, Polk City (Polk), 1963

Mogler, Howard P., Alvord (Lyon), 1981
*Mohr, Jim, Eldridge (Scott), 1982
Mohr, Ned O., Eldridge (Scott), 1982
*Moreland, Elmer, Guthrie Center (Guthrie), 1954
*Moreland, John J., Earlham (Madison), 1951
Morey, Jerry, Hazleton (Buchanan), 2004
*Morris, E.F., New Providence (Hardin), 1926
Morris, John D., Columbus Junction (Louisa), 1968
*Morris, Lewis, Grimes (Polk), 1926
*Mountain, Charles R. (Polk), 1940
Mueller, Howard, Waverly (Bremer), 1986
Murley, Harlan A., Aurora (Buchanan), 1984
*Myhr, A.B., Thompson (Winnebago), 1927

N

*Neal, Benjamin C., Mt. Vernon (Linn), 1938
*Neal, E.N., Shell Rock (Butler), 1940
*Neill, Harold, Corning (Adams), 1958
Neill, Ralph, Corning (Adams), 1994
*Nelson, Charles O., Creston (Union), 1949
*Nelson, Fred W., Nevada (Story), 1926
Newby, Donald D., Bondurant (Polk), 1989
Newell, Thomas Herbert, Columbus Junction (Louisa), 1959
*Newhouse, Maynard, Decorah (Winneshiek), 1969
*Newton, Lewis T., Knoxville (Marion), 1928
Nielsen, Donald L., Moneta (Clay), 1979
Noller, David, Sigourney (Keokuk), 1995
*Norman, Wayne E., Wellman (Washington), 1955
Northey, Wayne, Spirit Lake (Dickinson), 1987

O

*O'Hara, Joseph C., Shenandoah (Page), 1963
Odland, Arnold, Webster City (Hamilton), 2002
*Olerich, Henry F., Rolfe (Pocahontas), 1941
*Olson, Roy, Terrill (Dickinson), 1961
Oosterhuis, Merlin, Hospers (O'Brien), 1984
*Opsand, Harold, Elgin (Fayette), 1955
*Ormston, Lyle V., Waverly (Bremer), 1953

P

Paper, Elmer, Stockton (Scott), 1985
*Pellett, Clarence A., Atlantic (Cass), 1952
*Pellett, Wendell C., Atlantic (Cass), 1961
*Pennings, William, Orange City (Sioux), 1954
*Perrin, Ned E., Mapleton (Monona), 1956
Petersen, Duane A., Sumner (Bremer), 1997
Petersen, Roland D., Bryant (Clinton), 1984
Peterson, William Floyd, Davenport (Scott), 1988
Petty, David, Eldora (Hardin), 2006
Peyton, Harold, Sac City (Sac), 1995
Pflum, Curtis, Burlington (Des Moines), 1979
*Pike, Herbert W., Whiting (Monona), 1968
*Poundstone, Harry, Clarion (Wright), 1929
Pratt, Donald W., Glidden (Carroll), 1956
*Prestemon, Alvin, Waukon (Allamakee), 1941
*Pullen, R.T., Spencer (Clay), 1927
*Pullin, Donald, Waterloo (Black Hawk), 1953
*Puttmann, Dwight R., Kingsley (Woodbury), 1988

R

Raasch, Curtis A., Odebolt (Sac), 1999
*Rassmussen, Harry, Newell (Buena Vista), 1970
*Rawson, Robert, Kingsley (Cherokee), 1978
*Redfern, Ray, Yarmouth (Des Moines), 1927
*Reed, Alex, Bellevue (Jackson), 1930
*Reese, Harry, Prescott (Adams), 1948
*Reimer, Edward, Schleswig (Crawford), 1928
*Reis, Lawrence, Greenfield (Adair), 1953
Rempp, William, Montezuma (Poweshiek), 1979
*Ringoen, Marion, Ridgeway (Winneshiek), 1947
*Rinker, H.H., Rippey (Greene), 1930
*Rogers, S.T., Hancock (Pottawattamie), 1954
Rossiter, Myers M., Winfield (Henry), 1983
Ryan, Thomas, Cresco, (Winneshiek), 2000
*Ryon, Harold V., Laurens (Pocahontas), 1965

S

Sage, Ernest, Dunkerton (Black Hawk), 2006
Sage, James E., Waterloo (Black Hawk), 1980
*Sauerby, G.E., Oelwein (Fayette), 1929
Schager, C.B., Dows (Wright), 1952
*Schaper, Otto, Estherville (Emmet), 1957
Schlitzer, Marvin, Dubuque (Dubuque), 1987
*Schmidt, Fred (Clinton), 1960
*Schmidt, George, Delmar (Clinton), 1967
*Schmuecker, Ervin J., Marengo (Iowa), 1963
*Schnack, Alvin, Harlan (Shelby), 1958
*Schnack, John P., DeWitt (Clinton), 1948
*Schneckloth, Herbert, Davenport (Scott), 1939
*Schnittjer, D.J., Delhi (Delaware), 1926
*Schuelke, Bert, Storm Lake (Buena Vista), 1928
*Schuett, Loren A., Holstein (Cherokee), 1983
Schuiteman, Art J., Sioux Center (Sioux), 1970
*Schultz, Adolph, Malvern (Mills), 1927
Schultz, John Kenneth, Postville (Allamakee), 1999
*Schultz, Otto F., Malcom (Poweshiek), 1928
Schultz, Robert, Luana (Clayton), 1976
*Schweers, Arthur, Lenox (Adams), 1976
Scott, Wayne D., Nodaway (Adams), 1990
Seberg, Glen M., Mt. Pleasant (Henry), 1981
Sexton, Dale, Rockwell City (Calhoun), 1985
Shafer, Wesley J., Fairfield (Jefferson), 1972
*Shirer, Chester, Chariton (Lucas), 1961
Showalter, Kenneth, Hampton (Franklin), 1971
*Sidles, Peter, Centerville (Appanoose), 1948
*Siglin, Amos, Numa (Appanoose), 1957
Siglin, Courtney, Corydon (Wayne), 1973
*Slater, Ivan, Dayton (Webster), 1955
*Smith, C. Everett, Newton (Jasper), 1928
*Smith, John N., Center Junction (Jones), 1927
Snyder, Richard A., Cambridge (Story), 1997
Sorensen, Dale, Harlan (Shelby), 1975
Stadlman, Gaylord, Sac City (Sac), 1966
Stadtmueller, Dan, Monticello (Jones), 1994
*Steddom, Marion J., Grimes (Polk), 1957
Steele, Oscar E., Riverside (Washington), 1989
*Steen, George N., West Liberty (Muscatine), 1927

*Steffensen, DeVere, Leland (Winnebago), 1974
*Stephens, Richard, Ainsworth (Washington), 1948
Stevens, Alan L., Northwood (Worth), 1981
*Stevens, E.H., Farragut (Fremont), 1930
*Stevens, L.G., Northwood (Worth), 1952
*Stewart, Everett L., Washington (Washington), 1929
*Stewart, P.P., Marnard (Fayette), 1926
*Stille, Clifford, Macedonia (Pottawattamie), 1968
Stillman, Philip R., Emmetsburg (Palo Alto), 1982
Stillman, William H., Emmetsburg (Palo Alto), 1969
Stoneberg, Everett, Ames (Story), 1989
–Exceptional Service
*Strickler, Paul B., (Appanoose), 1928
Striegel, Virginia, What Cheer (Keokuk), 1979
Stroburg, Clark, Blockton (Taylor), 1950
Strohbehn, Kenneth Paul, Gladbrook (Tama), 1992
Sunde, Elvin L., Estherville (Emmet), 1956
*Sutton, Lyle, Delhi (Delaware), 1949
Svendsen, Doug, Marshalltown (Marshall), 2001
Svendsen, James, Marshalltown (Marshall), 2001
*Swalin, John, Pomeroy (Calhoun), 1931
Swanson, Ronald E., Galt (Wright), 1997
*Sylwester, Dr. E.P., Ames (Story), 1972
– Exceptional Service

T

*Thedens, P.C., Rowley (Buchanan), 1939
Thompson, Richard, Boone (Boone), 2003
Toale, Francis M., Independence (Buchanan), 1980
Tobin, J. Kelly, New Market (Taylor), 1999
Tonderum, Harlan A., Maquoketa (Jackson), 1969
*Tracy, E.E., Nashua (Chickasaw), 1927
Travis, Merle, Bedford (Taylor), 1953
*Trenary, G. Donald, Pocahontas (Pocahontas), 1953

Tronchetti, Louis, Jefferson (Greene), 1978

V

*Vaske, Henry C., Dyersville (Dubuque), 1928
Voss, Dr. Regis, Ames (Story), 1998 –
Exceptional Service

W

Wall, John P., Iowa City (Johnson), 1980
*Wall, Lawrence J., Iowa City (Johnson), 1980
Watkins, David, Moscow (Muscatine), 1998
*Watts, Earl, Shenandoah (Page), 1926
Weaver, Wiley, Rockwell (Cerro Gordo), 1977
*Webber, Ray, Stockport (Van Buren), 1957
*Weber, Dr. C.R., Ames (Story), 1967 –
Exceptional Service
*Welty, George K., Essex (Page), 1952
*Wendt, William, Waverly (Bremer), 1926
Wiese, Gene, Manning (Carroll), 2005
Willhoit, Carl, Batavia (Wapello), 1988
Williams, David L., Villisca (Montgomery),
1980
*Williams, Paul G., Villisca (Montgomery),
1951
*Winslow, Francis, Grundy Center (Grundy),
1967
Wright, Alvin, Tipton (Cedar), 1996
Wright, James, Collins (Story), 1965

Y

*Yates, Will, Osceola (Clarke), 1939
*Yungclas, William, Webster City (Hamilton),
1951

Z

Zacharias, Robert, Persia (Harrison), 1976
Zumbach, Earl, Ryan (Delaware), 1974

IOWA MASTER FARMER AWARD WINNERS BY CLASS YEAR

*deceased
ES Exceptional Service Award winner

1926
*George W. Christophel, Waverly (Bremer)
*George Godfrey, Algona (Kossuth)
*Lenus Hagglund, Essex (Page)
*Charles D. Kirkpatrick, Keota (Keokuk)
*Fred W. LaDoux, Spirit Lake (Dickinson)
*H.S. Martin, Newton (Jasper)
*William McArthur, Mason City (Cerro Gordo)
*E.F. Morris, New Providence (Hardin)
*Lewis Morris, Grimes (Polk)
*Fred W. Nelson, Nevada (Story)
*D.J. Schnittjer, Delhi (Delaware)
*P.P. Stewart, Marnard (Fayette)
*Earl Watts, Shenandoah (Page)
*William Wendt, Waverly (Bremer)

1927
*Carl T. Anderson, Wellman (Washington)
*H.D. Backhaus, Clear Lake (Cerro Gordo)
*Frank Heath, Corning (Adams)
*A.J. Blakely, Grinnell (Poweshiek)
*R.R. Clampitt, New Providence (Hardin)
*E.L. Hill, Minburn (Dallas)
*John M. Hunt, Ackley (Hardin)
*Oscar W. Johnson, LeGrand (Marshall)
*George W. Leffler, Stockport (Van Buren)
*A.B. Myhr, Thompson (Winnebago)
*R.T. Pullen, Spencer (Clay)
*Ray Redfern, Yarmouth (Des Moines)
*Adolph Schultz, Malvern (Mills)
*John N. Smith, Center Junction (Jones)
*George N. Steen, West Liberty (Muscatine)
*E.E. Tracy, Nashua (Chickasaw)

1928
*H.E. Barringer, Emmetsburg (Palo Alto)
*Earl E. Elijah, Clarence (Cedar)

*Frank F. Everett, New Sharon (Mahaska)
*Burrell C. Foster, Wellman (Washington)
*Theodore Gronna, Waterville (Allamakee)
*Hervey E. Hazen, (Lee)
*O.J. Kalsem, Huxley (Story)
*Seth N. Miller, Indianola (Warren)
*Lewis T. Newton, Knoxville (Marion)
*Edward Reimer, Schleswig (Crawford)
*Bert Schuelke, Storm Lake (Buena Vista)
*Otto F. Schultz, Malcom (Poweshiek)
*C. Everett Smith, Newton (Jasper)
*Paul B. Strickler, (Appanoose)
*Henry C. Vaske, Dyersville (Dubuque)

1929
*William C. Anderson, West Liberty (Muscatine)
*Harry J. Bode, Algona (Kossuth)
*James C. Davis, Millerton (Wayne)
*Z.T. Dunham, Dunlap (Harrison)
*Harry B. Fox, Odebolt (Sac)
*W.M. George, Denver (Bremer)
*John Hueck, Everly (Clay)
*Frank Holland, Milton (Van Buren)
*Sam Kennedy, Clear Lake (Cerro Gordo)
*John S. Knight, Strawberry Point (Clayton)
*R.C. McElhinney, Waterloo (Black Hawk)
*Charles B.F. Michel, Marion (Linn)
*Harry Poundstone, Clarion (Wright)
*W.H. Boyer, Dallas Center (Dallas)
*G.E. Sauerby, Oelwein (Fayette)
*Everett L. Stewart, Washington (Washington)

1930
*H.K. Baker, Beaconsfield (Ringgold)
*J.J. Boatman, Montezuma (Poweshiek)
*H.J. Grunewald, Blairstown (Benton)
*W.A. Hollowell, Melcher (Marion)
*R.C. Hopp, Sr., Glenwood (Mills)
*E.W. Houston, Dunlap (Harrison)
*W.F. Jager, Eddyville (Wapello)

*R.G. Kinsley, McGregor (Clayton)
*Joseph Lengeling, Carroll (Carroll)
*H.F. Lubkeman, Hampton (Franklin)
*John McKeegan, Rock Valley (Sioux)
*F.L. Miller, Beaman (Grundy)
*Alex Reed, Bellevue (Jackson)
*H.H. Rinker, Rippey (Greene)
*E.H. Stevens, Farragut (Fremont)

1931
*Walter Beck, Danville (Des Moines)
*Roscoe Blinks, Marion (Linn)
*Robert M. Clark, Mitchellville (Polk)
*John Collison, Arcadia (Carroll)
*Herman Franzenburg, Keystone (Benton)
*Louis Hadenfeldt, Sioux Rapids (Buena Vista)
*Mrs. J.E. Hoopes, Muscatine (Muscatine)
*D.F. Kruse, Sheldon (O'Brien)
*Fred Mitchell, New Providence (Hardin)
*John Swalin, Pomeroy (Calhoun)

1938
*H.W. Buck, Greenfield (Adair)
*Orie F. Irwin, Sac City (Sac)
*Allan B. Kline, Vinton (Benton)
*Benjamin C. Neal, Mt. Vernon (Linn)

1939
*Dayton W. Mather, Greene (Butler)
*J.D. Misbach, Williamsburg (Iowa)
*Herbert Schneckloth, Davenport (Scott)
*P.C. Thedens, Rowley (Buchanan)
*Will Yates, Osceola (Clarke)

1940
*Fred K. Bruene, Gladbrook (Tama)
*J.R. McKeown, Harlan (Shelby)
*Charles R. Mountain (Polk)
*E.N. Neal, Shell Rock (Butler)

1941
*Ray Coglon, Exira (Audubon)
*Henry Dall, Battle Creek (Ida)
*Henry F. Olerich, Rolfe (Pocahontas)
*Alvin Prestemon, Waukon (Allamakee)

1946
*G.D. Bellman, Indianola (Warren)
*E. Howard Hill, Minburn (Dallas)

1947
*Carney H. Conner, Glidden (Carroll)
Leigh R. Curran, Mason City (Cerro Gordo)
*William H. Davidson, Stanwood (Cedar)
*Henry Kernen, Villisca (Montgomery)
*Earl Lyon, Toledo (Tama)
*Marion Ringoen, Ridgeway (Winneshiek)

1948
*A.R. Clause, Grand Junction (Greene)
*Fred Dubbert, Laurens (Pocahontas)
Maynard Menefee, Fayette (Fayette)
*Harry Reese, Prescott (Adams)
*John P. Schnack, DeWitt (Clinton)
*Peter Sidles, Centerville (Appanoose)
*Richard Stephens, Ainsworth (Washington)

1949
*Dale Blackwell, Bloomfield (Davis)
*Wilbur E. Goodhue, Carlisle (Warren)
*Zeno Lapke, Dunlap (Harrison)
*Arthur Linder, Hartley (O'Brien)
*Charles O. Nelson, Creston (Union)
*Lyle Sutton, Delhi (Delaware)

1950
*Clyde M. Core, Pleasantville (Marion)
*J.E. Entz, Waterloo (Black Hawk)
John R. Holland, Milton (Van Buren)
*Peter J. Johnson, Inwood (Lyon)
*Hans A. Larsen, Spencer (Clay)
Clark Stroburg, Blockton (Taylor)

1951
*Herbert Campbell, Washington (Washington)
*Edwin Helming, Hornick (Woodbury)
Walter and Dorothy McConohy, DeWitt (Clinton)
*John J. Moreland, Earlham (Madison)
*Paul G. Williams, Villisca (Montgomery)
*William Yungclas, Webster City (Hamilton)

1952

*S.A. Barber, Kanawha (Hancock)
*Frank Christensen, Ogden (Boone)
*Lewis Greaser, Vinton (Benton)
*Orville N. Kalsem, Huxley (Story)
*Clarence A. Pellett, Atlantic (Cass)
C.B. Schager, Dows (Wright)
*L.G. Stevens, Northwood (Worth)
*George K. Welty, Essex (Page)

1953
*James D. Helmick, Columbus Junction (Louisa)
*Doyce Miller, Osceola (Clarke)
*Lyle V. Ormston, Waverly (Bremer)
*Donald Pullin, Waterloo (Black Hawk)
*Lawrence Reis, Greenfield (Adair)
Merle and Maggie Travis, Bedford (Taylor)
*G. Donald Trenary, Pocahontas (Pocahontas)

1954
*Clarence S. Hill, Minburn (Dallas)
*Wayne Keith, Algona (Kossuth)
*Sterling B. Martin, Melrose (Monroe)
*Dallas McGrew, Emerson (Mills)
*Elmer Moreland, Guthrie Center (Guthrie)
*William Pennings, Orange City (Sioux)
*S.T. Rogers, Hancock (Pottawattamie)

1955
*Whitfield Adamson, Cherokee (Cherokee)
*Alvin Christiansen, Nora Springs (Floyd)
*Wayne E. Norman, Wellman (Washington)
*Harold Opsand, Elgin (Fayette)
*Ivan Slater, Dayton (Webster)

1956
*Russell Eldred, Anamosa (Jones)
*C. Raymond and Eunice R. Fisher, Grand Junction (Greene)
*Lowell Hall, Griswold (Cass)
*Ned E. Perrin, Mapleton (Monona)
Donald W. Pratt, Glidden (Carroll)
Elvin L. Sunde, Estherville (Emmet)

1957
*William Blahauvietz, Harris (Osceola)
*William Darbyshire, Rockwell City (Calhoun)

*Oswell Fisher, Hubbard (Hardin)
*Donald Foutch, Woodbine (Harrison)
*Ralph A. Long, Mt. Ayr (Ringgold)
*Ray Mitchell, Charles City (Floyd)
*Otto Schaper, Estherville (Emmet)
*Amos Siglin, Numa (Appanoose)
*Marion J. Steddom, Grimes (Polk)
*Ray Webber, Stockport (Van Buren)

1958
*J. Merrill Anderson, Newton (Jasper)
*Glenn Christy, Garrison (Benton)
*Harold Neill, Corning (Adams)
*Alvin Schnack, Harlan (Shelby)

1959
*Larry Cain, Mason City (Cerro Gordo) ES
*Bernard Collins, Clarion (Wright)
*Floyd N. George, Janesville (Black Hawk)
Don and Doris Johnson, Fairfield (Jefferson)
Ervin J.J. Koos, Shelby (Pottawattamie)
Thomas Herbert Newell, Columbus Junction (Louisa)

1960
*Herbert Cline, Bussey (Marion)
Ralph and Geraldine Fox, Riceville, (Howard)
*Elmer J. Hamann, Eldridge (Scott)
*Donavan Kruse, Charles City (Floyd)
*Fred Schmidt (Clinton)

1961
*Edmund Groomes, Menlo (Guthrie)
William F. and Arlene Imlau, Kensett (Worth)
*Roy Olson, Terrill (Dickinson)
*Wendell C. Pellett, Atlantic (Cass)
*Chester Shirer, Chariton (Lucas)

1963
*Walter and Jean Hagen, Waterville (Allamakee)
*Harvey Moeckly, Polk City (Polk)
*Joseph C. O'Hara, Shenandoah (Page)
*Ervin J. Schmuecker, Marengo (Iowa)

1964
*Bert Ballou, Monticello (Jones)
*Glenn R. Brown, Grundy Center (Grundy)
*Elvie Dreeszen, Cushing (Ida)
*Willis A. McAlpin, Villisca (Montgomery)
Les and Gladys McGohan, Mt. Pleasant (Henry)

1965
*Hugh Black, Algona (Kossuth)
Leon and Ruby Haahr, Newell (Buena Vista)
J. Gordon Hollis, Waterloo (Black Hawk)
*Harold V. Ryon, Laurens (Pocahontas)
James, Sr. and Hazel M. Wright, Collins (Story)

1966
Norman and Ruth Barker, LeMars (Plymouth)
*Roy B. and Myrtle Keppy, Davenport (Scott)
*Paul McNutt, Iowa City (Johnson)
Gaylord Stadlman, Sac City (Sac)

1967
Horace and Mary Autenrieth, Paullina (O'Brien)
*Herbert C. Hinkhouse, West Branch (Cedar)
*Keith McAllister, Mount Union (Henry)
*George Schmidt, Delmar (Clinton)
*Francis Winslow, Grundy Center (Grundy)
* Dr. C.R. Weber, Ames (Story) ES

1968
*Louis Byrnes, Cresco (Howard)
*Ralph Calmer, Manson (Calhoun)
*Gene Dunphy, Creston (Union)
*Ed Hanrahan, Creston (Union)
John D. and Ruth E. Morris, Columbus
Junction (Louisa)
*Herbert W. Pike, Whiting (Monona)
*Clifford Stille, Macedonia (Pottawattamie)

1969
Donald F. and Opal Doolittle, Blairsburg
(Hamilton)
Paul Griffith, Lamoni (Decatur)
Irvin and Mildred Harvey, Oskaloosa (Mahaska)
*Maynard Newhouse, Decorah (Winneshiek)
William H. and Lois Stillman, Emmetsburg
(Palo Alto)

Harlan A. Tonderum, Maquoketa (Jackson)

1970
*Robert W. and Aylo Bell, Coggon (Linn)
*Leo Dunn, Clemons (Marshall)
*Jack M. Elliott, Mount Ayr (Ringgold)
*Harry Rassmussen, Newell (Buena Vista)
Art J. and Frances Schuiteman, Sioux Center
(Sioux)

1971
*Harvey C. Bolte, Silver City (Mills)
*Donald Hood, Bode (Humboldt)
*Edward Ladd, Rock Rapids (Lyon)
Kenneth Showalter, Hampton (Franklin)

1972
Marlowe and Myrna Feldman, Albert City
(Buena Vista)
*Delbert L. Grafft, Olin (Jones)
Garland and Betty Ann Hanson, Callender
(Webster)
John R. Livingston, Bedford (Taylor)
Wesley J. and Lenor Shafer, Fairfield (Jefferson)
*Dr. E.P. Sylwester, Ames (Story) ES

1973
George H. and Marie Busch, Allison (Butler)
Glenn and Donna Freese, Vail (Crawford)
Frank and Lee Hasenclever, Fort Madison (Lee)
Bud and Mary Jorgenson, Farragut (Fremont)
*Edward Klodt, Ottumwa (Wapello)
Courtney and Marge Siglin, Corydon (Wayne)

1974
*David Flint, What Cheer (Keokuk)
*Roland Jensen, Ida Grove (Ida)
*Glen Juelsggard, Gray (Audubon)
Marshall and *Donna King, Boone (Boone)
*DeVere and Clarine Steffensen, Leland
(Winnebago)
Earl and Edna Zumbach, Ryan (Delaware)

1975
Duane and Genevieve Boyd, Charles City (Floyd)
*Wilbert Frye, Independence (Buchanan)

*Lester Johnson, LeMars (Plymouth)
Morris and Janice S. Kluver, Britt (Hancock)
Dale and Ruth Sorensen, Harlan (Shelby)
William and Carla Greiner, Ankeny (Polk)ES

1976
*Ollie Kaldenberg, Albia (Monroe)
*Malcolm McGregor, Nashua (Chickasaw)
Robert Schultz, Luana (Clayton)
*Arthur Schweers, Lenox (Adams)
Robert and Lois Zacharias, Persia (Harrison)

1977
Gordon and Shirley Enyart, Prairie City (Jasper)
Farris and Patsy Gray, Bedford (Taylor)
Robert and Verana Johnson, Andover (Clinton)
*Bob Joslin, Clarence (Cedar)
*Ralph Mehl, Hornick (Woodbury)
Wiley and Evelyn Weaver, Rockwell
(Cerro Gordo)

1978
Loren and Wilma Eddy, Centerville
(Appanoose)
*Merlyn and Vara Groot, Manson (Calhoun)
*Ward and Margaret Handorf, Gladbrook
(Marshall)
*Robert Rawson, Kingsley (Cherokee)
Louis and Neva Tronchetti, Jefferson (Greene)

1979
Richard and Beverly Kuecker, Algona (Kossuth)
Donald L. and Marlene J. Nielsen, Moneta (Clay)
Curtis and Joan Pflum, Burlington (Des Moines)
William and Marjorie Rempp, Montezuma
(Poweshiek)
Virginia Striegel, What Cheer (Keokuk)

1980
George A. and Dolorys Helmers, Sibley
(Osceola)
James E. and Ann Sage, Waterloo (Black Hawk)
Francis M. and Clara Toale, Independence
(Buchanan)
John P. and Mary Ellen Wall, Iowa City
(Johnson)

*Lawrence J. Wall, Iowa City (Johnson)
David L. and Corrine Williams, Villisca
(Montgomery)

1981
John ("Ted") and Rachel Huser, Sac City (Sac)
James, Jr. and Helen Jorgensen, Hampton
(Franklin)
Howard P. and Lillian Mogler, Alvord (Lyon)
Glen M. and Louise Seberg, Mt. Pleasant
(Henry)
Alan L. and Mavis Stevens, Northwood (Worth)

1982
Donald L. and Shirley Doolittle, Duncombe
(Webster)
Alvin J. and Patricia Gilbert, New Hampton
(Chickasaw)
*Allen J. Korslund, Eagle Grove (Humboldt)
*Jim Mohr, Eldridge (Scott)
Ned O. and Norida Mohr, Eldridge (Scott)
Philip R. and Ann Stillman, Emmetsburg
(Palo Alto)

1983
Robert and Naomi Christensen, Hastings
(Mills)
G. Joe and Norma Lyon, Toledo (Tama)
*Howard H. Lyon, Toledo (Tama)
*Ralph C. ("R.C.") and Dorothy Mathis,
Elkhart (Polk)
Myers M. and Marlene Rossiter, Winfield
(Henry)
*Loren A. Schuett, Holstein (Cherokee)

1984
Kenneth J. and Evelyn Cook, New Providence
(Hardin)
Wilfred A., Jr. ("Bill") and Jeanette Groves,
Kamrar (Hamilton)
Richard F. ("Dick") and Donna Groves,
Webster City (Hamilton)
Albert ("Bud") and Lillian Knake, Bellevue
(Jackson)
Harlan A. and Karen Murley, Aurora
(Buchanan)

Marlin and Arlyce Oosterhuis, Hospers
(O'Brien)
Roland D. and Bette Petersen, Bryant (Clinton)

1985
Richard and Marie Anderson, West Branch
(Cedar)
Charles and Marilyn Bjustrom, Whittemore
(Kossuth)
George, Jr. and Ruth Hoffman, Ida Grove (Ida)
Elmer and Loretta Paper, Stockton (Scott)
Dale and Mary Sexton, Rockwell City (Calhoun)

1986
Walter Goeken, Monona (Clay)
*Alvin Hansen, Mason City (Cerro Gordo)
Loyd and Lois Martin, Marion (Linn)
Howard and Fran Mueller, Waverly (Bremer)

1987
*Don Burt, Marshalltown (Marshall)
Paul Copenhaver, Independence (Buchanan)
Wayne and Margaret Northey, Spirit Lake
(Dickinson)
Marvin and Barbara Schlitzer, Dubuque
(Dubuque)

1988
Edgar W. and Joyce Keith, Algona (Kossuth)
William F. and Marian Petersen, Davenport
(Scott)
*Dwight R. Puttmann, Kingsley, (Woodbury)
Carl and Eloise Willhoit, Batavia (Wapello)

1989
Arnold I. and Karen Grau, Newell (Buena Vista)
Ralph R. and Rita Howe, Clemons (Marshall)
Donald D. and Irene Newby, Bondurant (Polk)
Oscar E. and Wynne Steele, Riverside
(Washington)
Everett Stoneberg, Ames, (Story) ES

1990
*Stanley L. Bay, Albia (Monroe)
Edward and Bess Engstrom, Kanawha
(Hancock)

Edward F. and Dora Keast, Henderson
(Pottawattamie)
Wayne D. and Donna Scott, Nodaway (Adams)

1991
*Gerald E. Cornelius, Bellevue (Jackson)
Morris ("Mick") and Janet Greenley,
Independence (Buchanan)
David W. and Judy Hawkins, Orange City
(Plymouth)
David K. and Cheryl Kalsem, Huxley (Story)
Owen J. and Ann Kalsem, Huxley (Story)

1992
Vernon James Beernink, Sioux Center (Sioux)
Howard Lee and Leila Johnson, Ashton
(Osceola)
Keith G. Hora, Riverside (Washington)
Kenneth Paul and Barbara Strohbehn,
Gladbrook (Tama)

1993
Varel G. and Jacqueline Bailey, Anita (Cass)
Robert A. and Lucille Jardon, Randolph
(Fremont)
Kenneth and Janice Kassel, Ayshire (Palo Alto)
Ralph and Rita Manternach, Cascade (Jones)

1994
Bill and Judy Ellerman, Dallas Center (Dallas)
Jerry G. and Jean Goldsmith, Clarence (Cedar)
Ralph and Joyce Neill, Corning (Adams)
Dan and Diana Stadtmueller, Monticello
(Jones)

1995
Gary and Sally Ewoldt, Davenport (Scott)
Paul and Mary Hill, Ellsworth (Hamilton)
David Noller, Sigourney (Keokuk)
Harold and Sue Peyton, Sac City (Sac)

1996
Dennis and Janice Berger, Wellman
(Washington)
John and Mary Miller, Cedar Falls (Black Hawk)
Gary and Joyce Holst, Eldridge (Scott)

Alvin and Mary Wright, Tipton (Cedar)
Garren and Pat Benson, Ames, (Story) $\boxed{ES}$

1997
Donald R. and Grace Hertz, Laurens
(Pocahontas)
Duane A. and Ilene Petersen, Sumner (Bremer)
Richard A. and Shirley Snyder, Cambridge
(Story)
Ronald E. and Florine Swanson, Galt (Wright)

1998
David H. and Marlys Fisher, Hubbard (Hardin)
*Doug and Lynne Johnson, Fairfield (Jefferson)
Lucille ("Lu") and *Allyn Matthey, Sergeant
Bluff (Woodbury)
David and Marylu Watkins, Moscow
(Muscatine)
Dr. Regis D. and Mardy Voss, Ames, (Story) $\boxed{ES}$

1999
Kenneth I. and Helen Fawcett, West Branch,
(Cedar)
Curtis A. and Carol Raasch, Odebolt, (Sac)
John K. and Beverly Schultz, Postville,
(Allamakee)
J. Kelly and Irene Tobin, New Market, (Taylor)

2000
Larry and Judy Anton, LaPorte City,
(Black Hawk)
David and Theresa Anton, LaPorte City,
(Black Hawk)
Craig and LaVon, Ankeny, (Polk)
Ron and Judy Kielkopf, Fremont, (Keokuk)
Thomas and Elsie Ryan, Cresco, (Winneshiek)
Neil and Darlene Harl, Ames, (Story) $\boxed{ES}$

2001
Dean and Sandra Amstutz, Bloomfield, (Davis)
Maynard and Dorothy Lang, Brooklyn,
(Poweshiek)
Fritz and Jane Langguth, Fontanelle, (Adair)
James and Shirley Svendsen, Marshalltown,
(Marshall)

Doug and Linda Svendsen, Marshalltown,
(Marshall)

2002
Jim and Linda Anderson, Boone, (Boone)
Larry and Nancy Beyer, Marengo, (Iowa)
Wayne and Joan Demmer, Epworth, (Dubuque)
Arnold and Audrey Odland, Webster City,
(Hamilton)

2003
Lee and Martha Faris, Mt. Ayr, (Ringgold)
David and Donna Kunde, Manchester,
(Delaware)
Ronald and Judith Leistikow, Readlyn, (Bremer)
Richard and Sharon Thompson, Boone, (Boone)

2004
Jim and Bev Amdor, Corning, (Adams)
Jack and Dee Kintzle, Coggon, (Linn)
Dean and Harriett McWilliams, Montezuma,
(Poweshiek)
Jerry and Judy Morey, Hazleton, (Buchanan)

2005
Jerry and Leola Britten, Zearing, (Story)
Gary and Judy Burrack, Monona, (Clayton)
Karol and Rozanne King, Mondamin, (Harrison)
Gene and Jean Wiese, Manning, (Carroll)
Stewart and Carol Melvin, Ames (Story) $\boxed{ES}$

2006
Don and Marylou Ahrens, Osage, (Mitchell)
Howard and Velma Keitzer, Mediapolis,
(Des Moines)
David and Diane Petty, Eldora, (Hardin)
Ernest and Virginia Sage, Dunkerton, (Black
Hawk)
Dr. Alfred Blackmer, Ames (Story) $\boxed{ES}$

2007
Bill and Nancy Couser, Nevada, (Story)
David and Lisa Lubben, Monticello, (Jones)
Kenneth and Bethene Maass, Remsen,
(Plymouth)
Curtis and Brenda Meier, Clarinda, (Page)

IOWA MASTER FARMER AWARD WINNERS BY COUNTY

*deceased
ES Exceptional Service Award winner

ADAIR
1938   *H.W. Buck, Greenfield
1953   *Lawrence Reis, Greenfield
2001   Fritz and Jane Langguth, Fontanelle

ADAMS
1927   *Frank Beath, Corning
1948   *Harry Reese, Prescott
1958   *Harold Neill, Corning
1976   *Arthur Schweers, Lenex
1990   Wayne D. and Donna Scott, Nodaway
1994   Ralph and Joyce Neill, Corning
2004   Jim and Bev Amdor, Corning

ALLAMAKEE
1928   *Theodore Gronna, Waterville
1941   *Alvin Prestemon, Waukon
1963   Walter and Jean Hagen, Waterville
1999   John and Beverly Schultz, Postville

APPANOOSE
1928   *Paul B. Strickler
1948   *Peter Sidles, Centerville
1957   *Amos Siglin, Numa
1978   Loren and Wilma Eddy, Centerville

AUDUBON
1941   *Ray Coglon, Exira
1974   *Glen Juelsgaard, Gray

BENTON
1930   *H.J. Grunewald, Blairstown
1931   *Herman Franzenburg, Keystone
1938   *Allan B. Kline, Vinton
1952   *Lewis Greaser, Vinton
1958   *Glenn Christy, Garrison

BLACK HAWK
1929   *R.C. McElhinney, Waterloo
1950   *J.E. Entz, Waterloo
1953   *Donald Pullin, Waterloo
1959   *Floyd N. George, Janesville
1965   J. Gordon Hollis, Waterloo
1980   James E. and Ann Sage, Waterloo
1996   John and Mary Miller, Cedar Falls
2000   Larry and Judy Anton, LaPorte City
2000   David and Theresa Anton, LaPorte City
2006   Ernest Sage, Dunkerton

BOONE
1952   *Frank Christensen, Ogden
1974   Marshall and *Donna King, Boone
2002   Jim and Linda Anderson, Boone
2003   Richard and Sharon Thompson, Boone

BREMER
1926   *George W. Christophel, Waverly
1926   *William Wendt, Waverly
1929   *W.M. George, Denver
1953   *Lyle V. Ormston, Waverly
1986   Howard and Fran Mueller, Waverly
1997   Duane A. and Ilene Petersen, Sumner
2003   Ronald and Judith Leistikow, Readlyn

BUCHANAN
1939   *P.C. Thedens, Rowley
1975   *Wilbert Frye, Independence
1980   Francis and Clara Toale, Independence
1984   Harlan and Karen Murley, Aurora
1987   Paul Copenhaver, Independence
1991   Mick and Janet Greenley, Independence
2004   Jerry and Judy Morey, Hazleton

BUENA VISTA
1928   *Bert Schuelke, Storm Lake
1931   *Louis Hadenfeldt, Sioux Rapids

1965   Leon and Ruby Haahr, Newell
1970   *Harry Rasmussen, Newell
1972   Marlowe and Myrna Feldman, Albert City
1989   Arnold I. and Karen Grau, Newell

BUTLER
1939   *Dayton W. Mather, Greene
1940   *E.N. Neal, Shell Rock
1973   George H. and Marie Busch, Allison

CALHOUN
1931   *John Swalin, Pomeroy
1957   *William Darbyshire, Rockwell City
1968   Ralph Calmer, Manson
1978   Merlyn and Vara Groot, Manson
1985   Dale and Mary Sexton, Rockwell City

CARROLL
1930   *Joseph Lengelin, Carroll
1931   *John Collison, Arcadia
1947   *Carney Connor, Glidden
1956   Donald W. Pratt, Glidden
2005   Gene and Jean Wiese, Manning

CASS
1952   *Clarence A. Pellett, Atlantic
1956   *Lowell Hall, Griswold
1961   *Wendell C. Pellett, Atlantic
1993   Varel G. and Jacqueline Bailey, Anita

CEDAR
1928   *Earl E. Elijah, Clarence
1947   *William H. Davidson, Stanwood
1967   *Herbert C. Hinkhouse, West Branch
1977   *Robert Joslin, Clarence
1985   Richard and Marie Anderson, West Branch
1994   Jerry and Jean Goldsmith, Clarence
1996   Alvin and Mary Wright, Tipton
1999   Ken and Helen Fawcett, West Branch

CERRO GORDO
1926   *William McArthur, Mason City
1927   *H.D. Backhaus, Clear Lake
1929   *Sam Kennedy, Clear Lake
1947   Leigh R. Curran, Mason City
1959   *Larry Cain, Mason City **ES**

1977   Wiley and Evelyn Weaver, Rockwell
1986   *Alvin Hansen, Mason City

CHEROKEE
1955   *Whitfield Adamson, Cherokee
1978   *Robert Rawson, Cherokee
1983   *Loren A. Schuett, Holstein

CHICKASAW
1927   *E.E. Tracy, Nashua
1976   *Malcolm McGregor, Nashua
1982   Alvin J. and Patricia Gilbert, New Hampton

CLARKE
1939   *Will Yates, Osceola
1953   *Doyce Miller, Osceola

CLAY
1927   *Roy T. Pullen, Spencer
1929   *John Heuck, Everly
1950   *Hans A. Larsen, Spencer
1979   Donald and Marlene Nielsen, Moneta
1986   Walt Goeken, Moneta

CLAYTON
1929   *John S. Knight, Strawberry Point
1930   *R.G. Kinsley, McGregor
1976   Robert Schultz, Luana
2005   Gary and Judy Burrack, Monona

CLINTON
1948   *John P. Schnack, DeWitt
1951   Walter and Dorothy McConohy, DeWitt
1960   *Fred Schmidt, Maquoketa
1967   *George Schmidt, Delmar
1977   Robert and Verana Johnson, Andover
1984   Roland and Bette Petersen, Bryant

CRAWFORD
1928   *Edward Reimer, Schleswig
1973   Glenn and Donna Freese, Vail

DALLAS
1927   *E.L. Hill, Minburn
1929   *W.H. Royer, Dallas Center

1946   *E. Howard Hill, Minburn
1954   *Clarence S. Hill, Minburn
1994   Bill and Judy Ellerman, Dallas Center

DAVIS
1949   *Dale Blackwell, Bloomfield
2001   Dean and Sandra Amstutz, Bloomfield

DECATUR
1969   Paul Griffith, Lamoni

DELAWARE
1926   *D.J. Schnittjer, Delhi
1949   *Lyle Sutton, Delhi
1974   Earl and Edna Zumbach, Ryan
2003   David and Donna Kunde, Manchester

DES MOINES
1927   *Ray Redfern, Yarmouth
1931   *Walter Beck, Danville
1979   Curtis and Joan Pflum, Burlington
2006   Howard Keitzer, Mediapolis

DICKINSON
1926   *Fred W. LaDoux, Spirit Lake
1961   *Roy Olson, Terrill
1987   Wayne and Margaret Northey, Spirit Lake

DUBUQUE
1928   *Henry C. Vaske, Dyersville
1987   Marvin and Barbara Schlitzer, Dubuque
2002   Wayne and Joan Demmer, Epworth

EMMET
1956   Elvin L. Sunde, Estherville
1957   *Otto Schaper, Esterville

FAYETTE
1926   *P.E. Stewart, Maynard
1929   *G.E. Sauerbry, Oelwein
1948   Maynard Menefee, Fayette
1955   *Harold Opsand, Elgin

FLOYD
1955   *Alvin Christiansen, Nora Springs
1957   *Ray Mitchell, Charles City

1960   *Donavan Kruse, Charles City
1975   Duane and Genevieve Boyd, Charles City

FRANKLIN
1930   *H.F. Lubkeman, Hampton
1971   Kenneth Showalter, Hampton
1981   James and Helen Jorgensen, Hampton

FREMONT
1930   *E.H. Stevens, Farragut
1973   Bud and Mary Jorgenson, Farragut
1993   Robert A. and Lucille Jardon, Randolph

GREENE
1930   *H.H. Rinker, Rippey
1948   *A.R. Clause, Grand Junction
1956   C. Raymond and Eunice R. Fisher,
         Grand Junction
1978   Louis and Neva Tronchetti, Jefferson

GRUNDY
1930   *F.L. Miller, Beaman
1964   *Glenn R. Brown, Grundy Center
1967   Francis Winslow, Grundy Center

GUTHRIE
1954   *Elmer Moreland, Guthrie Center
1961   *Edmund Groomes, Menlo

HAMILTON
1951   *William Yungclas, Webster City
1969   Donald F. and Opal Doolittle, Blairsburg
1984   Wilfred and Jeanette Groves, Kamrar
1984   Richard and Donna Groves, Webster City
1995   Paul and Mary Hill, Ellsworth
2002   Arnold and Audrey Odland, Webster City

HANCOCK
1952   *S.A. Barber, Kanawha
1975   Morris and Janice S. Kluver, Britt
1990   Edward and Bess Engstrom, Kanawha

HARDIN
1926   *E.F. Morris, New Providence
1927   *R.R. Clampitt, New Providence
1927   *John M. Hunt, Ackley

1931   *Fred Mitchell, New Providence
1957   Oswell Fisher, Hubbard
1984   Kenneth and Evelyn Cook,
       New Providence
1998   David H. and Marlys Fisher, Hubbard
2006   David Petty, Eldora

HARRISON
1929   *A.T. Dunham, Dunlap
1930   *E.W. Houston, Dunlap
1949   *Zeno Lapke, Dunlap
1957   *Donald Foutch, Woodbine
1976   Robert and Lois Zacharias, Persia
2005   Karol and Rozanne King, Mondamin

HENRY
1964   Les and Gladys McGohan, Swedesburg
1967   Keith McAllister, Mt. Union
1981   Glen and Louise Seberg, Mt. Pleasant
1983   Myers and Marlene Rossiter, Winfield

HOWARD
1968   *Louis Byrnes, Cresco

HUMBOLDT
1971   Donald Hood, Humboldt
1982   *Allen J. Korslund, Eagle Grove

IDA
1941   *Henry Dall, Battle Creek
1964   *Elvie Dreeszen, Cushing
1974   *Roland Jensen, Ida Grove
1985   George and Ruth Hoffman, Ida Grove

IOWA
1939   *J.D. Misback, Williamsburg
1963   *Ervin J. Schmuecker, Marengo
2002   Larry and Nancy Beyer, Marengo

JACKSON
1930   *Alex Reed, Bellevue
1969   Harlan A. Tonderum, Maquoketa
1984   Bud and Lillian Knake, Bellevue
1991   *Gerald E. Cornelius, Bellevue

JASPER
1926   *H.S. Martin, Newton
1928   *C. Everett Smith, Newton
1958   *J. Merrill Anderson, Newton
1977   Gordon and Shirley Enyart, Prairie City

JEFFERSON
1959   Don and Doris Johnson, Fairfield
1972   Wesley J. and Lenor Shafer, Fairfield
1998   *Doug and Lynne Johnson, Fairfield

JOHNSON
1966   Paul McNutt, Iowa City
1980   John P. and Mary Ellen Wall, Iowa City
1980   *Lawrence J. Wall, Iowa City

JONES
1927   *John N. Smith, Center Junction
1956   *Russell Eldred, Anamosa
1964   *Bert Ballou, Monticello
1972   *Delbert L. Grafft, Olin
1993   Ralph and Rita Manternach, Cascade
1994   Dan and Diana Stadtmueller, Monticello
2007   David and Lisa Lubben, Monticello

KEOKUK
1926   *Charles D. Kirkpatrick, Keota
1974   *David Flint, What Cheer
1979   Virginia Striegel, What Cheer
1995   David Noller, Sigourney
2000   Ron and Judy Kielkopf, Fremont

KOSSUTH
1926   *George Godfrey, Algona
1929   *Harry J. Bode, Algona
1954   Wayne Keith, Algona
1965   *Hugh M. Black, Algona
1979   Richard and Beverly Kuecker, Algona
1985   Charles and Marilyn Bjustrom,
       Whittemore
1988   Edgar Wayne and Joyce Keith, Algona

LEE
1928   *Hervey E. Hazen
1973   Frank and Lee Hasenclever, Fort Madison

LINN

1929   *Charles B.F. Michel, Marion
1931   *Roscoe Blinks, Marion
1938   *Benjamin C. Neal, Mt. Vernon
1970   Robert W. and Aylo Bell, Coggon
1986   Loyd and Lois Martin, Marion
2004   Jack and Dee Kintzle, Coggon

LOUISA
1953   *James D. Helmick, Columbus Junction
1959   Thomas Herbert Newell, Columbus Junction
1968   John D. and Ruth E. Morris, Columbus Junction

LUCAS
1961   *Chester Shirer, Chariton

LYON
1950   *Peter J. Johnson, Inwood
1971   *Edward Ladd, Rock Rapids
1981   Howard P. and Lillian Mogler, Alvord

MADISON
1951   *John J. Moreland, Earlham

MAHASKA
1928   *Frank F. Everett, New Sharon
1969   Irvin and Mildred Harvey, Oskaloosa

MARION
1928   *Lewis T. Newton, Knoxville
1930   *W.A. Hollowell, Melcher
1950   Clyde M. Core, Pleasantville
1960   *Herbert E. Cline, Bussey

MARSHALL
1927   *Oscar W. Johnson, LeGrand
1970   *Leo Dunn, Clemons
1978   *Ward and Margaret Handorf, Gladbrook
1987   *Don Burt, Marshalltown
1989   Ralph R. and Rita Howe, Clemons
2000   Jim and Shirley Svendsen, Marshalltown
2001   Doug and Linda Svendsen, Marshalltown

MILLS
1927   *Adolph Schultz, Malvern

1930   *R.C. Hopp, Sr., Glenwood
1954   *Dallas McGrew, Emerson
1971   *Harvey C. Bolte, Silver City
1983   Bob and Naomi Christensen, Hastings

MITCHELL
1960   Ralph and Geraldine Fox, Riceville
2006   Don Ahrens, Osage

MONONA
1956   *Ned. E. Perrin, Mapleton
1968   *Herbert W. Pike, Whiting

MONROE
1954   *Sterling B. Martin, Melrose
1976   *Ollie Kaldenberg, Albia
1990   *Stanley L. Bay, Albia

MONTGOMERY
1947   *Henry Kernen, Villisca
1951   *Paul G. Williams, Villisca
1964   *Willis A. McAlpin, Villisca
1980   David and Corrine Williams, Villisca

MUSCATINE
1927   *George N. Steen, West Liberty
1929   *William C. Anderson, West Liberty
1931   *Mrs. J.E. Hoopes, Muscatine
1998   David and Marylu Watkins, Moscow

O'BRIEN
1931   *D.F. Kruse, Sheldon
1949   *Arthur Linder, Hartley
1967   Horace and Mary Autenrieth, Paullina
1984   Marlin and Arlyce Oosterhuis, Hospers

OSCEOLA
1957   *William Blahauvietz, Harris
1980   George and Dolorys Helmers, Sibley
1992   Howard L. and Leila Johnson, Ashton

PAGE
1926   *Lenus Hagglund, Essex
1926   *Earl Watts, Shenandoah
1952   *George K. Welty, Essex
1963   *Joseph C. O'Hara, Shenandoah

2007 Curtis and Brenda Meier, Clarinda

PALO ALTO
1928 *H.E. Barringer, Emmetsburg
1969 William and Lois Stillman, Emmetsburg
1982 Philip and Ann Stillman, Emmetsburg
1993 Kenneth and Janice Kassel, Ayshire

PLYMOUTH
1975 *Lester Johnson, LeMars
1991 David and Judy Hawkins, Orange City
2007 Kenneth and Bethene Maass, Remsen

POCAHONTAS
1941 *Henry F. Olerich, Rolfe
1948 *Fred Dubber, Laurens
1953 *G. Donald Trenary, Pocahontas
1965 *Harold Ryon, Laurens
1997 Donald R. and Grace Hertz, Laurens

POLK
1926 *Lewis Morris, Grimes
1931 *Robert M. Clark, Mitchellville
1940 *Charles R. Mountain, West Des Moines
1957 *Marion J. Steddom, Grimes
1963 *Harvey Moeckly, Polk City
1975 William and Carla Greiner, Ankeny $\boxed{ES}$
1983 *Ralph and Dorothy Mathis, Elkhart
1989 Donald D. and Irene Newby, Bondurant
2000 Craig and LaVon Griffieon, Ankeny

POTTAWATTAMIE
1954 *S.T. Rogers, Hancock
1959 Ervin J.J. Koos, Shelby
1968 *Clifford Stille, Macedonia
1990 Edward F. and Dora Keast, Henderson

POWESHIEK
1927 *A.J. Blakely, Grinnell
1928 *Otto F. Schultz, Malcom
1930 *J.J. Boatman, Montezuma
1979 William and Marjorie Rempp,
      Montezuma
2000 Maynard and Dorothy Lang, Brooklyn
2004 Dean and Harriett McWilliams,
      Montezuma

RINGGOLD
1930 *H.K. Baker, Beaconsfield
1957 *Ralph A. Long, Mount Ayr
1970 *Jack Elliott, Mount Ayr
2003 Lee and Martha Faris, Mount Ayr

SAC
1929 *Harry B. Fox, Odebolt
1938 *Orie F. Irwin, Sac City
1966 Gaylord Stadlman, Sac City
1981 Ted and Rachel Huser, Sac City
1995 Harold and Sue Peyton, Sac City
1999 Curt and Carol Raasch, Odebolt

SCOTT
1939 *Herbert Schneckloth, Davenport
1960 *Elmer J. Hamann, Eldridge
1966 Roy B. and Myrtle Keppy, Davenport
1982 *Jim Mohr, Eldridge
1982 Ned. O. and Norida Mohr, Eldridge
1985 Elmer and Loretta Paper, Stockton
1988 Bill and Marian Petersen, Davenport
1995 Gary and Sally Ewoldt, Davenport
1996 Gary and Joyce Holst, Eldridge

SHELBY
1940 *J.B. McKeown, Harlan
1958 *Alvin Schnack, Harlan
1975 Dale and Ruth Sorensen, Harlan

SIOUX
1930 *John McKeegan, Rock Valley
1954 *William Pennings, Orange City
1966 Norman and Ruth Barker, LeMars
1970 Art and Frances Schuiteman, Sioux Center
1992 Vernon J. Beernink, Sioux Center

STORY
1926 *Fred W. Nelson, Nevada
1928 *O.J. Kalsem, Huxley
1952 *Orville N. Kalsem, Huxley
1965 James Sr. and Hazel M. Wright, Collins
1967 *Dr. C.R. Weber, Ames $\boxed{ES}$
1972 *Dr. E.P. Sylwester, ISU, Ames $\boxed{ES}$
1989 Everett Stoneberg, ISU, Ames $\boxed{ES}$

1991   David K. and Cheryl Kalsem, Huxley
1991   Owen J. and Ann Kalsem, Huxley
1996   Garren and Pat Benson, Ames $\boxed{ES}$
1997   Richard and Shirley Snyder, Cambridge
1998   Dr. Regis and Mardy Voss, Ames $\boxed{ES}$
2000   Neil and Darlene Harl, Ames $\boxed{ES}$
2004   Stewart and Carol Melvin, Ames $\boxed{ES}$
2005   Jerry and Leola Britten, Zearing
2007   *Dr. Alfred Blackmer, Ames $\boxed{ES}$
2007   Bill and Nancy Couser, Nevada

TAMA
1940   *Fred K. Bruene, Gladbrook
1947   *Earl Lyon, Toledo
1983   G. Joe and Norma Lyon, Toledo
1983   *Howard H. Lyon, Toledo
1992   Kenneth P. and Barbara Strohbehn,
        Gladbrook

TAYLOR
1950   Clark Stroburg, Blockton
1953   Merle and Maggie Travis, Bedford
1972   John R. Livingston, Bedford
1977   Farris and Patsy Gray, Bedford
1999   J. Kelly and Irene Tobin, New Market

UNION
1949   *Charles O. Nelson, Creston
1968   *Gene Dunphy, Creston
1968   *Ed Hanrahan, Creston

VAN BUREN
1927   *George W. Leffler, Stockport
1929   *Frank Holland, Milton
1950   John R. Holland, Milton
1957   *Ray Webber, Stockport

WAPELLO
1930   *W.F. Jager, Eddyville
1973   *Edward Klodt, Ottumwa
1988   Carl and Eloise Willhoit, Batavia

WARREN
1928   *Seth N. Miller, Indianola
1946   *G.D. Bellman, Indianola
1949   *Wilbur E. Goodhue, Carlisle

WASHINGTON
1927   *Carl T. Anderson, Wellman
1928   *Burrell C. Foster, Wellman
1929   *Everett L. Stewart, Washington
1948   *Richard Stephens, Ainsworth
1951   *Herbert Campbell, Ainsworth
1955   *Wayne E. Norman, Wellman
1989   Oscar E. and Wynne Steele, Riverside
1992   Keith G. Hora, Riverside
1996   Dennis and Janice Berger, Wellman

WAYNE
1929   *James C. Davis, Millerton
1973   Courtney and Marge Siglin, Corydon

WEBSTER
1955   *Ivan Slater, Dayton
1972   Garland and Betty Ann Hanson,
        Callender
1982   Donald L. and Shirley Doolittle,
        Duncombe

WINNEBAGO
1927   *A.B. Myhr, Thompson
1974   DeVere and Clarine Steffensen, Leland
2000   Thomas and Elsie Ryan, Cresco

WINNESHIEK
1947   *Marion Ringoen, Ridgeway
1969   *Maynard Newhouse, Decorah

WOODBURY
1951   *Edwin Helming, Hornick
1977   *Ralph Mehl, Hornick
1988   *Dwight R. Puttman, Kingsley
1998   Lucille "Lu" and *Allyn Matthey,
        Sergeant Bluff

WORTH
1952   *L.G. Stevens, Northwood
1961   William F. and Arlene Imlau, Kensett
1981   Alan L. and Mavis Stevens,
Northwood

APPENDIX C

WRIGHT

1929	*Harry Poundstone, Clarion
1952	C.B. Schager, Dows
1959	*Bernard Collins, Clarion
1997	Ronald E. and Florine Swanson, Galt
1929	*Harry Poundstone, Clarion
1952	C.B. Schager, Dows
1959	*Bernard Collins, Clarion
1997	Ronald E. and Florine Swanson, Galt